THE MAKER'S FIELD GUIDE

THE ART & SCIENCE OF MAKING ANYTHING IMAGINABLE

UPDATED AND EXPANDED **GOLD** *EDITION*

CHRISTOPHER ARMSTRONG

Dedicated to the 1,192 backers who helped bring this project to life on

www.themakersfieldguide.com

Contents

PREFACE TO THE EXPANDED *GOLD* EDITION

A hardcover version of *The Maker's Field Guide* has been both a dream and a goal of mine ever since the first book was released in the middle of 2018. So, why go through the trouble of writing not just an updated, but a substantially expanded version of the book? The simple answer is that after the first book was released, I've had the opportunity to spend time touring the country and attending multiple different trade shows, expos, industry events and workshops — all where I've been exposed to a vast network of makers, renowned industry experts, and trailblazers out front of the Maker Movement phenomenon from all corners of the globe. Although some of them might appear as unassuming geeks tinkering with new technologies as if they were new playthings, every single one of them has a sense that what the future holds is as malleable as a piece of clay. This has given me a renewed sense of awe and fascination about the potential for the Maker Movement to have profound, far-reaching impacts on society at large — not just in America or in the developed nations of the West, but on a global scale. One of the the other things that has happened over the last year and a half that the first book was published, is that I've had a chance to see how people all over have interpreted the material in the first book, which has produced many great new insights about which specific subjects or content people were resonating with, and what they felt was lacking or wanted to see more of. This time around, I wanted to write a book with the true professional in mind, by including what I feel are some of the most important, relevant, and up to date scientific developments in science and technology — mostly because I've been frustrated by what I've been seeing taught in most schools, that's at least a few years if not a decade or more behind (extremely dogmatic at that), and has been more concerned with protecting the status quo than with preparing the next generation of students, young professionals, and entrepreneurs for the profound shifts ahead.

One of the comments about the first book is that while it was a good primer into the subjects covered, it may have been lacking depth in a few areas. I should have known going into writing a book with the subtitle, *'The Art & Science of Making Anything Imaginable'* that I was shooting myself in the foot — since compiling a book of such magnitude was indeed quite a bold claim to make. Even still, it is my firm belief that when you start *combining* all of these disparate technologies and processes together in new, synergistic, and often unexpected ways, that this is truly when things really starts to become powerful. Therefore, I still stand behind the first books as very strong resources in their own right, since having a solid understanding and exposure to the fundamentals and to the basics is the most important all. Often it's the folks who connect the dots in new and never-before-seen ways who become the true breakthrough innovators and pioneers in their respective fields. So, this time around is I've dug deep to think holistically about what an aspiring maker would truly need to set himself or herself up for success, making sure that no stone has been left unturned. I've also dedicated some much needed TLC to the sections that needed it. Most notably, you'll find almost thirty new pages dedicated to state-of-the-art 3D printing technologies — an area that's sure to blow your mind, even if you happen to be a seasoned pro who's been around this world for some time now. My goal here is to to provide a set of tools in your toolbox that are suitable for any skill level, including tips and tricks that even the most seasoned professional are bound to find useful "aha" nuggets of wisdom in. What the new *GOLD* edition strives to do is to give you the most kick-ass, one stop-manual that's going to be your secret weapon in making your project dreams become a reality — no matter how small or large scale. What's included throughout these pages are photographs spanning literally over a twelve year time period, with the best information I've distilled down from many archival notes that I've pulled directly from multiple different notebooks, sketchbooks, and my time spent working in the R&D industry at some of the highest levels. I understand that many of you reading this may not have access to all of the tools covered inside, and that's totally okay. It's best to start right where you are with the tools that are currently at your disposal — just as RTV silicones and resins were all that I had to draw from in the beginning. Then, once you gain access to some of the more sophisticated pieces of tools and equipment, you can grow into them accordingly. Even still, no matter what you have available to you at this very moment, I still strongly suggest you strive to at least become familiar with the basics of all of the tools, processes and terminology covered here. This will give you a solid understanding of their capabilities, as well as the different roles they play within the realm of design, prototyping, and manufacturing to bring real products to life.

I. THE BEGINNING OF A LIFELONG ~~PASSION~~ OBSESSION

If you were to lay me down on the proverbial psychiatrist's table and try to trace it all back to the very beginning, I'd attribute my intense curiosity and obsessive quest to learn more about the physical makeup behind the physical world of atoms all around us undoubtedly started one summer morning while out riding my shiny new, canary yellow GT Dyno BMX bike. I had just forked over more cash than I had ever dared to spend on any one single item up until that point on this bike — using up an entire nest egg of savings which I had scraped together from monthly allowances, occasional odd-job chores, and a lifetime's worth of birthdays and Christmas's. This decision cost me somewhere in the ballpark of $300 at a local bike shop for this purchase acquisition, which was the result of many months research and years of desperately seeking to upgrade from my sub-$100 budget bike, bought as a Wal-Mart special. In my mind at the time, a GT was quite a significant improvement on even the best-of-the-best models that Wal-Mart had to offer, and I felt confident enough to finally pull the proverbial trigger and take it home with me that day. However, the rug would soon be pulled out from under my excitement when one of the neighborhood bullies (known to be a serious BMX snob), caught glimpse of me riding by that morning on summer break. When I rode past him on my glistening new machine, his eyes quickly locked on the bright yellow frame like a homing missile, and without hesitation he blurted out an insult that hit me like a ton of bricks: "I can't believe you like that bike!" Almost in an instant, what I had thought just minutes earlier as a laudible purchase, now had me second-guessing as I continued to ride by. Teen-aged pride wounded, I quickly stole a glance at the bike he was perched on top of — a flashy, chrome purple Diamondback. At the time, Diamondback was widely known to be one of the most coveted brands in all of BMX. And at a starting price of $800, it was also way out of my budget. When I rode off, crushed by this older kids' incendiary bike snobbery, I became absolutely determined to answer the question, "What's the big difference between a cheap Wal-Mart bike, the bike I'm currently riding, and one of the fancier bike brands, anyway?" At the time, all of them looked so similar that it was difficult to distinguish whether or not they had any *real* differences in their structural build qualities beyond mere brand name or marketing hype alone. It was at this pivotal moment in time that I swore to try and find answers to this question, beginning with a thorough investigation into the origins of where the frames were made and assembled, then onto how they were fabricated from a special type of steel known as 4130 Chrome Moly, or Chromoly. This coveted 'Cro-Mo' steel had been the chief culprit behind the higher sticker price of the top-tier bikes. Peeling back the layers even further, I started to learn about how the delicate mix of Chromium and Molybdenum alloys created just the right balance between a hard (stiff) frame and one that was flexible (ductile) enough to avoid breaking when subjected to heavy loads, stresses or impacts — similar to how razor-sharp steel blades of Japanese Samurai swords are carefully forged together using only the finest quality metals, which have been carefully hand-selected to be devoid of any imperfections. In the BMX world, this unique blend of Chromoly would mean the ultimate difference between a bike frame that could handle anything a young trickster could throw at it, and one which adorned the dreaded disclaimer, "This bike is not intended for off-road or stunt jumping use" (like my new GT did). Upon further inspection, the Haro's, Diamondback's, and Schwinn's of the world did not come attached with such an embarrasing label — one that was likely crafted by an over-zealous legal team afraid of the retaliation from swarms of angry mothers. Even though I couldn't afford it at the time, I vowed that I someday I would own one of these dream bike brands, and eventually scraped together enough money to buy a used Schwinn Automatic on eBay a few years later. That frame had been made from none other than *Chromoly steel.*

Around the same time, I became hooked on episodes of the show *How It's Made* when they first aired on TV in the 1990's. Something about the show caused my young brain to click, and for the first time ever, I was being exposed to the inner workings of how *real products* were brought to life — usually from unimpressive raw materials that were mined from the ground. The curtain had just been lifted, and while I was captivated by these newfound insights, I was also profoundly confused. How was it that nobody I knew was talking about this kind of stuff? Why is it that I've never seen or been to one of these factories — much less ever heard from anyone who had worked inside of one? If I'm the one enjoying these products, there must be someone *somewhere* making them for me to consume, after all? Even years later when I started to work in retail, again I felt a knawing sense that I was simply selling the things that *other* people had made, but which I was powerless to have any input or influence on. "Just sell what you're given to sell" was what I was taught to do; it was my job. So I started asking myself, "Why couldn't I be on the other side of the glass? Why couldn't I join in on becoming a *producer* myself, rather than just a hapless *consumer*?"

This was around the same time that I had just graduated from high school, and when I became obsessed with behind-the-scenes film featurettes and began experimenting with RTV silicone molding and casting, which would later prove to be a "gateway" into industrial design. The ability to custom create and sell things was a liberating experience, and from that point on there was no turning back. Years later I came across this qoute by the pioneering design icon Steve Jobs, which has stuck with me ever since:

> "When you grow up you tend to get told that the world is the way it is and your life is just to live your life inside the world. Try not to bash into the walls too much. Try to have a nice family life, have fun, save a little money. But that's a very limited life. Life can be much broader once you discover one simple fact, and that is: everything around you that you call life was made up by people that were no smarter than you. And you can change it, you can influence it. You can build your own things that other people can use. And the minute you understand that you can poke life and something will pop out the other side; and that you can *change* it — you can *mold* it. That's maybe the most important thing — to shake off this erroneous notion that life is *there*, and you're just gonna live in it — versus embrace it, change it, improve it, make your mark upon it. I think that's very important. And however you learn that, once you learn it you'll want to change life and make it better...Once you learn that, you'll never be the same again."

II. THE RISE OF THE MAKER MINDSET & DIY CULTURE

Fast forward fifteen years later, and we're now in the midst of what's being called the Maker Movement, a dramatic shift towards the democratization of design, engineering, education, jobs and manufacturing. Advancements in new technologies such as desktop 3D printing and CNC machining are now putting powerful tools that were once only available to large research institutions like NASA in the hands of millions of creators worldwide. This rapid pace of disruption is creating a paradigm shift and playing-field leveler like no other in history, opening up many new opportunities for independent makers and entrepreneurs that were once thought to be unimaginable. As a result, this is leading to what's known as the small-batch or "lean manufacturing" revolution giving rise to the "maker" and maker culture. Put simply, the Maker Movement is a collective group of empowered individuals who are becoming much less dependent on large manufacturers for the production of their goods and services. Add to that an increasing level of interest and investment into corporate R&D (research and development) programs that are leveraging the use of new technologies as a way of gaining a competitive advantage in the marketplace. All of these combined factors have placed an emphasis on STEM and engineering educations or skill-sets as the path forward to success in this new era of uncertainty and globalization — with tens of thousands of grade-schools worldwide now rushing to build their own Makerspace facilities out of both a fear of missing out, and in an attempt to stay out front of this lighting-fast pace of change in today's volatile job marketplace. Because of the tectonic shifts in technology and connectivity, we are now at an inflection point, with many far-reaching implications that traverse far beyond America or any national borders — but which will be felt globally. Here are just a few of my thoughts on how to best navigate the coming changes, including insights from great minds that are much smarter than myself:

THE MAKER MOVEMENT or THE FOURTH INDUSTRIAL REVOLUTION

In his book, *The Fourth Industrial Revolution*, technologist and engineer Klaus Scwhab outlines the coming cataclysmic global, social, and economic shifts. In the past, factories were expensive to operate, and so it was more often than not the individual with the deepest pockets who controlled production. Enter the Maker Movement, and now the scales have tipped in favor of the individual, with new disruptive technologies vastly lowering barriers to entry by empowering and putting the power of production in the hands of almost anyone. A new breed of makers around the world with a dream, a vision, and the wherewithal to connect the dots have taken full advantage of these game-changing technologies. We're on the cusp of a revolution that many are claiming is as big as the countercultural revolution that swept through the West in the 1960's-70's, where manufacturing is becoming more and more decentralized on a global scale. The Maker Movement is one of the most dramatic paradigm shifts in human history, since the First Industrial Revolution of 1760. The mindset of a maker is quintessentially changing the meaning of what it means to be a manufacturer, and as a result reflects a fundamental shift towards valuing practice over theory.

THE FUTURE OF WORK

Many concerns have been raised about the future of work, even pre-COVID-19. Will the "gig economy" be here to stay? Will robots and automation render large swaths of the human workforce redundant and / or obsolete? If one thing is for certain, it's that change is inevitable. The future will not look anything like what it looks like today. Therefore, those who fight change are destined to be victims of the consequences, while those who learn to embrace it are the ones who will thrive in the years and decades ahead — no matter how uncertain the economic or geopolitical landscape becomes. Peter Drucker, the legendary business philosopher and inventor of modern management as we know it, pioneered the concept of the "knowledge worker" in the 1960's, forseeing massive shifts away from industrialized societies dominated by manual labor and management, and into knowledge-based societies led by intellectual capacity and creative entreprenuership. This is why I'm personally so excited about the Maker Movement, as it represents one possible solution to the challenges facing a global, interconnected society. If we can give more people the tools of production, we can empower them to become much more self-sufficient in their careers and in their own lives.

THE FUTURE OF EDUCATION

Dale Dougherty, in his book *Free to Make*, wrote this about hands-on learning, "The process of makers might be informal, messy, and organic. It's a process that includes but overcomes repeated failures, misunderstandings, and kludges. It's their own process that reflects real life rather than an ideal or model. A maker thinks: if it works for me, it works. If it doesn't, keep changing it. Also, makers learn from others; they can reflect on their own process, compare it to others, and borrow what they need." This informal process is in stark contrast to what many see as the over-formalization and institutionalization of the public education system as a whole. In order to keep up wih the lighting-fast pace of change, factory-style education systems simply cannot rest on their reputations or on their laurels; instead they will need to change their act dramatically if their true aim is preparing individuals for a rapidly evolving workforce. I am a huge believer in non-accredited bootcamps, professional training workshops, and continuing or alternative educations. Most importantly of all, you want to learn from someone who has achieved the results you seek, and who practices what they preach. This is a big problem plaguing the academic tenure system, where bureaucracy and job security at many schools have taken priority over actually preparing the next generations with relevant knowledge and hirable skills.

LIFELONG STUDENT & THE BEGINNER'S MIND (SHOSHIN)

The industrialist Henry Ford was known to have said, "Anyone who stops learning is old, whether at twenty or eighty. Anyone who keeps learning stays young. The greatest thing in life is to keep your mind young." Shoshin is the Zen concept of the beginner's mind, or having the humility to show up day-in and day-out as a day-one beginner. Socrates was known for being the wisest philosopher of his time, yet even he is remembered to have said, "I know that I know nothing." Once you *think* you know everything, that's when you stop growing, expanding, or advancing. Peter Drucker once wrote, "Knowledge has to be improved, challenged, and increased constantly, or it vanishes," and that "The most important thing to learn in school is *how to learn* — the habit of continuous learning. Knowledge makes itself obsolete very fast." Lifelong learning can only be cultivated through an insatiable sense of curiosity, combined with continual training dedicated to personal development and sharpening your sword. Most CEO's and executives read 50-60 books per year. The moment you stop learning, you stop leading. Leaders are learners.

"SCIENTISM" VS. REAL SCIENCE

Real science seeks clarification and simplification, rather than unnecessary overcomplication. In his book *Skin in the Game,* mathematician and risk analyst Nassim Nicholas Taleb shatters the myth that all scientists wear white lab coats and work for large academic or government research centers, writing, "What looks scientific is usually *scientism*, not science...Science and business must not be decorative. Scientism *looks* more scientific than real science." Elaborating that, "Scientism is a naive interpretation of science as complication, rather than science as a process and a skeptical enterprise. Using mathematics when it's not needed is not science, but *scientism*," and that, "Skin in the game is about the real world, not appearances. In any type of business or activity divorced from the direct filter of skin in the game, the great majority of people know the jargon, play the part, and are intimate with the cosmetic details, but are clueless about the subject...Elaborate rituals, titles, protocols and formalities hide this deficit."

GATEKEEPERS & THE "OLD GUARD"

Due to the democratization of technology and manufacturing brought about by the Maker Movement, as well as interconnected global networks, gatekeepers have largely disappeared. This is either good or bad depending on what lens to choose to look at it from. For some, it is one of the most liberating times in human history. For others, this massive level of disruption spells a serious threat to entrenched institutions and interest groups. Physicist Max Planck famously said, "A new scientific truth does not triumph by convincing its opponents and making them see the light, but rather because its opponents eventually die, and a new generation grows up that is familiar with it." In one of Jeff Bezos' letters to shareholders, he noted, "Even well meaning gatekeepers slow innovation. When a platform is self-service, even the improbable ideas can get tried, because there's no expert gatekeeper ready to say 'that will never work!' And guess what — many of those improbable ideas actually do work, and society is the beneficiary of that diversity." The internet, crowdfunding, and independent ecommerce stores are all self-service platforms.

BUILDERS (DOERS) > BUREAUCRATS (TALKERS)

The antithesis of a builder is a bureaucrat. As a creative builder myself, I've loathed bureaucracy my entire life — I've just never had a precise label to describe it. True builders are busy building, not shuffling paperwork, filling out forms, or wrapping themselves up in endless red tape and meetings. Jim Collins, in his book *Good To Great*, calls bureaucracy "the cancer of mediocrity" and arrives at the conclusion, "The purpose of bureaucracy is to compensate for incompetence and lack of discipline." A bias for disciplined action and an ethic of entrepreneurship — the "fail fast" engineering-first culture at the heart of Silicon Valley — are the antidotes to bureaucratic creep. Jamie Dimon, Chairman & CEO of Chase Bank, affirmed, "Bureaucracy is a disease. Bureaucracy drives out good people, slows down decision making, kills innovation and is often the petri dish of bad politics...Leaders must continually drive for speed and accuracy to eliminate waste and kill bureaucracy. When you get in great shape, you don't stop excercising."

BEING A PIONEER & CONTRARIAN

Albert Einstein proclaimed, "Great spirits have always encountered opposition from mediocre minds. The mediocre mind is incapable of understanding the man who refuses to bow blindly to conventional predjudices and chooses instead to express his opinions courageously and honestly." On leading his team of designers and engineers, James Dyson has said, "I want people who feel as though they are pioneers, and want to do something in a different and better way...Wrong thinking is the best way to start. Eventually you'll come to a solution that no one has ever thought of." If you're brave enough to challenge conventional wisdom and follow your own path, be prepared to be misunderstood at first, but realize at this edge is where breakthroughs occur.

ENTREPRENEURIAL MINDSET & SELF-RELIANCE

As Erick Ries, author of *The Lean Startup* puts it, "Anyone who is creating a new product or business under conditions of extreme uncertainty is an entrepreneur." Entrepreneurs are ultimately creative problem solvers who naturally seek out and take it upon themselves to engineer risk in their lives to the benefit of others. That's what an entrepreneur does — they provide value to people and they help people solve their problems and challenges. Chances are likely that with an increasingly changing technological landscape, the world of work is likely to become even more unpredictable, *not* less. So, even large businesses are finding they must still think like a startup to ensure they're constantly building, constantly expanding, constantly evolving and improving. Even if you are operating within a large business unit, it is still best to think of yourself as an entrepreneur (or "intrapreneur" as Ries calls it), and to start by asking What can I contribute? The most successful and well paid employees are always the ones who see themselves as part owners in the businesses they go to work for. They are self-motivated and self-managing — therefore they don't need to be managed. Again, in the words of the great Drucker, "A knowledge-based organization has to be an entrepreneurial organization, in the sense that it always starts out to make itself obsolete. Because that is the characteristic of knowledge. It is not the characteristic of a skill." So whatever your job title may be, you are first and foremost a PROBLEM SOLVER.

DEGREE VS. NO DEGREE (FORMAL VS. INFORMAL EDUCATION)

Soichiro Honda, the late founder and chief engineer of Honda Motor Corporation, said of his own educational pursuits, "I don't give a damn for the diploma. What I want is the knowledge." Society tends to overweight formalized credentials, and underweight actual knowledge, skills, and the ability to get results. While the classroom setting can be very valuable for multiple different reasons (including peer pressure, feedback loops and a sense of tribe accountability), choosing self-education or formal educated makes no difference in one's actual performance or results. The real proof is always in the pudding — if you're good, you're good — especially in creative or technical fields where the results can be shown concretely. Is an "alternative" form of education inferior by default, because it has not been vetted, formalized and / or accredited? Is a name-brand education automatically superior because of the name it carries? Education should be treated as a means to an end, not an end in itself. I've personally learned much more from workshops taught by leading industry pros and from reading books than I ever did in academia. I've also witnessed many of my peers think they can stop learning the minute they get their diploma. Jamie Dimon put it best in his 2017 letter to shareholders: "In less mutable times, a degree meant that formal learning was complete. You had aquired what you needed for a successful career in your field. A degree in today's world cannot mean the end of your studies. New discoveries, new advancements, new technologies and new terminology all mean that a degree will not carry you as far into the future as it once did. We must place a higher premium on lifelong learning." *Real* experience and on the job training are the most important of all — and the best way to get them when first starting out is to drop your ego and volunteer for anything and everything you can.

THE MYTH OF 'PROGRESS' FOR THE SAKE OF PROGRESS

Making something out of newer, more advanced materials doesn't automatically make it an improvement on what's come before. For instance, when I was younger (and a non-skateboarder, I might add) I was absolutely convinced that a company making aluminum skateboards, a brand named Yocaher, would come to totally supplant traditional plywood skateboard manufacturers as the technology caught on. At the same time, there were other companies who were developing carbon fiber skateboards, claiming that they were virtually indestructable and built to last a lifetime. However, both were terribly unsuccessful — because they missed the point: most skateboarders actually *preferred* the non-permanence and natural pliability of a wood board (known as the spring feel or "pop"). Also, the softness of the wood makes it better suited for grinding rails, lips and other features — something the other hi-tech brands missed. Early in my design studies, a green I.D. student proposed a line of carbon fiber kitchen utensils. But does assuming because they were made from the latest materials mean they were somehow better by default? Perhaps forks, knives, and spoons have remained as steel for centuries for good reason. There's nothing wrong with trying to push the envelope and make an honest try at making things better — but just keep in mind that along the way, sometimes the test of time can be the best filter for evolutionary change — what author and former stock trader Nassim Taleb refers to as the "Lindy Effect." Even in the year 3000, for better or worse I can almost guarantee that people will still be walking around in Chuck Taylors (casual), suit & tie (formal), and drinking Coca-Cola — because these are the "classics" that society is comfortable with.

DESIGN VS. ENGINEERING

Design is more than just skin deep. There's so much overlap between the meaning of design and engineering that they're often misconstrued or used interchangeably. To meet the challenges of the future, both disciplines will need to approach the field of R&D differently. Instead of being separated and siloed, the two must be better integrated holistically (end-to-end) or "full stack." Engineers are categorically good at building things and making them work, but less so when it comes to polishing, packaging, or finessing the finer cosmetic details. Designers are categorically good at creating visionary concept pieces, but tend to carry a "that's not my job" mentality when it comes to actually building or implementing them in the real world. In the words of James Dyson (an industrial designer by trade), "It's very important to be a designer *and* an engineer. There's no reason why the two should be separate. In the 21st century, it's time to bring design and engineering together. Engineering and design go hand-in-hand for me. They're not separate professions." For this reason, Dyson even created the special job title "design engineer."

THE MAKER PORTFOLIO

A maker portfolio is a collection of projects which showcases an individual's core competencies, as well as practical problem-solving capabilities, that is accessible online. What this collection of case studies and "spec projects" serves to do is to provide an alternative system that's better than testing or grades at evaluating an individual student's or job candidate's talents and abilities. Through evidence-based portfolios, the emphasis can and should be on *results* rather than on mere effort or inputs. Serial Kickstarter or Indiegogo campaign creators serve as an ultimate case-in-point example to the fact that a talented project creator's ability to get results and deliver on their promises can be evidenced outside of standardized testing and blasé résumés.

PRODUCERS (MAKERS) VS. CONSUMERS (USERS)

One of the most profound implications of the decentralization of manufacturing is that more and more people in society will be empowered to see themselves as makers and producers, rather than simply as consumers or users. The Maker Movement represents a bottom-up approach to change, rather than one that's traditionally top-down. Dale Dougherty, one of the leading voices of the movement, writes this about the new level of individual empowerment: "Manufacturing could be viewed as a creative process. What you can do with a 3D printer is manufacture a 3D object yourself...[The] message shouldn't be about jobs in manufacturing, but what people can do to become manufacturers. Those people were makers, and they looked at manufacturing in a different way. It actually wasn't about factories. It was about what you could build if you had access to the tools of production."

DECENTRALIZATION, GLOBALIZATION & CROWDFUNDING

The nature of desktop 3D printers, CNC machines, and laser cutters are opening up entirely new possibilities in the realm of decentralized manufacturing. Small batch size means that a handful of iterations can be made at a time, anywhere, and without the need for expensive tooling, dies, or production assembly equipment. This frees up products to be made to order or "on-demand," thereby opening up massive new possibilities in the way products are made, sold, and distributed to end users. In the past, supply and demand were limited by individual region, which often relied on the size of the customer base within that small territory. Now, instant global interconnectivity via the internet makes it possible for a person in a remote village town to sell a product of his or her own making to a worldwide customer base reaching all corners of the globe. This allows for extremely specialized or bespoke products within a specific market niche to gain traction with a large enough audience of independent consumers globally — not only to help those products thrive, but to potentially succeed as exciting new businesses that think and operate unconventionally. This is a trend that I see only increasing over time, as more and more people come online, and as more and more people gain access to the tools of production. This book you are holding in your hands would not be possible without the help and support of thousands of different Kickstarter backers across the globe, and is a testament to the power of these online communities. After successfully launching this book on Kickstarter and having gone through the process myself, I can honestly speak to the unlimited potential of the crowdfunding platform, and look forward to seeing what the future holds for peer-to-peer / bottom-up trade networks in general.

LEARNING FROM FAILURE (ANTIFRAGILE TINKERING)

No one illustrates the process of learning from failure better than James Dyson, who spent four and a half years and built 5,127 prototypes in order to nail down the final design of his original bagless cyclonic vacuum cleaner. Thomas Edison, one of Dyson's heroes, put it this way, "Genius is one percent inspiration and ninety-nine percent perspiration." In his books *Antifragile* and *Skin in the Game*, Nassim Taleb parallels these sentiments, providing a compelling arguement that more learning is actually done by self-directed tinkering, iteration, and explorative testing — including *failure* — rather than from academic reasoning, writing, "The abrasions of your skin guide your learning and discovery." Steve Jobs referred to learning from painful mistakes as "scar tissue."

RESOURCEFULNESS > RESOURCES, or "WWTSD?"

In the first Iron Man film, there's a scene where a frustrated businessman confronts his team of stumped research scientists, who are struggling to reduce the form factor of a room-sized power supply down to a handheld-sized device. When his head scientist exclaims that it's an impossible task, the boss snaps back, "Tony Stark was able to build this in a cave...with a bunch of SCRAPS!!" My heuristic for resourcefulness, or making the very most with the very least, is WWTSD — or "What Would Tony Stark Do?" The Wright Brothers were two bicycle mechanics up against armies of heavily funded, government-sponsored academic research committees. Although they had no more than a public high school education, little money and no contacts — they were far from unschooled, making the most of their situation and teaching themselves through ceaseless curiosity instead. Because the house they lived in had no electricity or indoor plumbing, they resorted to non-stop reading of books that were supplied by their father. In the end, it was the brothers who went down in history for first pioneering manned aerial flight, through their sheer grit, courage, determination and ingenuity — helping to push the human race forward as a result. Fast forward more than a century later, and a brave entrepreneur / technologist named Elon Musk has been able to outperform NASA with his tiny little rocket startup, SpaceX. When asked how he acquired the knowledge and expertise to become the CTO of a rocketship company (apart from a generic background in physics), he replied, "I read a lot of books and talked to a lot of smart people...I don't have an aerospace degree." Even one of the largest corporations of our time, Amazon, forced its executives in the early days (an example set by Bezos himself), to work on DIY "door desks" made literally from unpainted doors bought from Home Depot. Money is a resource, time is a resource, technology is a resource, knowing the right people is a resource; but lacking the *resources* is not the problem — lacking *resourcefulness* is the real problem. If you grew up with little or no resources, realize that you're playing the game on "hard mode" and that your only solution is to learn to become very resourceful. If you're creative enough, if you're determined enough, if you're passionate enough, if you're strong enough, if you're bold enough, if you're disciplined enough, you will always find what you need to succeed. Where there's a will there's *always* a way. THE ULTIMATE RESOURCE IS RESOURCEFULNESS!

III. THE FUTURE IS WHAT WE <u>MAKE</u> IT

Although interest in STEM fields seems to be at an all time high, many makers are still looked upon by professional scientists and engineers as mere hobbyists or amateurs. My mission in writing this expanded *GOLD* edition is to help bridge the gap between the amatuer and the professional, by giving the starry-eyed tinkerers out there an exhaustive exposure to as many of the different tools and processes available. This will also help to unveil the *Matrix code* behind the physical world that so many of us take for granted. Success in R&D today requires one to be bilingual or even trilingual in order to communicate seamlessly between the designer, engineer, and manufacturer. For this reason, at the back of the book I've also included a list of important terminology which will help you to understand and to start speaking the language. Having a firm grasp of this key industry terminology might sound trivial at first, but will serve as true superpowers when it comes time to tackle the nitty-gritty of product development from a solid engineering standpoint. I can't overemphasis how important this is — because even if you yourself are not the one who will ultimately be building your idea, you will still need to be able to clearly communicate with the folks who will be! Perhaps one of the more instructive stories of this all-important fact is from Soichiro Honda, after a Formula 1 engine designed by a green engineer had failed. When Honda found out who was responsible, he then roared, "No wonder the piston gets burned. You have changed the thickness. I hate college graduates. They only use their heads...I have been making and touching pistons for several tens of years. I am fully aware how critical half a millimeter is here...A company does not need people like you who use only their heads. Before you laid out this design, why didn't you listen to the opinions of those experienced people in the shop? If you think academic study in college is everything, you are totally wrong. You will be useless in Honda unless you spend more time on the spot for many years to come. You will go to the machine shop and apologize to every person there, for wasting their efforts."

I firmly believe the age-old wisdom, "Give a man a fish, feed him for a day; teach a man to fish, feed him for a lifetime." In going to great lengths to make this book as explicitly detailed as possible, I hope I've not only shown you how to fish, but also how to research, develop, and build new rod & reel technologies; source the proper materials for their construction; and arm yourself with a powerful set of tools in your tacklebox which will ensure the most successful catch — no matter your unique setting or situation. However, it is not enough to simply dream up a better future, we must take action on those dreams to make them a reality!

Au·to·di·dact

ˌôdōˈdīdakt/

noun

1.a self-taught person.

MERRIAM-WEBSTER DICTIONARY

Introduction

Working on a plaster head cast in my original "innovation kitchen" (aka home garage work shop) — Katy, Texas Circa 2008.

THIS IS THE BOOK I ALWAYS WISHED I HAD.

The path leading to where I am today is an unlikely story. Many years ago, I started out in a much different place than where I am today. Unlike many of my professional peers, friends, and colleagues who have enjoyed successful design careers — I did not come from a family of designers, engineers, businesspeople, or intellectuals. Both of my two parents worked for the United States Post Office all of their lives. Because of this, I had no set path to follow early on. I had no template to turn to. What I learned early on was entirely empirical — through trial, error and experiment, which I would conduct in the family garage. Being born and raised in a small local community near Houston, Texas, I have to admit there was not many opportunities for creative individuals. I had always coveted places such as California, where creativity and innovative new ideas seemed to be in unlimited supply. So, many years ago, as my first stint in entrepreneurship (and to keep myself entertained) I would hand make Batman look-alike movie props and reproduce them in the home garage — using many of the RTV silicone molds and urethane castings covered in this book. I would then sometimes sell these reproductions on eBay, where I would earn extra income on the side while attending community college and lifeguarding in the summertime.

Back in those days (around 2005-2008) there was a local forum just for Batman prop makers called the Brotherhood of The Bat (BOTB). This was a die-hard community where fans of the Batman film series would come together to discuss home-made DIY costumes, props, and even homemade life-sized driving Batmobiles. The forum was populated with active members from all across the country; a community of autodidacts who came together to share their knowledge while lending positive support, tips & tricks, and constructive criticism to learn and grow from. This was long before the days of 3D printing technologies, where the internet was still in its crude infancy — and before the term "maker" became a household name. Many of these people simply had a passion for making and collecting film props after their routine 9-5 day jobs, many of them parents with families. Some of the favorite techniques used among the BOTB community were Super Sculpey clay sculpture, RTV silicone molding & casting, and latex plaster casting — these are many of the same techniques used in the film industry, but on a homemade DIY scale. It was here that I developed my curiosity for making things, my love for working with my hands, and the satisfaction of building professional quality models using only availably sourced materials. Shortly after, I took a job at Lowe's Home Improvement with the gaol of eventually attending design university. I used my short tenure here to become a connoisseur of sorts on the tens of thousands of different tools and materials available — from sand papers, to spray paints, and much more. Afterward, this passion was carried into design school, both at the University of Houston and later the Art Center College of Design — where I finally settled out on the same West Coast I had always dreamed of. Having never set foot in a professional model shop prior to that time (I was clueless when it came to using tools in gradeschool, having never attended a single shop class), it was during this time that I developed a more formal expertise working with more advanced tools and machinery, which would later be refined through years of working as a professional Industrial Product Designer in a handful of different industries. Although today much of design is done either through digital sketching or 3D CAD software, making prototypes is still a part of my everyday work life — no matter the size of the company or client. Although even myself I am relying more heavily on CAD and 3D printing, there is still no replacement for or greater satisfaction than getting back to the tactile touch and feel of building physical things. These are critical skills to have for anyone considering a professional career in design or engineering, or simply for recreational entertainment purposes and the love of making.

My purpose in writing this book is to provide a practical, condensed guide to almost all of the major tools and materials available for making things — in a non-formulaic, overly technical, or jargon-filled textbook. Instead, *The Maker's Field Guide* has been written as a practical reference guide to reveal some of the closely guarded secrets of professional designers and model makers, touching on everything from traditional "old school" manual techniques to the most cutting-edge tools like 3D printing and robotic CNC machining. I am a visual learner, so seeing real world case studies has always been the best way for me to learn. I feel I am not unique here, so I've taken the time to make this book as clear and visually instructive as possible. Whereas there may be many books out there specializing on individual subjects such as woodworking or 3D printing, there has yet to be a single volume distilling them all in one complete package — until now. I truly believe there is no one single tool that's adequate for every job, and just as the professional chef will be able to craft more elaborate dishes given a wider access to a variety of ingredients, I feel the more tools the designer or maker has in his toolkit will give him (or her) the opportunity to use the best *set* of ingredients to tackle the particular project at hand. While not every tool or material will be needed all the time or for every scenario, it's up to the individual to choose what works best for him in his specific situation. In this way, the professional learns to be resourceful — being able to perform successfully in a variety of different environments without limitation or excuses (i.e. one may work in a school or an office where expensive machines like 3D printers and scanners are unavailable, yet where there may be open access to a number of different clays and modeling foams). In this way, one learns to make the most of the cards he is dealt with — instead of waiting for that perfect hand to arrive. The best chef is the one who will be able to craft and deliver the highest quality food & experience regardless of whether there's a shortage of certain ingredients at market. These tips & techniques can simply be regarded as "golden standards" when it comes to working with each tool or application, to be used on a case-by-case basis or as needed. I truly feel having the right tools — and knowing how to use them properly — is half the battle to professional quality results. Otherwise, one can experiment and fail year after year (as I did in the beginning) will little to no progress being made. Hopefully this guide will inspire and empower creative tinkerers and entrepreneurs alike as an essential tool used literally in "the field" or on the shelf, and in the garage of every student or professional machinist, machine operator, shop technician, Hollywood special FX film-making or model making crew, engineer, industrial designer, architect, environmental or set designer, and DIY makers — creating the future one project at a time in garages, labs and makerspaces all across the world.

You can't make a world-class project in a world-class mess!

Clark Acton

MODEL SHOP MANAGER

Chapter 1 — Work Shop Overview

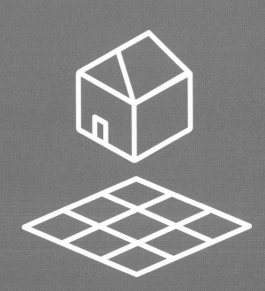

1 SHOP OVERVIEW

2 MACHINES

3 HAND TOOLS

4 MATERIALS

5 APPLICATION

6 ADV. PROJECTS

Shop Overview

SHOP BASICS

Typically, best practices in most professional shops call for each area of the shop to be divided into subsets, organized by machine type or application type (such as woodworking). This will help keep sanding dust away from a spray painting lab (one of the biggest no-no's, since dust in the air will ruin paint quality), and some of the noisier tools will also be separated into an area all by themselves. The professional shop mindset often is, "when you're not working on projects, you're working on shop infrastructure." Organization can help elevate the efficiency of shop work. "First order retrievability" is a term used to describe frequently used tools within quick reach.

SHOP INFRASTRUCTURE

The different areas of a professional shop will typically be divided as follows:

Wood Shop / Woodworking Room - a room specifically for woodworking tools like the lathe, band saw, table saw, router table, planer, and drill press.

Metal Shop / Metalworking Room - a separate area for metalworking tools like the metal lathe, welding torches, metal grinders, sheet metal foot shear, and chop saw. Red PVC screens will typically be placed to shield other people from sparks, noise, UV light and other potential hazards.

Spray Booth - a fully enclosed, well ventilated, clean room set up for spray painting applications only. This room must be as dust-free as possible, with special filtration to pull dust particulates and harmful paint chemicals from the air.

Drying Room - a completely separate area from the spray booth, where models are left to dry undisturbed.

Sanding Room - a separate room where models are sanded, using tools like the disk sander, belt sander, spindle sander, and sand blaster. This room must be as far away from the spray booth as possible.

PRO TIPS

Keep your shop area as clean as possible, making it a daily practice to clean up after yourself. One of my favorite qoutes is "you can't make a world-class project in a world-class mess." Some production lines, such as McLaren's Design & Technology Centre in the United Kingdom, will immediately drop everything they're doing just to clean up a small oil spill immediately after it hits the factory floor. This fanatical obsession with cleanliness is a testament to the OCD level of care and pride taken towards the production of their high-performance production cars as well as their Formula 1 specialty race cars — and pays dividends in the overall quality of the final products coming off the assembly line (an area I mistakingly neglected years ago, which can easily be seen by the clutter of my former garage in this book's intro).

DO NOT SPRAY BOOTH WALLS
$100 FINE PER OCCURRENCE

Above: A typical spray booth will be clean, well-lit, with a strong ventilation system. A dust-free environment is key to a professional paint finish.

17

Shop Safety

PROTECTION

Safety Glasses / Goggles - are an essential safety piece, with many styles available. Whichever style you select, make sure they are safety rated. Some shop technicians who wear prescription eyewear that's already safety rated feel they can get by without wearing goggles.

Disposable Gloves - nitrile is the most protective type of disposable gloves available. Nitrile is protective against harsh chemicals like acetone (which will dissolve latex), also better for people with latex allergies. Usually blue or black in color. Latex gloves are less protective than Nitrile, and are usually an off-white natural rubber color. Vinyl gloves are clear in color, and are the least protective. They are typically for the budget minded, or for people with latex allergies.

Hearing Protection - another must-have safety item to have, especially if you want to protect your long-term hearing, is a set of ear plugs or muffs. Several types are available, including over-ear style earmuffs (or "shooting" muffs), expanding EVA foam earplugs, and EVA foam headband plugs — at far right. The EVA headband plugs are my personal favorite, since they are lightweight and not easily misplaced like the loose foam earplugs.

Respirator Mask - NIOSH (National Institute for Occupational Safety and Health) rated respirators feature replaceable carbon filter catridges, which will filter most toxic chemicals. As a rule of thumb, If you can smell toxic fumes through the mask, it's time to replace the filters. Small dust masks work fine for sawdust or sanding dust, but will not protect against harsh chemical vapors. Follow the manufacturer's recommendations when replacing filter cartridges and don't skimp on buying a high quality mask.

PRO TIPS

Storing respirator masks in a zip-lock bag will help to extend the life of the filter cartridges between uses. To this day, I still re-use disposable gloves if possible — which cuts down on trips to the hardware store. Pinch the lower palm area with gloved hand, then once halfway off, repeat on the other side to until removed.

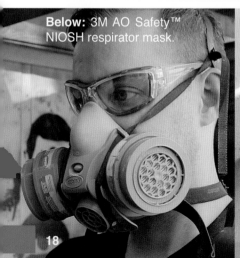

Below: 3M AO Safety™ NIOSH respirator mask.

Below: Blue nitrile gloves.

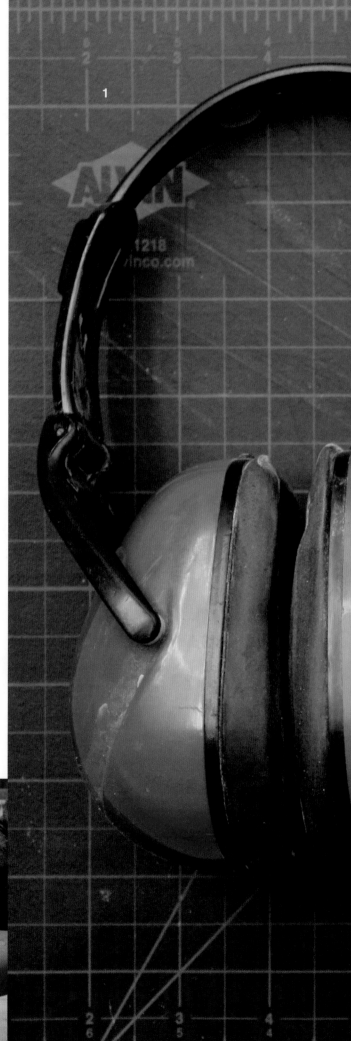

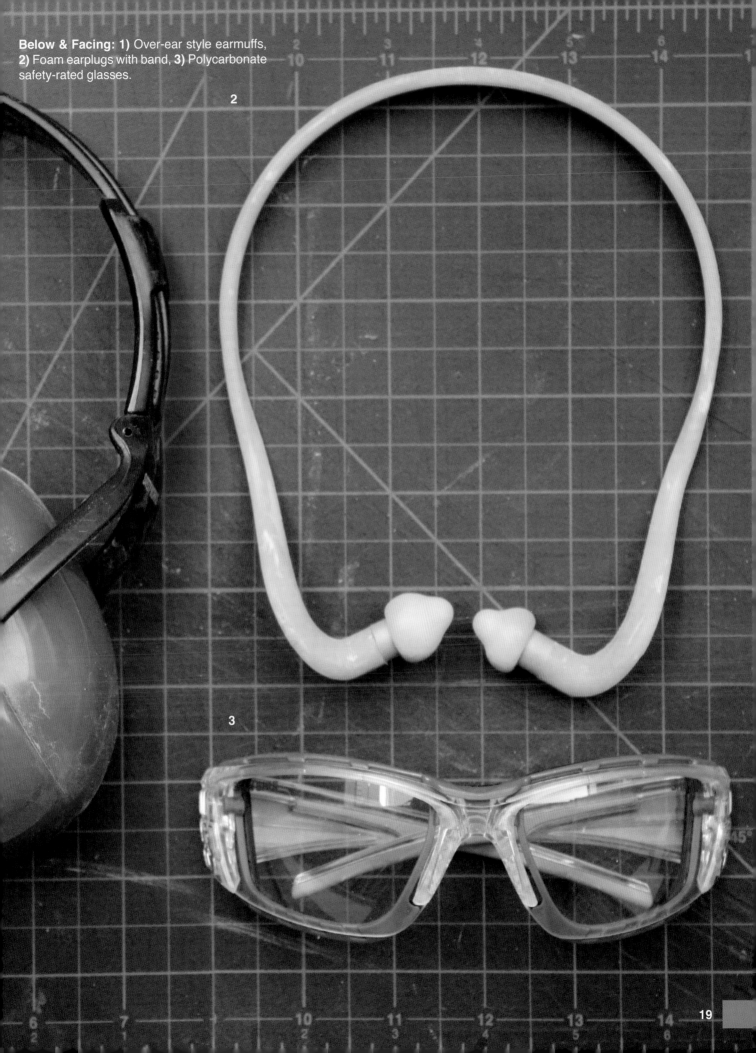

Below & Facing: 1) Over-ear style earmuffs, **2)** Foam earplugs with band, **3)** Polycarbonate safety-rated glasses.

2

3

POWER DRILL
PG. 94

BATTERY POWERED
SHOP FAN

CUSTOM-BUILT
STORAGE SHELVES
PG. 12

TOOLBOX
PG. 90

work·shop

/ˈwərkˌSHäp/

noun

noun: **workshop**; plural noun:
workshops

> 1. a room or building in
> which goods are
> manufactured or repaired.
> synonyms: workroom, studio,
> atelier; factory, plant

Ted Fossum's home garage work shop in Atlanta, Georgia.
Ted specially designed and organized his space to meet the
needs of the different types of projects he works on — from
repairing cars and motorcycles, to creative woodworking
and metalworking projects.

For more information on Ted's work shop, he also hosts
a YouTube channel — Ted's The Great Shop — where
he shares his DIY projects and custom workshop design
elements.

Stay Safe!

Not too fast.
Not too tired.

**BATTERY POWERED
SHOP LIGHTS**

**DREMEL TOOL
PG. 98**

**EAR MUFFS
PG. 8**

**CROSS-CUT SAW
PG. 38**

**SHOP VAC
PG. 96**

Right: A custom vertically mounted, collapsible tool storage unit constructed from plywood saves precious shop space. Many shop owners prefer to build their own custom storage solutions, to fit the exact measurements and infrastructure requirements of their particular workspace.

Below: When unfolded, custom storage solutions like these keep every tool close at hand with minimal to no setup time. This is also known as "first order retrievability."

Above: Custom tool storage shelves keep shops neat, clean and organized. Ted's garage is only slightly larger than a one-car garage, so he must utilize every inch of available space on hand. Larger tools like the table saw are fitted with rolling caster wheels so they can be quickly rolled out during use, or tucked away for larger projects — including car mechanic work.

23

POWER OUTLET

mak·er·space

/ˈmākərˌspās/

noun

noun: makerspace; plural noun: makerspaces

> 1. a place in which people with shared interests, especially in computing or technology, can gather to work on projects while sharing ideas, equipment, and knowledge.

Urban Workshop's Makerspace in Costa Mesa, California is one of the most impressive spaces in the country, with over $1 million in equipment — including wood shop, electronics lab, computer lab, 3D printers, CNC mills, laser cutters, fabric areas, and co-working space.

Membership-based Makerspaces like these are popping up constantly in major creative / entrepreneurial business hubs across the USA and in other parts of the world — popular amongst engineering startups, small businesses, and hobbyists alike.

ASSEMBLY

LASER CUT
ACRYLIC SIGNAGE

LASER
CUTTER AND ENGRAVER

DUST COLLECTION
VAC HOSES

COMPUTER
WORKSTATION

LASER CUTTER

Above & Below: High-end Makerspaces will stock the most advanced, high-tech automated machinery with a wide variety of low-tech, traditional (manual) machines. Urban Workshop's California facility is on par with even the most elaborate of in-house corporate R&D labs.

Above & Below (clockwise from top): Custom shop signage cut on the CNC router table, a dedicated sewing lab with materials for screen printed logos and graphics, vacuum forming & pressure casting lab.

ELECTRONICS   PRESSURE CASTING   VACUUM FORMING   fabric & sewing   SILKSCREENING

man cave

noun

1. a room or other area in a home that is primarily a male sanctuary, designed and furnished to accommodate the man's recreational activities, hobbies, etc.

Kris Petrat's man cave garage space in Long Beach, California. Kris's garage is custom-built to suit his passion for racing Motocross and working on motorcycles, featuring relics from the Southern California races he's participated in — such as Red Bull's infamous Day in The Dirt. The Man Cave can become a highly personalized sanctuary, uniquely designed to reflect each individual owner's character and personality.

TOOL BOX

INSPIRATION

CUSTOM-BUILT SHELVING

TUNES

INSPIRATION

MORALE
BOOSTERS
(TROPHIES,
ETC.)

SHOP LIGHTS

PAPER
TOWELS

AIR HOSE

CUSTOM-BUILT
SHELVING

Below & Facing: A fun helmet Kris and I custom built while I was Lead Designer at LIFT Aviation / EVS Sports. Take your pick — Miller or Red Bull?

Optimizing Space: Kris's garage isn't the biggest space around, so this is where he had to get creative with vertical and wall shelf storage. This is where you may want to hire a professional — Kris gave his carpenter a brief sketch to communicate his intent, and the rest was up to the builder to figure out how to make it all work.

A study done of the most successful CEO's in America (not celebrity CEO's, but those who, without fanfare and jumping jobs every few years, get the work done) found one factor they all have in common: They enjoy working with their hands. The older ones had cars that they worked on in high school (when you could still work on your own car) or had wood shops in their garages where they made furniture. When a faucet needed a washer or a door wouldn't close properly, they did it themselves. The longevity of a CEO's career is directly proportional to his or her problem-solving skills and ability to adapt and grow with the job.

Yvon Chounaird

**FOUNDER/CEO,
PATAGONIA -** *LET MY PEOPLE GO SURFING*

Chapter 2 —
Machines

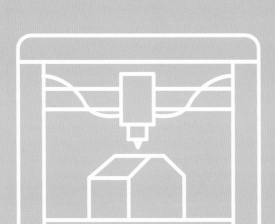

1 SHOP OVERVIEW

2 MACHINES

3 HAND TOOLS

4 MATERIALS

5 APPLICATION

6 ADV. PROJECTS

Table Saw

TOOL BASICS

The table saw is the most fundamental of all machines in the shop and is by far the best machine to use for cutting pieces square. It is one of the fundamental tools of woodworking, and If used correctly can precisely cut through many different material types. A different blade should be used for cutting plastic versus wood or metal.

Blade Height / Angle - two blade adjustments knobs are located beneath the saw's table — a height adjustment knob at front, and an angle adjustment knob on the side.

Cross Cut - a cut through the width (shortest side) of a piece of material. Keep the material down to the table and against the fence at all times. On this particular saw, a vacuum tube has been installed in order to help with saw dust cleanup.

Cross-Cut Fence - this fence fits into a groove on the tabletop of the saw. These can be pre-made or specially built jigs.

Cross-Cut Sled - is also used for cross-cutting, but is more accurate. This sled is a pre-made or custom-built jig which slides along two guide rails located in the table saw's surface. The sled keeps the material from moving to the left, right, or at an angle during a cross cut.

Cross-Cut Sled Fence - rollers located on the back side of the saw's table, to support longer pieces of material. Also works as a cross-cut sled support.

Rip Cut - a cut through the length of a piece of material.

Rip Fence - a variable-position moving wall, or "fence" used to guide a piece throughout the entire length of a cut.

Miter Cut - angle cut or bevel (i.e. 45° joint = 90° corner).

Dado Cut - a groove or slot cut into one piece of material into which another piece of material will fit snugly.

Rabbet Cut - similar to a dado, but where the recess or notch is cut into the edge of a piece of material — ie. joining two 90° box faces together to be flush at corner.

Top Suppliers: Delta™, Laguna™

SAFETY TIPS

Keep your part to be cut down to the table at all times. Always turn off the machine after your cut is finished.

PRO TIPS

Always make sure the blade is sharp. The sharper the blade, the more clean & accurate the cut.

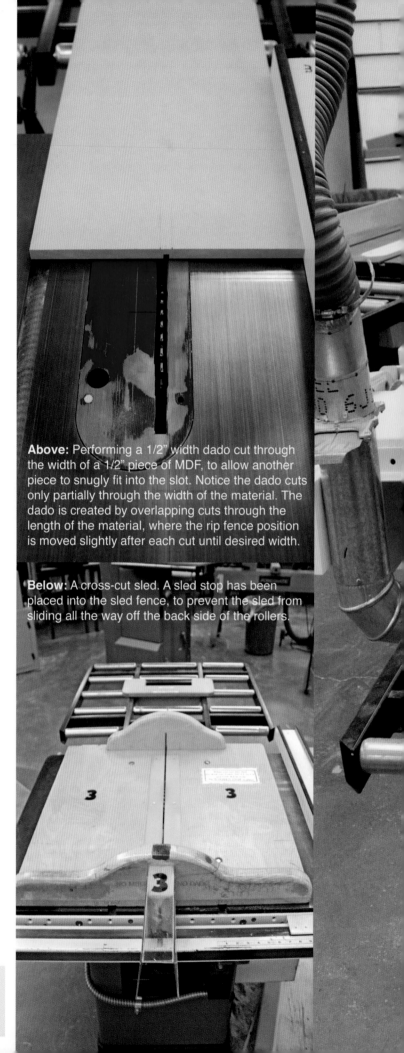

Above: Performing a 1/2" width dado cut through the width of a 1/2" piece of MDF, to allow another piece to snugly fit into the slot. Notice the dado cuts only partially through the width of the material. The dado is created by overlapping cuts through the length of the material, where the rip fence position is moved slightly after each cut until desired width.

Below: A cross-cut sled. A sled stop has been placed into the sled fence, to prevent the sled from sliding all the way off the back side of the rollers.

RIP
FENCE

CROSS-CUT
SLED GUIDE
RAILS

WORK
TABLE

BLADE

CROSS-CUT
SLED FENCE

Cross-Cut Sled: Adjusting blade height using a cross-cut sled. There is a slotted groove running down the center of the sled, allowing the blade to peak through. Ideally, the blade should have no more than three teeth exposed above a piece of material — anything more becomes dangerous.

Cross-Cut: 1) For cutting through the middle of a board, the piece is supported by both hands at both ends. **2)** After the cut, the two halves are pulled away from the blade. Continue to push the sled all the way through the blade and onto the sled fence, located at the back-side of the table.

Above: 1) To adjust blade height, use the knob below the saw's table. **2)** The blade angle can also be adjusted, using a knob at the side of the table. When these two adjustments are used in combination, the table saw can become an extremely precise cutting tool. **3)** A rabbet cut on the edges of a plywood box **4)** A dado cut made by overlapping blade cuts.

Rip Cut: To start a rip cut, position the rip fence according to the final desired part measurements. Turn the blade on, then guide the material along the fence, being mindful to keep fingers safely away from the blade at all times. Continue to follow all the way through the material, then turn the blade off before safely removing leftover pieces.

Band Saw

TOOL BASICS

The band saw is also one of the fundamental machines in the model shop. This machine is designed for cutting through muscle and bone in the meat-packing industry — so extreme caution must be used with the blade. The blade can cut through various woods, plastics, and soft metals like aluminum. To begin a cut, turn the machine on. While keeping the material down to the table, push the material through the blade. Keep your fingers as far away from the blade as possible. Follow through the cut by reaching around the backside of the blade, keeping hands and fingers clear and away. "Backing Up", or moving the material backwards is also possible.

Blade Type - the blade's depth will determine the size of curves you'll be able to cut. The smaller the depth of the blade, the smaller, tighter, and rounder the cut can be — useful for finer details or curvy organic shapes.

Blade Height - a knob on the back of the blade allows for height adjustment. Make sure the blade height adjustment is set so that no more than 1/2" is exposed over the top surface of the material to be cut.

Table Angle - the band saw's table can be adjusted from 0-45° angle. Below the table are a set of knobs — loosen the knobs below the table, adjust to the desired angle, and re-tighten to set back into place.

Rip Fence - like the table saw, the band saw has a variable-position, moving fence used to guide a piece throughout the entire length of a cut.

Top Suppliers: Delta™, Laguna™

SAFETY TIPS

Keep your part to be cut down and to the table at all times. Push the piece into the cut at the start, then pull the piece through at the end. Always turn the machine off after your cut is finished.

PRO TIPS

Replace the blade when it wears out. The sharper the blade, the more clean & accurate the cut. Blades that are dull can cause burning and smoking in the material.

Below: Properly positioning a rip fence at left so that the part is where marked (shown here through the center). Notice correct blade height.

CUT WIDTH

SAFE ZONE   SAFE ZONE

Above: Correct reach-around position where hands are held away from the blade. The part is pulled all the way through the blade at the end of the cut.

DRIVE
WHEEL

BLADE
SERVICE
ACCESS
DOOR

POWER
SWITCH

BLADE
GUARD

BLADE

CROSS-CUT
SLED GUIDE

WORK TABLE

DUST VAC
HOSE

SAFETY FIRST
PLEASE POST THESE SAFETY RULES
NEAR YOUR MACHINE FOR REFERENCE
SAFETY RULES for DELTA
BAND SAWS

DELTA

Do your part
Please clean up
and place your
bits in the can

No cutting
Plaster

39

Blade Height: A knob on the side of the blade allows for height adjustment. There should be no more than 1/2" of blade exposed above the piece of material being cut. Blade speed and tension can also be adjusted. Blades are interchangeable, with different teeth shape and size & shape configurations specially suited for wood or steel.

Table Adjustment: The saw's table can be adjusted from 0-45° for angled cuts. After the is table has been locked into place, the material is then guided along the rip fence during the cut.

Cutting: Showing 1/2" of blade exposed above the material. Parts can be rotated and "backed up" during a cut — however, make sure to reach around the blade and keep hands and fingers clear and away at all times.

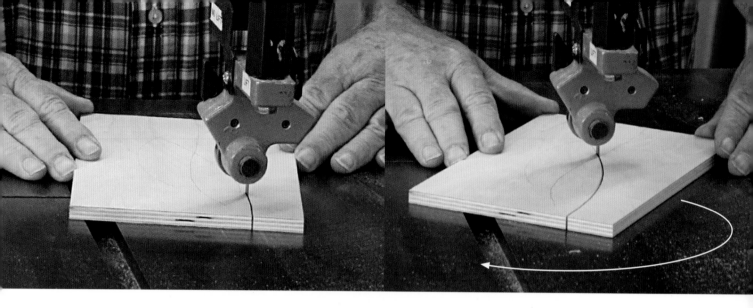

Above: Starting a proper entry and exit of a cut. Unlike a scroll saw, a band saw will need to create an entry cut, which will be an artifact left in the finished piece. Use a scroll saw or handheld reciprocating saw (jig saw) if a clean hole cutout is needed.

Below: This piece shows an expert level of saw control — the piece has been "backed out" through the entry cut of the blade.

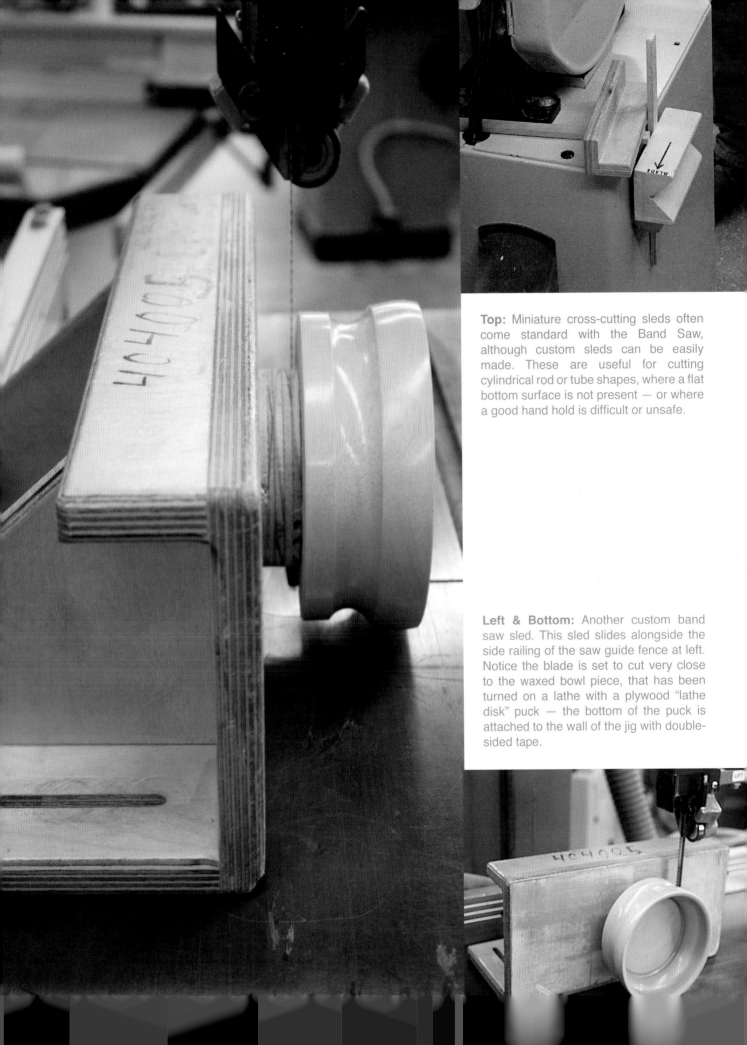

Top: Miniature cross-cutting sleds often come standard with the Band Saw, although custom sleds can be easily made. These are useful for cutting cylindrical rod or tube shapes, where a flat bottom surface is not present — or where a good hand hold is difficult or unsafe.

Left & Bottom: Another custom band saw sled. This sled slides alongside the side railing of the saw guide fence at left. Notice the blade is set to cut very close to the waxed bowl piece, that has been turned on a lathe with a plywood "lathe disk" puck — the bottom of the puck is attached to the wall of the jig with double-sided tape.

Scroll Saw

TOOL BASICS

The scroll saw essentially functions much like a mini band saw. This machine is able to cut fine detail in small pieces. A small lamp can be positioned around your work, and a tiny air hose sprays the work area to keep clear of saw dust. Unlike the band saw, the scroll saw can cut inside a part without the need for an entry or exit cut. Blade tension can be adjusted through a knob on the top of the saw. Hand-held equivalents to the scroll saw are the jigsaw and the reciprocating saw — which are much more difficult to control and lack some of the finer precision of the scroll saw, since both lack a workable table surface to cut on.

Top Suppliers: DeWalt™

SAFETY TIPS

As with the band saw, as a general rule position the blade roughly 1/2" above the part being cut.

PRO TIPS

Always make sure the blade is sharp. The most dangerous blade is a dull blade, and the sharper the blade, the more clean & accurate the cut. Different blade types with special tooth patterns can be used to cut different materials.

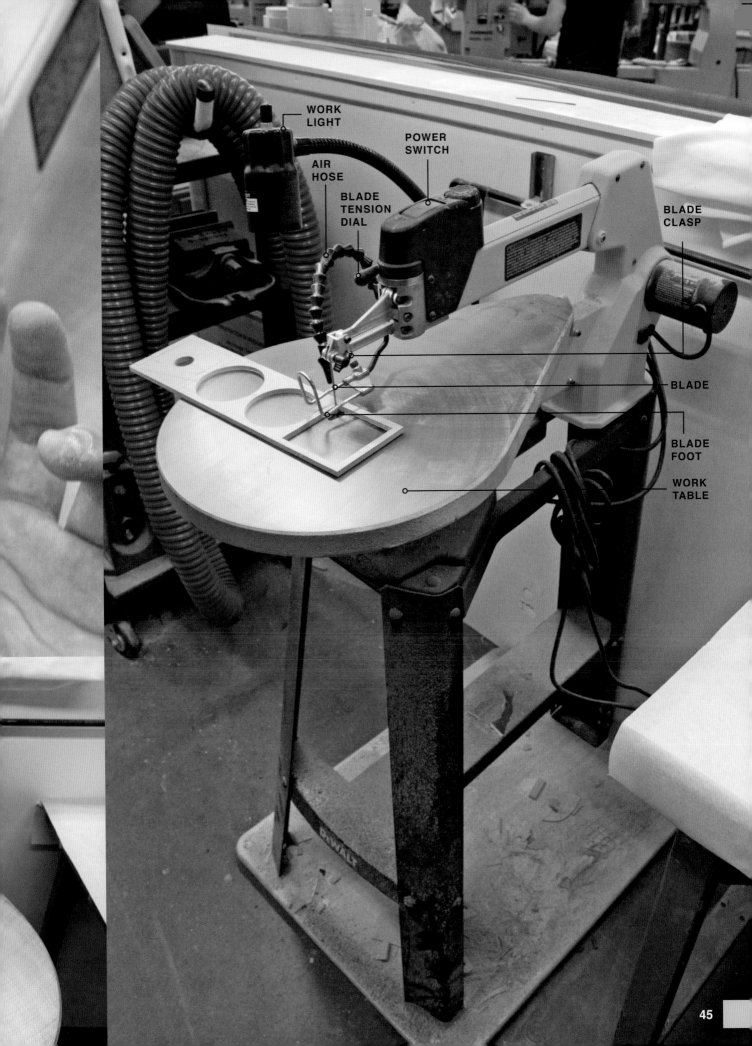

WORK
LIGHT

AIR
HOSE

POWER
SWITCH

BLADE
TENSION
DIAL

BLADE
CLASP

BLADE

BLADE
FOOT

WORK
TABLE

45

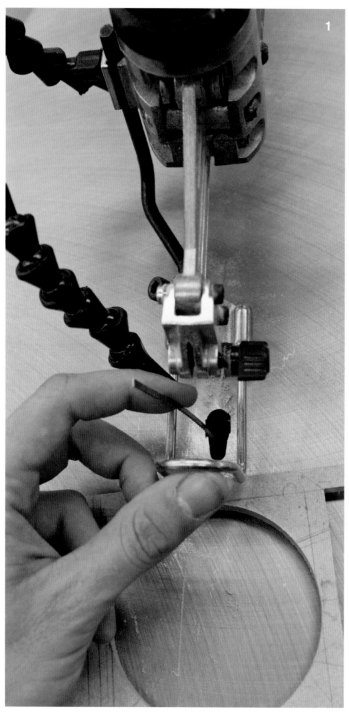

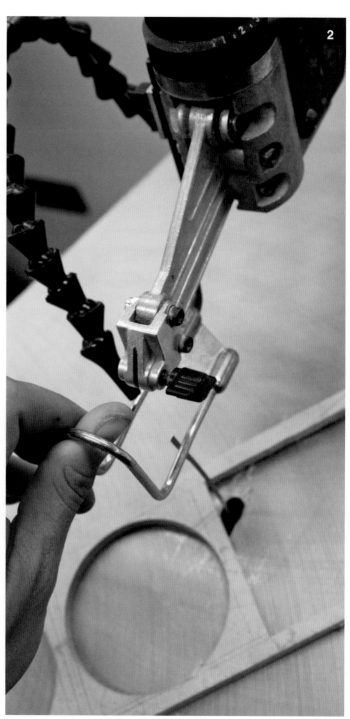

1) To make a cut inside of a part, first remove the blade. Blade tension must be released and the blade carefully loosened.

2) Next, the blade head is lifted and the material is placed through the blade. The blade clasp knob is then re-tightened.

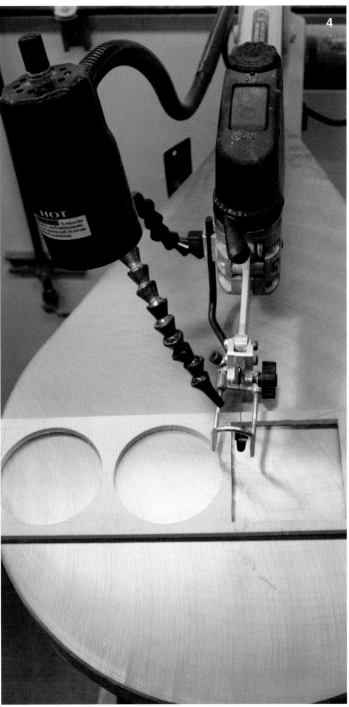

3) Once the blade is tight, tension and speed can be adjusted using the control knob on the top of the saw.

4) A small lamp can be positioned around your work, and a tiny air hose sprays the work area to keep the work area clear for precision cutting.

Cross-Cut Saw

TOOL BASICS

The cross-cut saw is the best way to quickly cross cut a material through a horizontal dimension. It is not as accurate as the table saw, but much quicker — since there is no need to set up a sled or cross-cut fence. This saw produces ragged edges that aren't as reliably square as on the table saw.

The cross-cut saw is basically a circular saw mounted on a pull system, which is perpendicular to its table.

Top Suppliers: Delta™

SAFETY TIPS

Wait until the blade comes to a complete stop before trying to make any measurements on material. Measurements can be cut to the left or to the right of the blade.

PRO TIPS

Use this machine to cut larger pieces than the chop saw can handle, but aren't large enough to need to be cut on the panel saw.

DUST VAC HOSE

SLIDING RAIL
POSITION LOCK

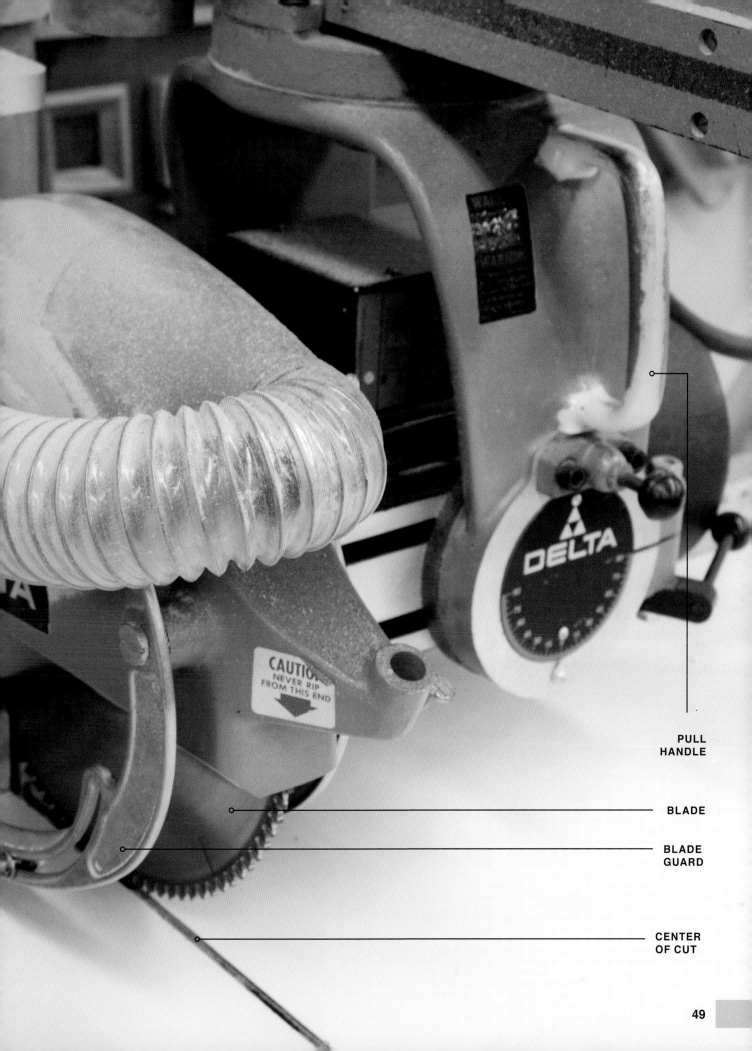

PULL
HANDLE

BLADE

BLADE
GUARD

CENTER
OF CUT

CAUTION
NEVER RIP
FROM THIS END

DELTA

Chop Saw

TOOL BASICS

The chop saw, or miter saw, is a circular saw that cuts in a quick, chopping motion. The saw can rotate on a swivel for cutting different angles in materials. Use this saw for rapid cutting (rough cuts only). It is not intended for precise work requiring accurate measurements. A vacuum hose helps to collect sanding dust, which can ignite in the air. Freestanding models are also available, and are a fantastic option for working on remote or outdoor projects.

SAFETY TIPS

Wait until the blade comes to a complete stop before trying to make any measurements in material. Measurements can be cut either to the left or to the right of the blade.

Top Suppliers: DeWalt™, Makita™, Milwuakee™, RIGID™

PRO TIPS

Use this saw when needing to make many cuts. Use it to roughly divide up a long wood board, or other material, into smaller, more manageable sized pieces. These pieces can then be taken to the table saw for more precise cuts, if needed.

Below: Free-standing chop saw.

Below: A custom built saw table setup made from MDF.

MITER ANGLE
ADJUSTMENT LATCH

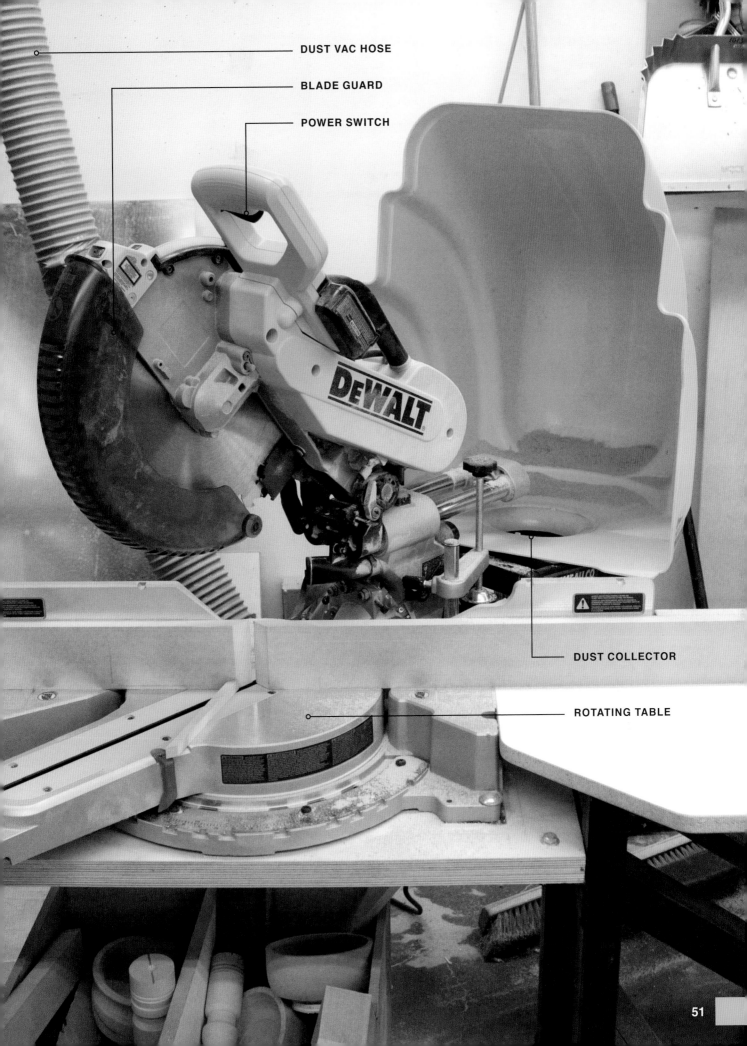

DUST VAC HOSE

BLADE GUARD

POWER SWITCH

DUST COLLECTOR

ROTATING TABLE

Panel Saw

TOOL BASICS
The vertical panel saw is used for cutting large panels of material. The saw only moves in a vertical, up-and-down direction. The basic mechanism functions almost the same as the cross-cut saw, except this saw is mounted vertically. The saw can move left and right depending on the size of the pieces needed.

SAFETY TIPS
This is saw is quite loud, so hearing and eye protection will be needed.

PRO TIPS
This machine is one of the most expensive machines that can be purchased in the shop, making it suitable only for the most sophisticated work shop facilities.

PULL HANDLES   BLADE GAURD

Cut this way only

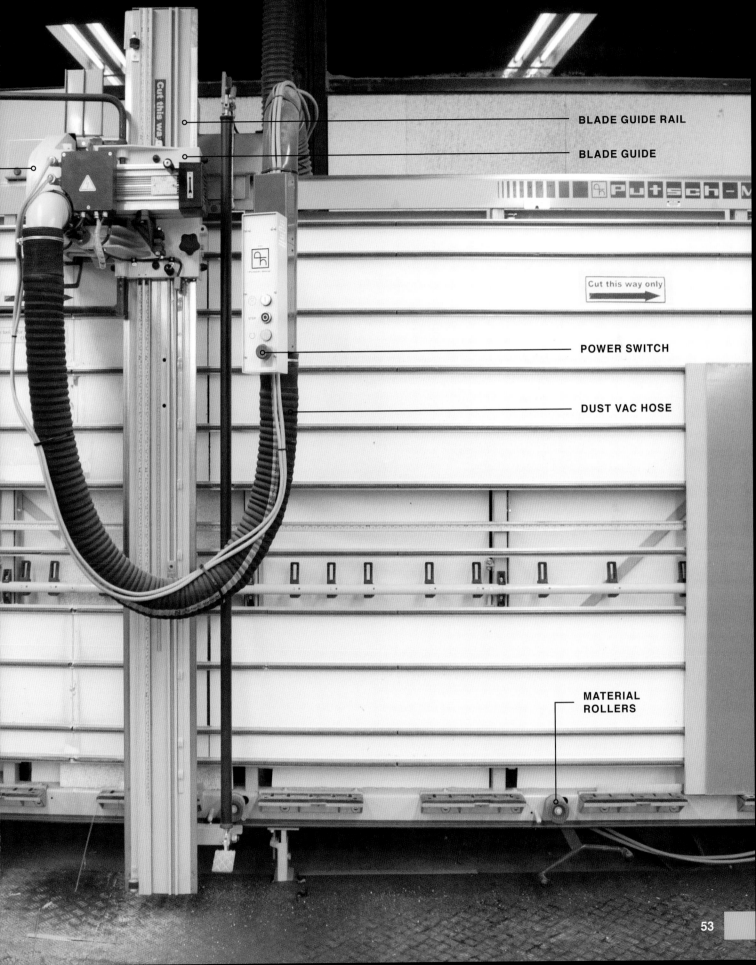

BLADE GUIDE RAIL

BLADE GUIDE

Cut this way only

POWER SWITCH

DUST VAC HOSE

MATERIAL
ROLLERS

Wood Lathe

TOOL BASICS

The lathe works on the principle of rotational force, spinning materials into shape. It is a great tool for making things round. It is the only machine in the shop that can build itself: "you can make a lathe with a lathe." It is perhaps most widely known as the famous baseball-bat making machine. A vacuum is built into the lathe, for collecting dust — however, it is still a good idea to wear a dust mask, especially with tooling foams. An air hose on the end of the lathe is used for cleaning the machine and the cut parts.

Shield Guard - can be used to safely guard against projectiles.

Instrument Panel - includes a digital readout showing the RPM (revolutions per minute) of the material being turned. Also included is a switch to control the rotation direction — either forward or in reverse.

"Turning Between Centers" - this is the most common configuration where the material being turned is held between the drive spur (on the motor side) and the live center (in the tailstock vice opposite the motor side — example on facing page).

Tool Rest - locks into the tool rest vice, and is used to steady the blade on the cutting tool for more accuracy and control.

Top Suppliers: Powermatic™, Laguna™

SAFETY TIPS

Tie back loose clothing and hair, and wear eye and hearing protection. A dust mask is recommended when cutting tooling foams.

PRO TIPS

The best way to get a smooth part is to turn at high speeds with a sharp cutting tool. However, at much higher speeds (1800 RPM) sawdust becomes uncomfortably warm. Slower speed (300 RPM) is good for initial rounding, and for sanding. Reverse spin direction is useful for sanding, or to remove raised grains in wood — usually caused by dull lathe cutting tools.

POWER SWITCH

POWERMATIC
MODEL 4224

DRIVE SPUR

DUST VAC HOSE

DUST COLLECTOR

TOOL REST

TAILSTOCK VICE

SHIELD GUARD

POWERMATIC

POWER CORDS KEPT TIDY

AIR HOSE

Turning Between Centers: 1) Proper holding of a cutting tool — notice the tool tip positioned at the edge of the adjustable tool rest. The tool should be gripped with both hands for better precision & control.

2) Using a pointed cutting tool to score into Jelutong wood. Use this tool to score cut when sectioning off pieces of a long material.

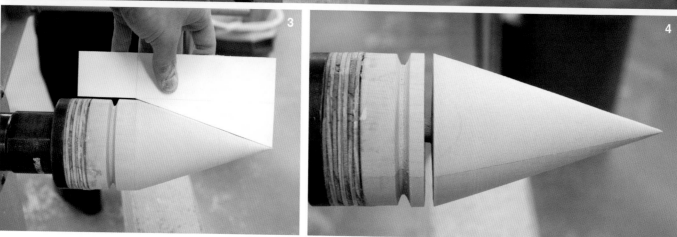

Using Templates: 3) Geometric shapes can made from a template cut from styrene. Here, a simple angled template is used to verify a cone cut out of a cylindrical block of wood (cut with a steel cutting tool, not the template!). 4) Use a pointed cutting tool to score into a cut as deep as possible, the rest will be removed with a hand saw.

Left: 5) The results after cutting the middle cone post with a handsaw. The left-over raised post area will be sanded down with a sanding file or sandpaper.

Below: 6) An example of geometric forms which can all be cut on the lathe — sealed with shellac, then a light coat of paint.

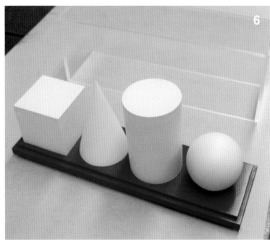

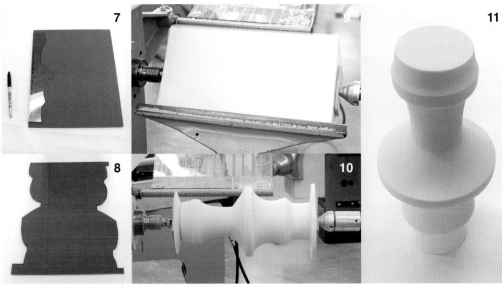

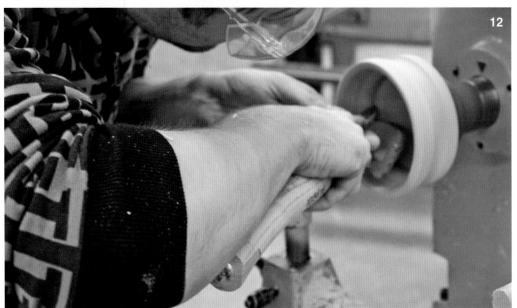

Cutting Pattern: Tooling foam can also be turned on the lathe. **7-8)** Here, a volumetric 'half silhouette' pattern is cut from an 1/8" board of masonite (using bandsaw and scroll saw). **9-11)** Once this pattern is pushed into the spinning foam block, the block will begin to take on the form of the silouette (see page 145 for the same volumetric pattern design cut from foam core).

Inside Cut: 12) Showing use of a special tool rest for cutting the inside of a round shape. For the cleanest and best cutting results, keep your tool as sharp as possible.

Metal Lathe

TOOL BASICS

The metal lathe or "machinist's lathe" uses the same principles as the wood lathe. It is specially suited for turning harder alloy materials. High-precision part production is possible with this machine. Special end-mills and drill bits are available.

Top Suppliers: LeBlond™, Kent USA™, Bolton Tools™, Precision Matthews™

SAFETY

Notice the red PVC screen at right — this screen in used to shield other people and machines from sparks, slags, UV light and other potential hazards.

PRO TIPS

It's a wise idea to keep all metal tools in a room or space of their own, due to high temperatures and flying sparks.

Above: A pro machinist in a typical machine shop.

DRIVE SPUR

SPEED DIAL

POWER SWITCH

PVC SCREEN

TAILSTOCK VICE

Disk Sander

TOOL BASICS

The disk sander is by far the best tool for sanding away material quickly. The machine works by spinning a wheel of textured sandpaper. The sander's table and blade guard are adjustable. A vacuum hose helps to collect sanding dust — which can ignite in the air. Only sand on the side of the sanding wheel that is spinning downwards — NEVER use the part of the disk that is coming up at you.

SAFETY

Make sure to wear safety glasses and keep hands and fingers clear and away from the sanding wheel. You may get very close to the spinning disk, but make sure never to touch.

PRO TIPS

Custom jigs can be created to give parts a custom "draft angle." This draft angle will allow for parts to be more easily separated from a vacuum form, or from a silicone RTV mold. Parts need at least +5° draft angle, since perfectly vertical, 90° side walls will not release properly from a mold or vacuum form.

DISK ROTATION

CUTTING ZONE

DO NOT wear gloves or loose clothing while operating this machine

Above: Before sanding anything, always check that the table is square. If not, you will ruin your piece. A compound square works best here.

DISK
GUARD

SANDING
DISK

MOTOR

WORK
TABLE

WORK
TABLE
ANGLE
ADJUST
LEVER

61

Above: In the middle of a cut — notice hands and fingers are clear and away from the sanding disk. Be sure to only cut on the downward spinning half of the disk (in this case, the right side). Using a "cheater board" jig to add a 5° angle to the sides of a part.

Cheater Board: A custom made cheater board to slide in the guide rail of the disk sander, to a part a precise draft angle. This draft angle will help in releasing the part from a mold, if using in RTV molding & casting applications.

Above: A straight scrap piece can be used as a sled when feeding a piece into the sander. Here, a scrap piece of MDF is double-stick taped onto the sanding table platform itself.

Right: A smaller disk sander — notice this disk sander spins counter-clockwise, so parts will need to be sanded on the left-hand side (or the side that is spinning downwards). Mini tabletop sanders are also available.

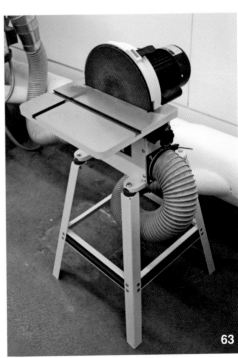

Belt Sander

TOOL BASICS

The belt sander functions the same as the disk sander, only with the sandpaper on a belt system instead of a spinning disk. Larger or more awkwardly shaped pieces should be sanded on the belt sander instead of the disk sander. A vacuum hose helps to collect sanding dust, which can ignite in the air.

Different sanding belts are available, from 80-800 grit range, and come standard in four different types:

Aluminum Oxide - used for leathers and rubbers.
Zirconia Alumina - used for wet sanding / smoothing.
Silicone Carbide - used for metals, ceramics, and glass.
Garnet Style - used for fine woodworking.

SAFETY

Make sure to keep hands and fingers clear and away from sanding belt. You may get as close to the belt as possible, without touching.

PRO TIPS

Use the right belt for your material type, and replace belts when the textured tooth becomes clogged.

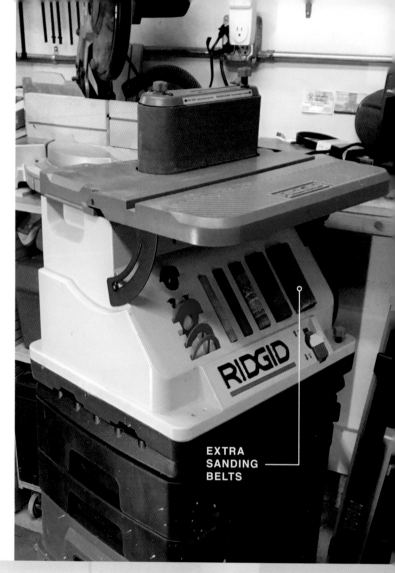

EXTRA SANDING BELTS

SANDING BELT

WORK TABLE

NO SANDING OF PLASTER
ON THIS TOOL!

POWER SWITCH

Spindle Sander

TOOL BASICS

The spindle sander can go where the disk & belt sanders cannot. While the other sanders work great for convex surfaces (outside bends), it cannot reach concave surfaces (inside bends) — this is where the spindle sander comes in. The spindle sander works by reciprocating (moving up and down) a cylindrical "spindle" wrapped in sandpaper. The spindle spins continuously while moving up and down, increasing cutting efficiency.

The spindle sander has an adjustable table, which can be adjusted using the crank on the side. Possible table angles range anywhere from 0°-45°. Keep your piece down to the table at all times. A dust collecting vacuum can be re-positioned on the table, helping to keep sawdust away from your piece while sanding.

SAFETY

Keep in mind that while you can get in close to sand smaller pieces, be sure to keep fingers safely away from the spindle.

PRO TIPS

A "fall line" is marked on the surface of the table, showing a zone that is perpendicular to the spindle — this is the most accurate area to sand. Variable-sized spindles may be attached — larger spindles work best for larger curves, and smaller spindles work best for smaller pieces.

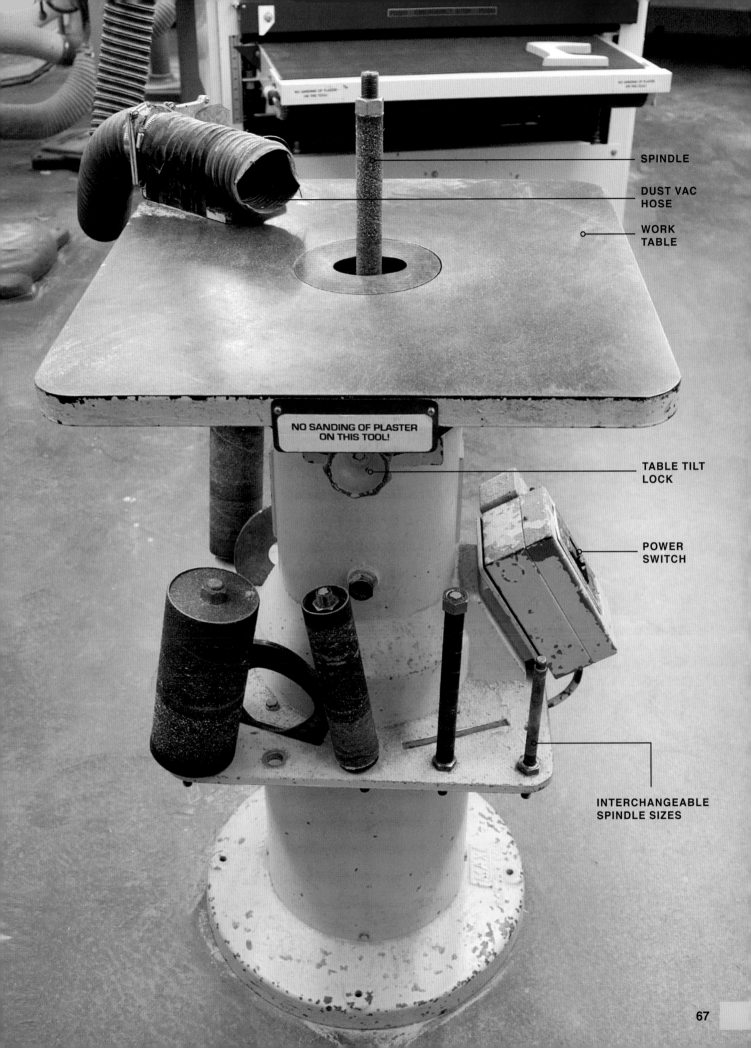

SPINDLE

DUST VAC
HOSE

WORK
TABLE

NO SANDING OF PLASTER
ON THIS TOOL!

TABLE TILT
LOCK

POWER
SWITCH

INTERCHANGEABLE
SPINDLE SIZES

1) To change a spindle, remove the metal ring in the center of the table, then grasp the top of the spindle and loosen the bottom nut with a wrench.

2) Afterward, attach the desired spindle with a wrench. This larger spindle size work best for larger curves.

3) Finally, replace the center metal table ring, then tighten to fit.

4) On / Off switch located below the table.

Router Table

TOOL BASICS

The router table is a useful machine for adding finished edge treatments (i.e. edge radius, bull nose, chamfer, etc.) to wood, MDF, or plastic. The router bit can either cut a flat or a radius edge.

A round wheel bearing located at the top of each bit keeps direct contact with the material being cut. This is referred to as a flush cut. Router bits cannot cut through solid material, and are used for trimming edges only.

Various different shapes and sizes of router bits are available, for creating a multitude of different edge treatments.

SAFETY TIPS

Keep the part down to the table at all times.

PRO TIPS

Custom jigs can be created for cutting into uniquely shaped parts.

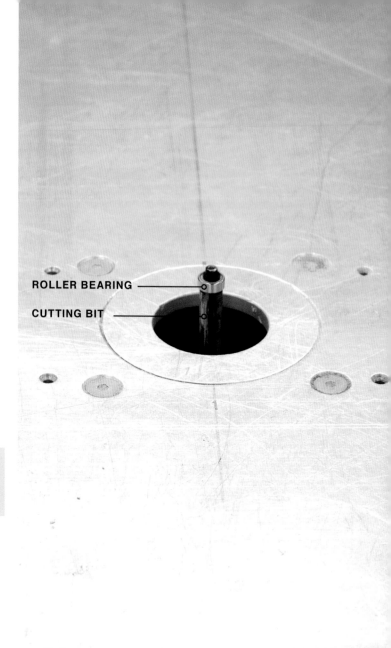

ROLLER BEARING

CUTTING BIT

Right: An assortment of different carbide router cutting bits.

ROUTER BIT

WORK TABLE

POWER
SWITCH /
MOTOR

Standard Edge Bevel: With a firm grip on the part, start at one edge and follow all the way through to the other side. Always apply downward pressure, keeping the part down to the table at all times.

Router Bit: The top bearing wheel of the router bit must remain in contact with the piece. The lower spinning bit cuts the material while this bearing wheel stays still.

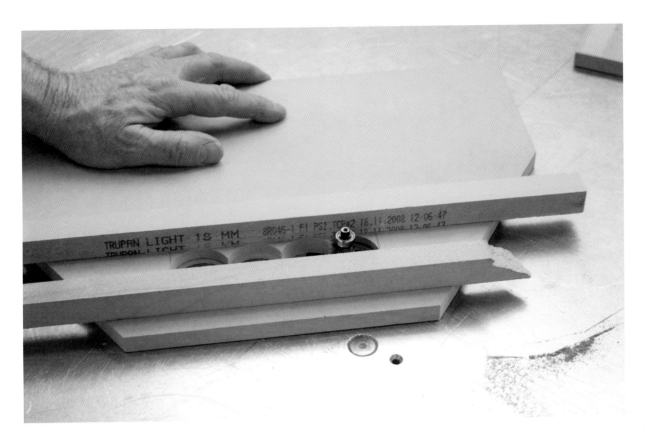

Interior Edge Cut: Trimming the leftover material from a drill press. The top bearing wheel of the router bit must come into direct contact with a flat surface of a piece. Here, a custom jig is made from scrap wood and double-stick tape. Never underestimate the power of double-stick tape!

Edge Burning: The final radius-ed edge added to the corners of an MDF box. Burning around the corners can occur from the heat given off by the router bit. This can easily be sanded off before a wax or other finish is applied.

Sheet Metal Foot Shear

TOOL BASICS

The foot shear is used for cutting sheet materials like steel, styrene, PETG, blue steel, etc. The shear cuts very cleanly and easily, and is especially useful for cutting materials not suitable for the table saw. One of its many handy uses is for cutting blue steel scrapers, where rough edges left by the shear can then be grounded down on the disk sander. The foot shear blade drops down when pressing down on the front foot lever. Leftover material scraps drop behind the shear.

Top Suppliers: Tennsmith™, Roper Whitney™

SAFETY TIPS

The foot shear is used to cut flat sheet material only — absolutely NO wire or anything round should be cut on this machine. This will put an excessive amount of pressure on one small area of the blade, which can cause it to chip and loose its edge.

PRO TIPS

Parts can be rotated during a cut, effectively creating curved pieces like the blue steel "pickles" on page 216.

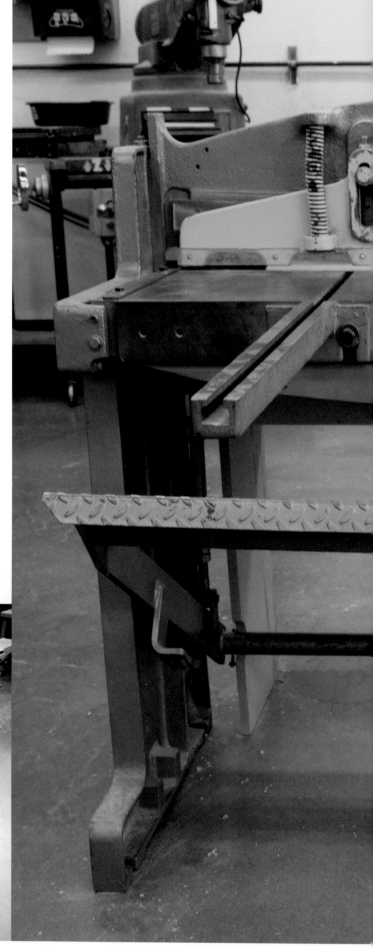

WORK
TABLE

BLADE

PEXTO

FOOT
LEVER

Drill Press

TOOL BASICS

The drill press is essentially a power drill on steroids. It is a very useful tool when precise drilling is necessary. The drill can only move or "press" up and down. Different bits can be used in the press — from drill bits, Forstner bits (small holes & countersinking), and hole saws (larger holes). A crank arm on the side of the press lowers and raises the drill. The RPM (revolutions per minute) speed of the drill may be controlled via an adjustment dial at the top.

Top Suppliers: Powermatic™

SAFETY TIPS

Tie back long hair, wear safety glasses, and remove all loose jewelry.

PRO TIPS

As a general rule, smaller bits should run at faster RPM's and larger bits at slower RPM's.

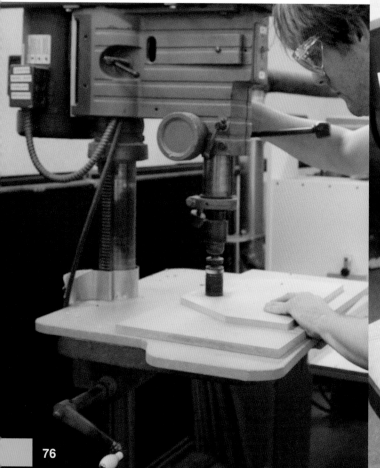

SPEED DIAL

POWER SWITCH

CRANK ARM

DRILL CHUCK

WORK TABLE

TABLE HEIGHT ADJUST LEVER

1) The chuck key is needed to install or uninstall cutting bits. Here, a hole saw bit has been selected. Notice the bit is essentially a large cylindrical shape with saw teeth at the bottom.

2) Installation of a bit: first, the bit's upper shank is placed into the collar of the press. First, hand tighten the collar, then use the chuck key to tighten firmly.

3) The drill depth can be set, depending on the width of material needing to be drilled. With the depth gauge, it is possible to bore countersunk holes, or to cut completely through the material.

4) During a drill — a "sacrificial board" should be placed under the cutting material, to protect the press's underlying table. The height of the table can also be adjusted.

Above: Custom jigs can be helpful for cutting into shapes that are hard to grasp. C-Clamps are useful for stabilizing parts. Here, a Forstner bit is being used to bore small 1/2" holes into a plywood box.

Mill

TOOL BASICS

Before CNC (computer numerical control), there was the standard, manual mill. The Mill is essentially a variable-position version of the drill press, and is known as a standard machinist's tool. It is most useful for creating precise duplicate parts, such as wheels for a car. The depth of the cut can be set or varied. The drilling angle can also be modified, where the part can be rotated while the drill is still in motion. Unlike the high-tech, digitally automated CNC machines and laser cutters of today, the Mill is a completely manual machine. Many different chocks, jigs, and cutting tool parts are available —custom ones can be made.

Top Suppliers: Bolton Tools™

SAFETY TIPS

Treat the Mill with the same caution as the Drill Press.

PRO TIPS

Various different bits and chocks are available for creating unique effects — many of them are custom made.

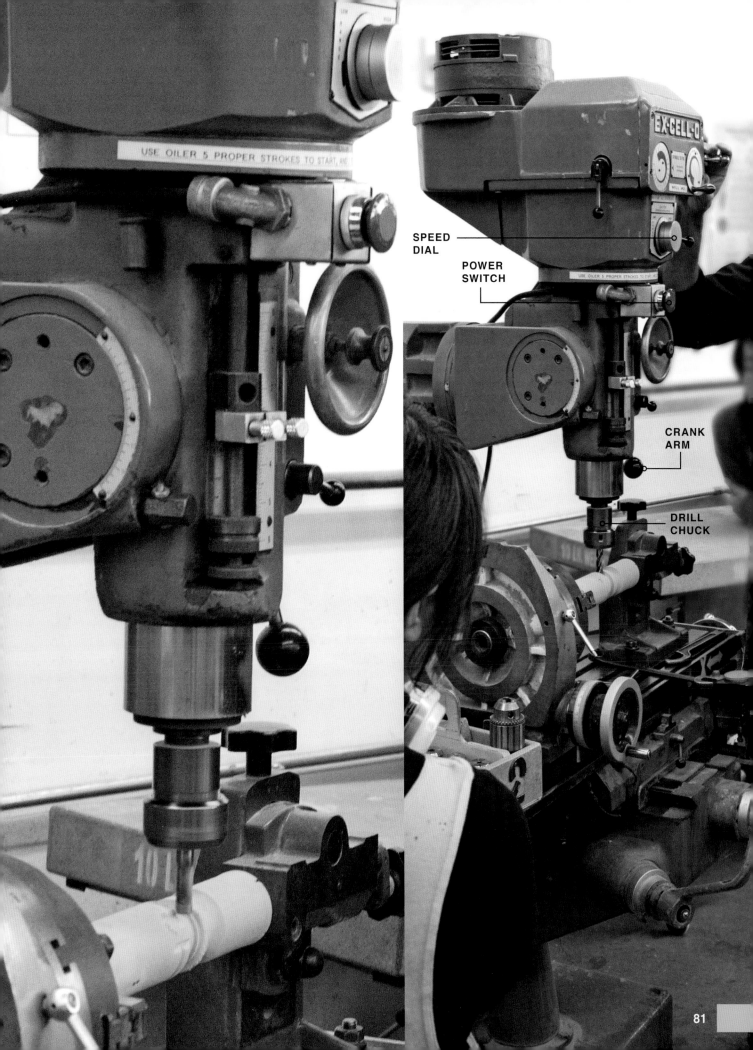

SPEED
DIAL

POWER
SWITCH

CRANK
ARM

DRILL
CHUCK

USE OILER 5 PROPER STROKES TO START, AND

EX·CELL·O

81

2.5 & 5-Axis CNC Mill

TOOL BASICS

CNC, or Computer Numerical Control, is a programmable robotic piece of machinery driven by stepper motors. CNC technology is commonly known as "subtractive manufacturing", in that material can be taken away, but cannot be added. It is used in a wide range of engineering applications, from flat-pattern furniture, production tooling and moldmaking, machined metal hardware, and signage. Digital CAM (Computer Aided Manufacturing) software can program and run digital tool path simulations in the computer before an actual part is cut. This will help the CNC programmer spot any issues up front, which will save time and money. Tool parts can also be specified in CAM — the size of the machine lends itself to the machining of larger models, including 1:1 full size cars. Large scale models like these would be grossly inefficient using 3D printers.

5-Axis (A,B,C,Y, Z axis) - this mill is one of the most sophisticated and expensive tools in the Work Shop. It is capable of producing very high levels of 3-Dimensional quality/detail. The machine is capable of tooling both foam and soft MDF — and is capable of producing super fine details like small treads and groove patterns in a shoe outsole. Special router milling bits will be needed in depending on the application — such as de-burring, trimming, engraving, etc.

2.5 & 3-Axis (A,B,Z axis) - used for cutting flat parts. The machine moves along the A and B axis, and cutting tool bit moves up/down along the Z axis.

Popular CAD / CAM Software: Autodesk Fusion 360™, PTC Creo™, ProEngineer™, CATIA™, MasterCAM™, Solidworks™, Mach 3™

Top Suppliers: HAAS™, Laguna™, Roland™, Fadal™, Cincinnati™, Servo-Tec™

SAFETY

These machines can be noisy, so it's a good idea to keep them partitioned in a separate room. To ensure proper safety, they should be used by experienced CNC programmers or trained operators only.

PRO TIPS

Large parts will typically be tooled using soft foam (12-20LB) using large cutting bits. Harder foam takes longer to mill and is better for smaller parts with more detail, where a smaller cutting endmill bit will be used. A controller box will house all of the electronics for the machine, which will also need a standard PC to run. Mach 3 is a standard CNC control software interface.

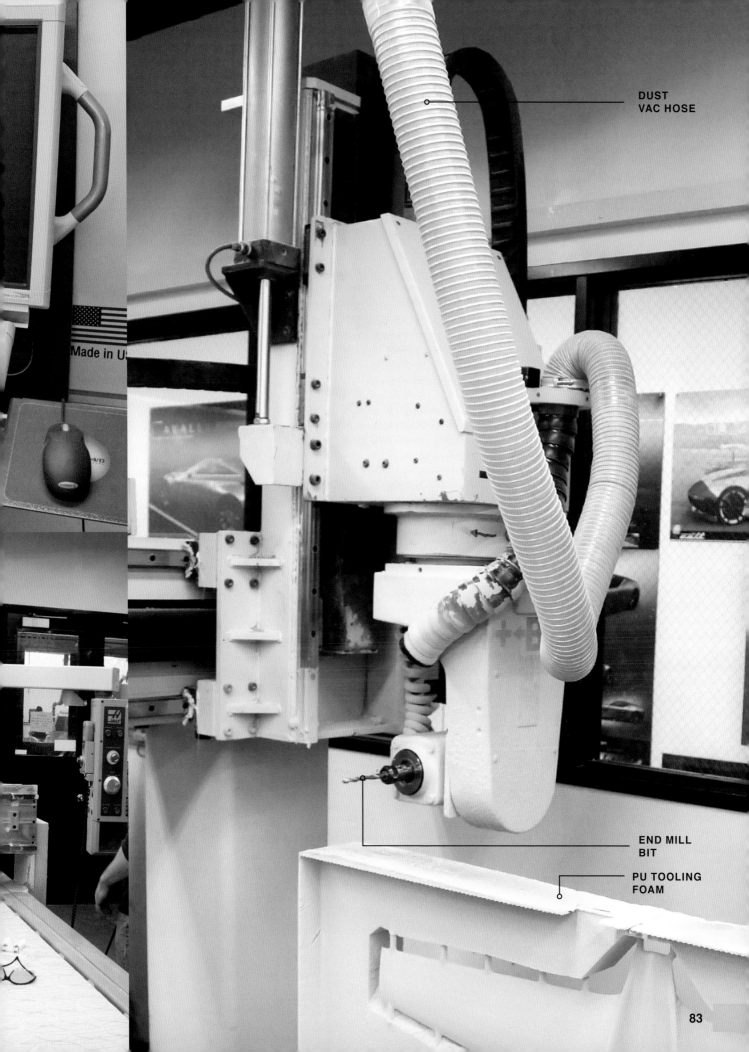

DUST
VAC HOSE

END MILL
BIT

PU TOOLING
FOAM

Made in US

83

Spread: A 5-axis CNC can cut almost 360° full rotation around the material — 5-axes of the machine are visible (B, C, X, Y, & Z).

2.5-Axis: Some CNC machines are the size of a large table, and can even be as big as a warehouse. Works much like an inkjet printer, only moving in an additional up-and-down, or Z-axis. 2D engraving or cutting is often referred to as routering, while 3D cutting is known as milling.

Small Format: Small format Roland mills cutting into 20LB tooling foam.

5-Axis: A 1:4 scale automotive car model being cut from a large a block of 10LB tooling foam

Below: Special end mill bits are used — here, a ball end mill spiral flute is used. A ball end mill is typically used on surfaces that are 3D shaped, so the mill bit doesn't leave any hard edges anywhere.

Above: A 5-Axis part will have support posts, which can be removed later with a pull saw.

Vacuum Former

TOOL BASICS

Vacuum forming, also known as vacuum casting, is a process whereby a plastic is heated until malleable, pulled over a hard surface form, then formed to the surface by vacuum suction. Since the vacuum forces the plastic down to the form, the soft material will conform to whatever shape is underneath. After the original underlying form is removed, a thin-walled plastic shell piece is left behind. This process is much more economical in comparison RTV to molding and casting. Volumetric surface forms can be made from hard materials like MDF, or soft materials such as tooling foam.

Platen - the platform the surface form will sit on. A valve in the center allows for the vacuum suction. Platen sizes can be customized according to the size of your form.

Material Types- some of the most common vacuum forming plastics are Acrylic, Styrene, PETG, Polypropylene (PP), and Polyethylene (PE), PVC, and ABS. Each material will need to be calibrated for proper heat and time settings. Sheet material from 1/16" to 1/8" thickness can be used for forming. Brackets must be adjusted depending on the size of the plastic used.

SAFETY

Keep hands and fingers clear and away from the heating elements and moving parts.

PRO TIPS

With a little design ingenuity and minimal investment costs, a homemade DIY vacuum forming machine can be built using simple, readily available parts.

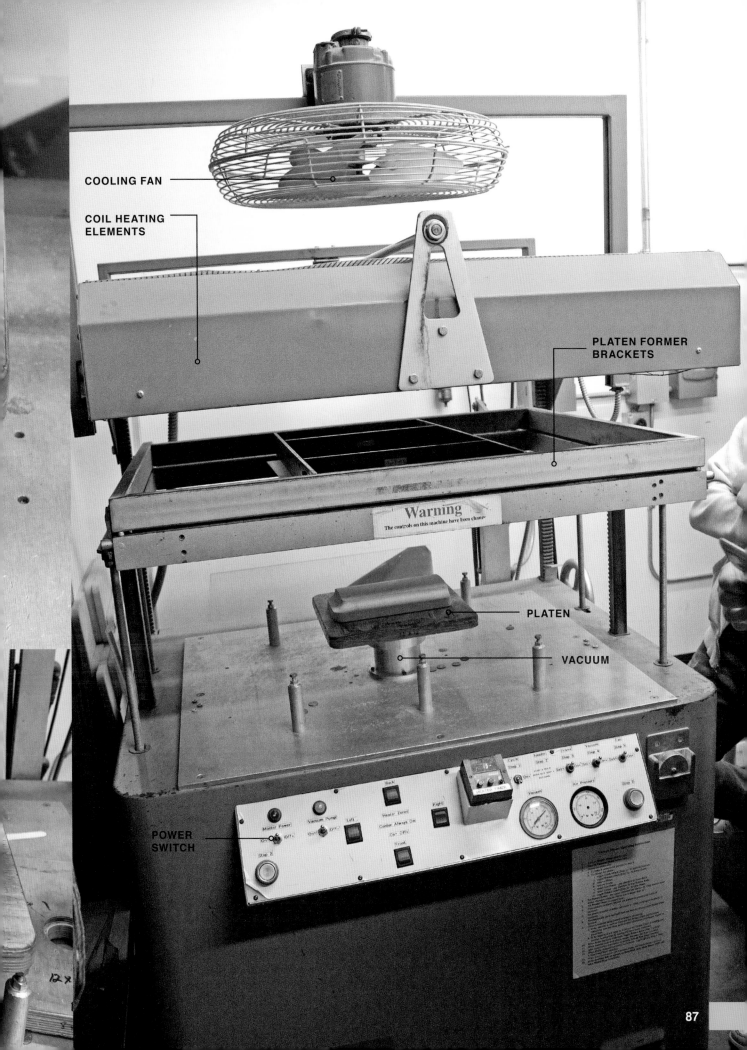

COOLING FAN

COIL HEATING
ELEMENTS

PLATEN FORMER
BRACKETS

Warning
The controls on this machine have been change

PLATEN

VACUUM

POWER
SWITCH

Industrial & Automotive Clay Oven

TOOL BASICS

The clay oven is a simple commercial food warmer, and is commonplace in the automotive industry. It is used to warm industrial clay billets to the proper temperatures. Drawers allow for different clay types / brands to be heated separately. When heated, the clay becomes malleable and easily spreadable. Within minutes, it then cools and hardens at room temperature and can be sculpted with clay wires and rakes. Each drawer has it's own temperature dial — make sure the temperature settings are set according to the brand and type of clay being used.

Top Suppliers: Toastmaster™

SAFETY

Turn off the oven when not in use. Avoid overheating clays, which can lead to burning when handled.

PRO TIPS

Clay types should not be mixed, since they consist of different formulas with wildly different consistencies. Have a fan or other form of circulation in the room, to blow away the strong smell from the clay.

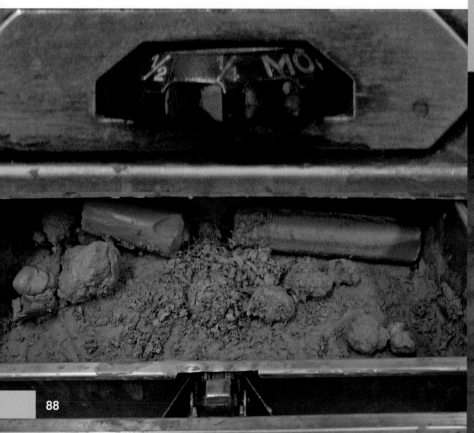

TEMPERATURE
DIAL

HEATED
DRAWERS

THERMOMETER

Laser Cutter

TOOL BASICS

The laser cutter works just like an inkjet printer, where a laser raster head swipes back-and-forth. Depending on the power and speed settings, the laser can either cut completely cut through a piece, or it can etch into the surface — this is known as etching or "rastering." The depth of a raster depends on the laser settings. A laser set to too much power, or too slow a speed will create unsightly edge burning. Getting the settings right will take experimentation to calibrate correctly, and will depend on the material being used.

Top Suppliers: Trotec™, Legend™, Epilog™, Universal Laser™, Laguna™

Top Software: Corel Draw™, Adobe Illustrator™, AutoCAD™

SAFETY

Never stare directly at the laser while it is cutting, or it can lead to temporary blinding. Also, be careful not to set the laser settings too high, or the material will burn and smoke which can potentially lead to a fire.

PRO TIPS

After some experimentation, save the speed / power settings that work well for each type of material. This can be used as reference for all future applications (pg. 256).

Below: A flat-packed furniture scale model cut from 1/8" masonite board (at right). This model was used to test construction joinery on a small-scale first, before the full-scale furniture design is cut on the CNC router.

LASER HEAD

MATERIAL

LASER BED

Greg

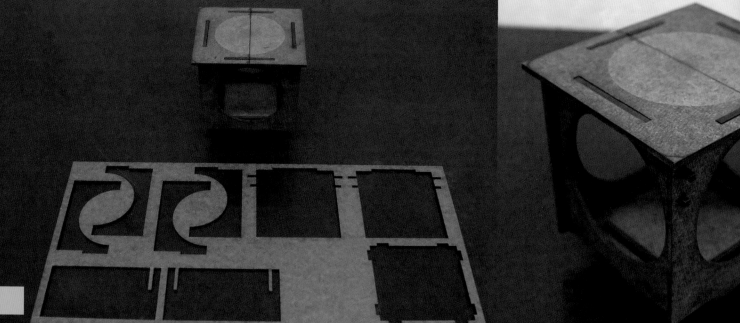

Above: Laser etching into the surface of a plywood panel. The depth of the raster can be adjusted using the machine's speed and power settings.

3D Printer

TOOL BASICS

3D printing, also known as "Rapid Prototyping" or "Additive Manufacturing," represents a true revolution in prototyping. Once only available to large government-funded R&D institutions like NASA, this powerful technology is now in the hands of everyday home consumers. This represents a dramatic shift in the way prototypes are made, and how physical objects are now being brought to life. 3D printers are being used by large companies and small startups alike to dramatically cut down on the time it takes to develop and bring new products to market. This technology is almost single-handedly responsible for giving rise to what's known as the "Maker Movement", or de-centralized manufacturing. Along with hard resin plastics, rubbers can now be 3D printed in different hardnesses, and on the same machine. Specialty printers can even print aluminum, titanium, gold, ceramics, wood polymer, and carbon fiber composites. And just like a home inkjet printer, 3D printers can print in different colors as well. Desktop units are becoming more and more affordable all the time, and third party services are also available. These services allow you to upload your 3D CAD data to a server, where the part is printed and shipped back to you.

FDM (Fused Deposition Modeling) - the most common type of desktop printer. Works by melting a thin spool of plastic nylon filament over a raised print bed that gradually lowers, printing or "fusing" material layer by layer. Fairly inexpensive, FDM can print a wide variety of materials such as ABS plastic.

SLA (Stereolithography) - uses a laser to solidify liquid resin with UV light. This is the oldest 3D print technology, and is capable of high-quality results.

SLS (Selective Laser Sintering) - similar to SLA, except SLS uses a laser to cure a powder of material instead of a pool of liquid. Two most common printable plastics are ABS and PLA.

Polyjet - uses a UV-cured liquid resin just like SLA, however Polyjet 3D printers use an inkjet-like print head to deposit the resin onto the print bed. This eliminates the need for a messy pool of resin. Polyjet prints in the finest layer resolution of any 3D print technology, and is typically the most expensive.

Top Suppliers: Maker Bot™, Form Labs™, Ultimaker™, Stratasys™, Shapeways™, Dimension™, 3D Platform™, Raise 3D™, 3d Systems™, Prusa Research™, EOS™, Markforged™, Carbon™, HP™

PRO TIPS

Part layer resolution (measured in microns) will depend on the type of printer and material used. These visible layers will need to be sanded out and prepped by primer for appearance models. Coring out or shelling the non-visible inner part volume will help to reduce material / weight, lower print times, and decrease overall print costs. This process is known to as "splicing," and most 3D software packages have plug-ins for this very purpose.

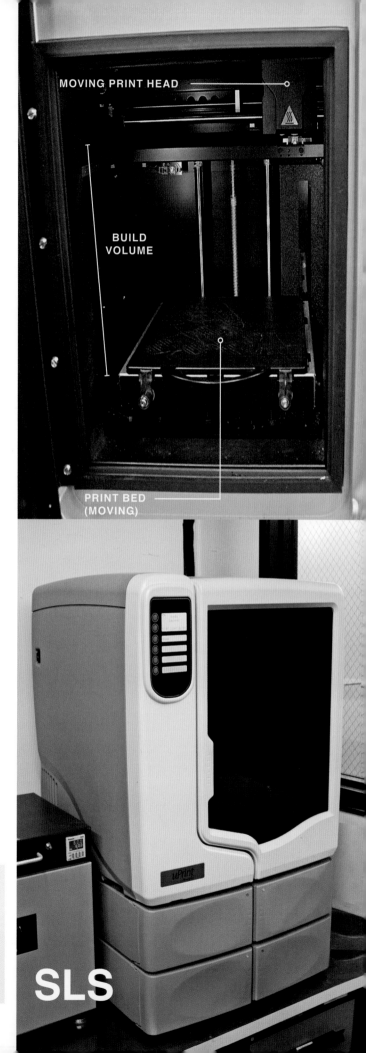

MOVING PRINT HEAD

BUILD VOLUME

PRINT BED (MOVING)

SLS

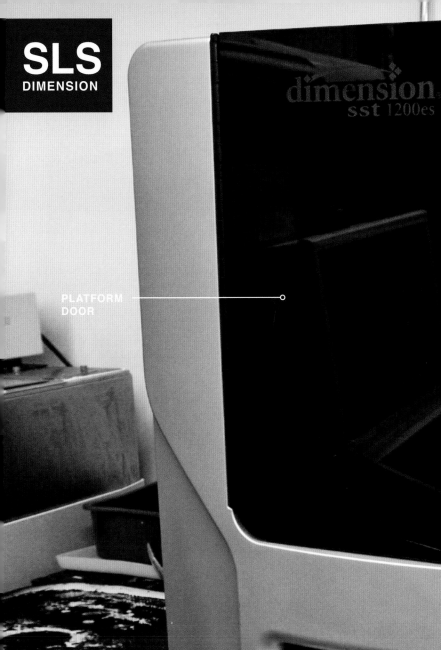

PLATFORM
DOOR

MACHINE
SETTINGS

BLACK

POWER
SWITCH

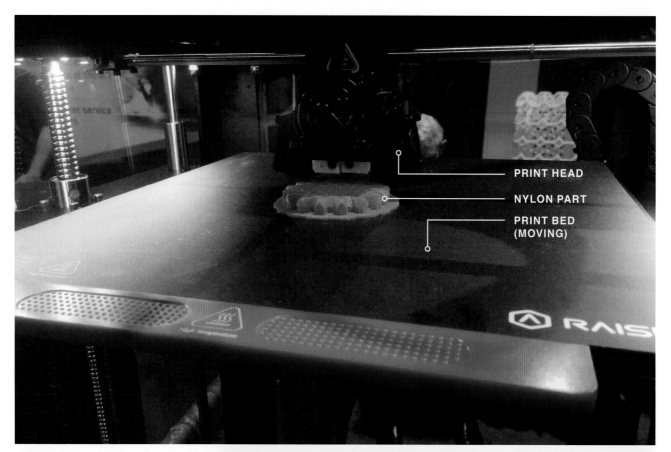

PRINT HEAD

NYLON PART

PRINT BED
(MOVING)

Above: An FDM filament part being 3D printed. The melted nylon plastic material is fused layer by layer to "grow" the part — where the 3D print head sweeps back and forth very much like an inkjet printer. After each layer is complete, the print bed moves down fractions of a milimter (microns) to allow for the new layer to be layed on top. This process repeats itself until the final part is complete. The amount of steps, layers, or "striations" in the part will depend on how many layers are laid down during this process. More layers = higher part resolution / detail, and more time to complete. Less layers = lower part resolution / detail, and less time to complete.

Right: This particular model of 3D printer has a convenient LCD touch screen, which shows key instrumentation like part progess, nozzle temperature, time remaining, and remaining nylon plastic filament stock levels.

FILAMENT (A)
FILAMENT (B)

FILAMENT
SPOOL (A)

BUILD
VOLUME

FILAMENT
SPOOL (B)

LCD DISPLAY

PLATFORM
DOOR

FDM
RAISE 3D

STORAGE
BIN

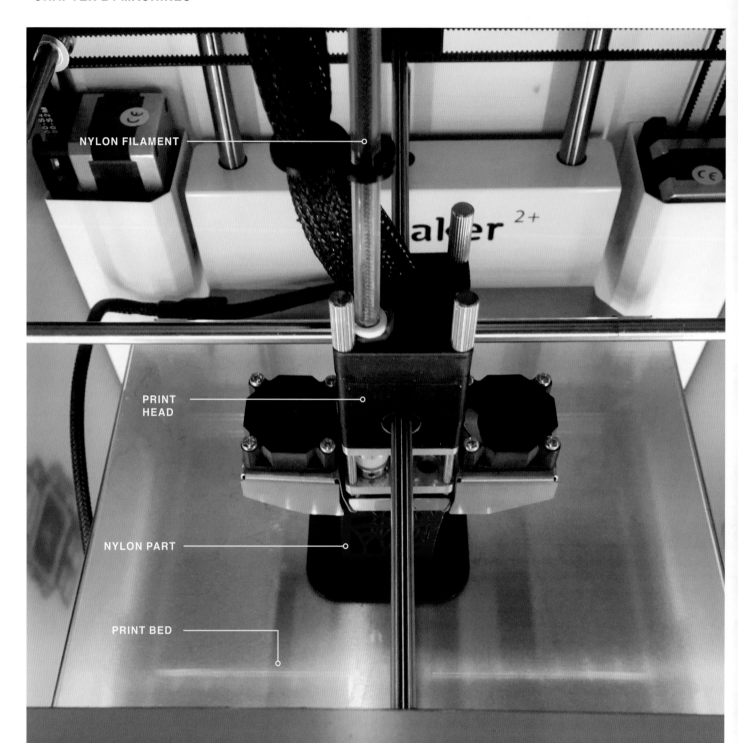

NYLON FILAMENT

PRINT
HEAD

NYLON PART

PRINT BED

Above & Facing: A popular FDM 3D printer from Ultimaker. This desktop unit has a much smaller build volume than the ones shown earlier, meaning that the size of the part possible will not be as large. That said, this size of 3D printer is most popular for startups and small-scale makers or development teams, because of their portability and affordability. If larger parts are needed, they can be tiled together — a process involving the different "tile" sections to be printed separately, then bonded together using a strong glue like epoxy.

NYLON FILAMET

PRINT HEAD

Ultimaker²⁺

BUILD VOLUME

PRINT BED
(MOVING)

PLATFORM
DOOR

POWER SWITCH

LCD DISPLAY

97

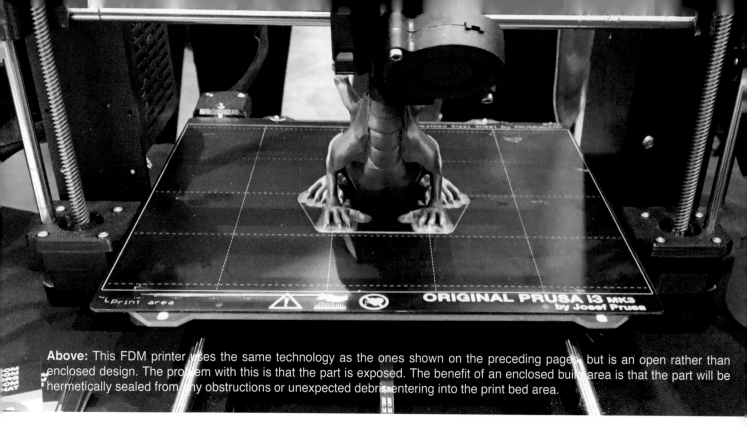

Above: This FDM printer uses the same technology as the ones shown on the preceding pages, but is an open rather than enclosed design. The problem with this is that the part is exposed. The benefit of an enclosed build area is that the part will be hermetically sealed from any obstructions or unexpected debris entering into the print bed area.

Below & Facing: Nylon filaments are available in a wide spectrum of colors, depending on the supplier. Some filaments even have a metallic sheen to them, such as the printed bullfrog below. Color printing with FDM technology is much more limited than SLA, SLS or polyjet, and typically lays down only one color at a time (color will depend on the filament color loaded into the machine). Some FDM printers can print dual colors, such as the two filament spools loaded at bottom right. The unique steam punk printer at right has been customized by Prusa 3D's team — using parts that were 3D printed on their own machines.

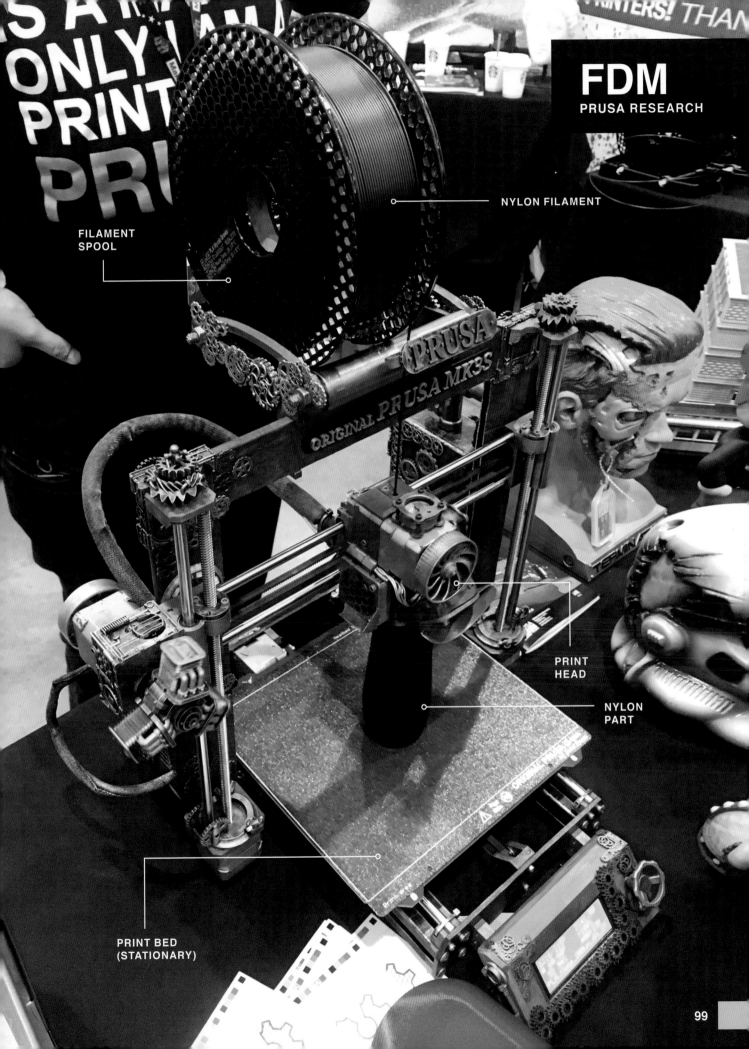

FILAMENT
SPOOL

NYLON FILAMENT

FDM
PRUSA RESEARCH

PRINT
HEAD

NYLON
PART

PRINT BED
(STATIONARY)

Welder & Waterjet Cutter

TOOL BASICS

MIG Welding (Metal Inert Gas) - uses a continuous spool of wire that burns, melts and fuses parts together. MIG is the most versatile and the easiest type of welding to learn, and can weld mild steel, stainless steel, or aluminum.

TIG Welding (Tungsten Inert Gas) - uses long welding rolls that are manually fed and melted into a weld puddle. TIG is the most aesthetically pleasing weld type, and can be used for thinner gauge materials with lower temperatures. A finer and more delicate welding process, good for car bodies, motorcycles, or sculpture. TIG can weld many different types of metals.

Stick Welding - shielded metal arc welding (SMAW), is a type of arc welding and one of the oldest welding types. Uses less expensive materials than other welding types, and common in heavy construction applications.

Arc Welding - or flux core welding, is for use with heavier/thicker materials. Most common in heavy steel construction and industrial machinery applications.

Waterjet Cutter - uses a highly pressurized, extremely focused stream of water mixed with an abrasive grit propellant to cut through material. Functions much like a laser cutter, but can cut through much thicker, stronger materials like titanium and heavy gauge steel — anywhere from 1/2" up to 4" of solid material. Waterjet can also be used to cut through soft foams.

Soldering - similar to a low-temperature form of welding, but unlike welding soldering does not involve melting the work pieces. Routinely used in hardware or electronics engineering, for joining together PCB (printed circuit board) components, prototype breadboards, robotics. Available as electric, propane, or butane pens (the pens tend to get hotter, heat up quickly and are more reliable).

SAFETY

Wear an arch flame light-activated welding mask at all times to prevent being blinded by bright welding torches.

PRO TIPS

Practice makes perfect — expert level welding takes time to achieve, so take time to practice on scrap metal pieces first, before committing to the final welded part. Beginners should learn simple MIG welding or soldering techniques before progressing onto some of the more difficult welding types listed.

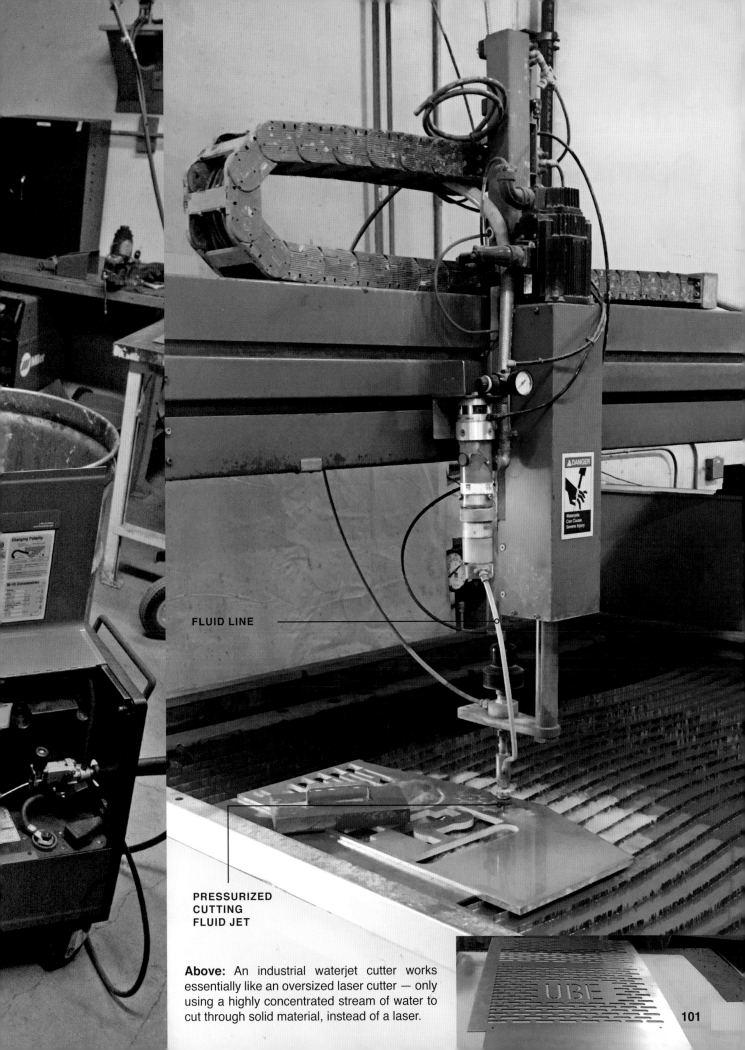

FLUID LINE

PRESSURIZED CUTTING FLUID JET

Above: An industrial waterjet cutter works essentially like an oversized laser cutter — only using a highly concentrated stream of water to cut through solid material, instead of a laser.

Industrial Sewing Machine

TOOL BASICS

Many fully-stocked shops or R&D labs will be outfitted with an industrial sewing machine for cut & sew prototyping or development. These machines create an "interlock stitch", which simulates hand sewing but only sews through one side of the fabric material — standard for mass manufacture.

Heavy Duty Single Needle "The Walking Foot" Machine - uses higher power than typical home machines, and can be used for thick leather and carpentry work.

Double / Triple Needle Machine - machines for sewing heavier reinforced double or triple stitches.

Serger Machine - special machine creates a flatlock stitch (chain stitch) for stretch fabrics and hemming (edging) fabric.

Top Suppliers: JUKI™, Suzuki™, Singer™, Janome™

SAFETY

Keep material down to the table at all times. Replace needles when broken.

PRO TIPS

Practice makes perfect — expert level sewing takes time to achieve. Large curves = easier, tight curves = harder to sew.

Below: Serger machine.

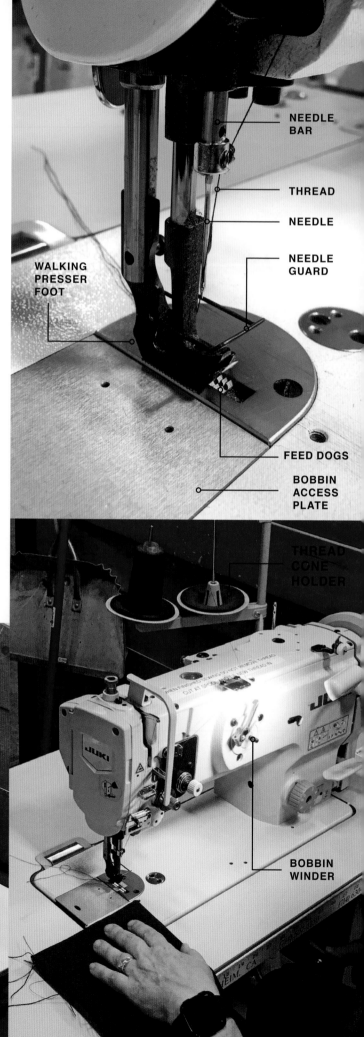

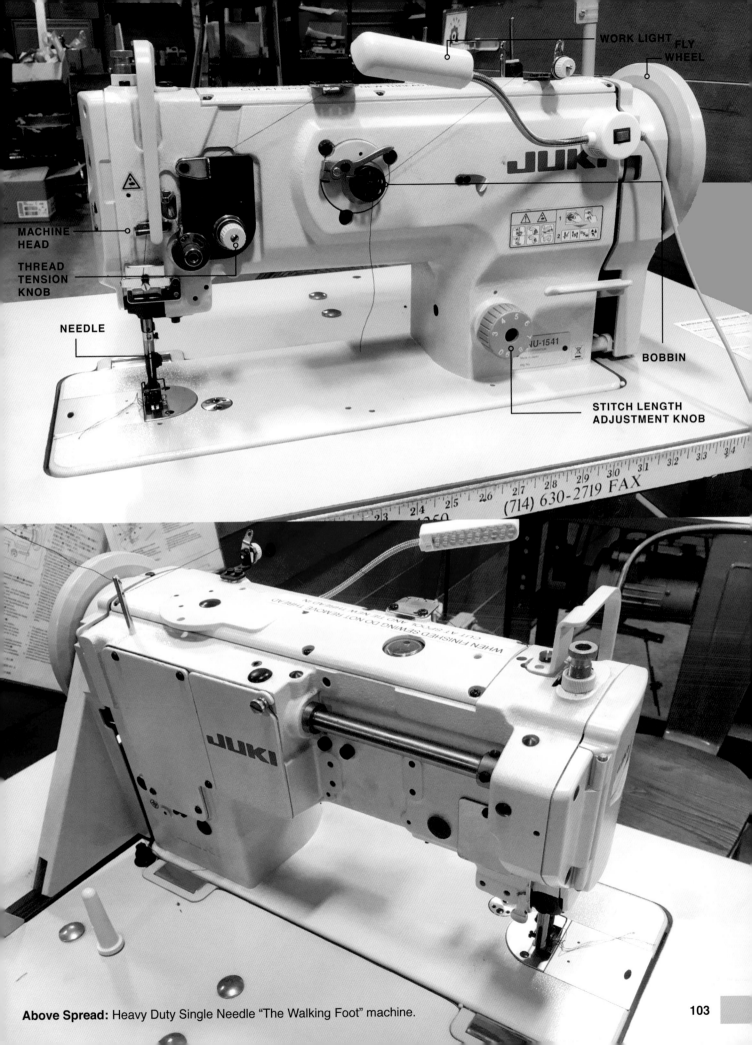

WORK LIGHT

FLY WHEEL

MACHINE HEAD

THREAD TENSION KNOB

NEEDLE

BOBBIN

STITCH LENGTH ADJUSTMENT KNOB

Above Spread: Heavy Duty Single Needle "The Walking Foot" machine.

Below: Another heavy duty single needle walking foot sewing machine model by JUKI.

JUKI

SEWING
THREAD
SPOOLS

Left: Body forms are used for proper fit & form (shaping) in apparel / fashion. Forms are male and female specific.

Bottom & Right: Custom tailoring is an art form. Companies like Patagonia repair used clothes as part of their Worn Wear program, in an effort to reduce, re-use, and recycle

THE TAILOR IS IN

ALTERATIONS

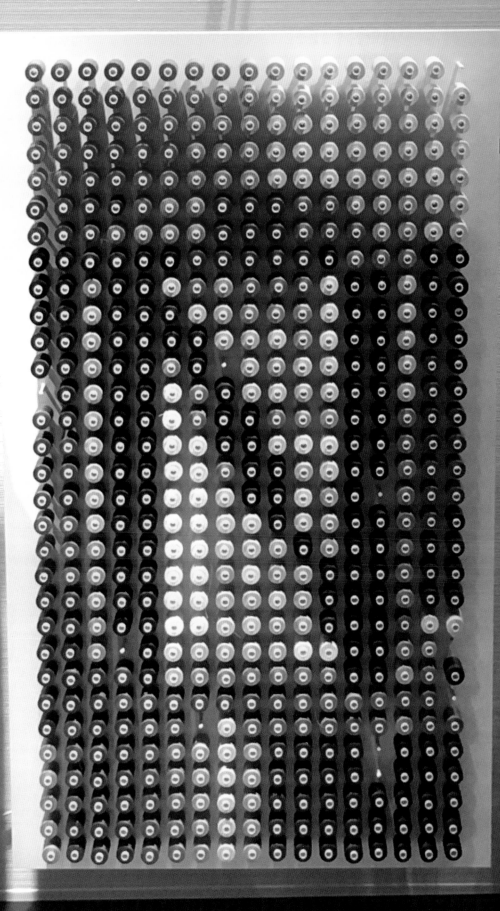

Injection Molder

TOOL BASICS

Injection molding has been one of the true cornerstones of mass manufacturing for decades. Chances are, if you've seen a product made from plastic or rubber (or a combination of the two) in a store, that product has been produced using injection molding. An injection molding machine literally shoots or "packs" a molten plastic fluid into a steel mold cavity at very high pressure, using a pneumatic press. A finished part is produced after the two mold halves separate and the cooled part is pushed out by a steel ejector plate with ejector pins. Each time that a part is injected is known as an injection cycle. Steel mold cavities are machined by a CNC mill, in a process commonly known as "cutting steel." Because the molds are metal, they can withstand much more repeated use and abuse, and are therefore able to produce many more parts versus softer molds like silicone, which will start to break down and tear after a few hundred castings are made. Parts are also 100% finished straight out of the mold, often needing little or no no post-processing. However, a parting line (where the mold halves come) together will be visible on the part after de-molding.This can be removed by deburring or deflashing in post production. The two major types of injection molding are thermoplastic (the most common type) and thermoset.

Top Suppliers: Morgan Industries™, Robot Digg™, Nissei™

SAFETY

Parts and heating elements will be hot, so avoid touching.

PRO TIPS

Proper heat and pressure settings (combined with proper mold design) must be dialed-in properly for your part, in order to minimize flashing — excess plastic squeezed out from the sides. Since Delrin plastic can be melted and re-used, be sure to save any flawed parts or scrap material for re-use later on.

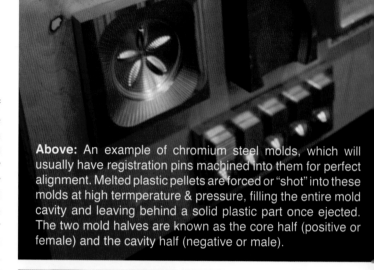

Above: An example of chromium steel molds, which will usually have registration pins machined into them for perfect alignment. Melted plastic pellets are forced or "shot" into these molds at high termperature & pressure, filling the entire mold cavity and leaving behind a solid plastic part once ejected. The two mold halves are known as the core half (positive or female) and the cavity half (negative or male).

Right: PP (Delrin) thermoplastic resin pellets, ready to be loaded into the injection molding machine. Delrin can be pigmented with colorants to match almost any color, and is re-cyclable — meaning that it can be ground down, re-melted, and re-injected several times. Re-cycled material can also be mixed (up to 15%) with brand new pellets, so there's virtually no waste involved.

Large Batch: A large injection molding machine oriented on a production assembly line.

6

WARNING

WEAR SAFETY GLASSES NEAR MACHINE

DO NOT OPERATE THIS MACHINE UNLESS
THOROUGHLY INSTRUCTED ON OPERATING
PROCEDURES AND SAFETY RULES.

CONTACT MANUFACTURER BEFORE
ALTERING THIS EQUIPMENT.

WIRE
SAFETY
GAURD

VALVE
PRESSURE
GAUGE (PSI)

CLAMP FORCE
(TONNAGE)
GAUGE

TEMPERATURE
CONTROL
SETTINGS

MATERIAL
LOADING
CHUTE

DANGER
HIGH TEMPERATURE

MATERIAL
MELTING
CYLINDER

STATIONARY
PLATEN (HOLDS
COVER HALF)

SLIDING
WIRE
GUARD

STANCTION
POSTS
(TRACK)

MOVEABLE PLATEN
WITH PRE-HEAT
PLATE (HOLDS
EJECTOR HALF)

Small Batch: This is a two-ton (13,500 psi) pneumatic Morgan press, which is a miniature version of what is ultimately used on mass-production assembly lines like the machines on facing page. Machines like these are great to learn on, but are ultimately only suitable for small-batch production due to their limited size. Also useful for testing of injection molded prototype parts to later be used in larger production batches.

MACHINCE
SETTINGS

THERMO-
PLASTIC
PELLETS

FORCE & PRESSURE
AIR COMPRESSOR
HOSES

CLAMP & PRESSURE
REGULATORS

INJECTION FUNCTION
REGULATION & CONTROL

When my son, Fletcher, was a teenager, I told him it didn't matter to me what he wanted to do for work in the future as long as he also learned some sort of craft that involved working with his hands. He chose shaping surfboards, which was a good fit since he is slightly dyslexic, and dyslexics often have a great sense of proportion. They make good sculptors.

Yvon Chounaird

FOUNDER/CEO, PATAGONIA - *LET MY PEOPLE GO SURFING*

Chapter 3 — Hand Tools

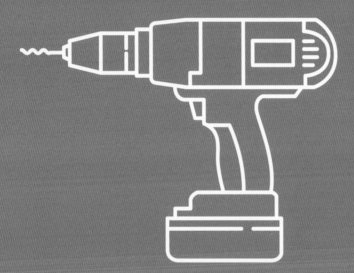

Toolbox

TOOL BASICS

For all of the tools in your shop, you'll need a system to organize them all. A quality tool box is worth it's weight in gold. I've tried many different types of toolboxes over the years, and one that I swear by is a simple toolbox made by Craftsman. A box with sliding drawers is also useful, so you don't need to take out all of the compartments to access your tools inside. The best sliding drawer box is from Matrix Concepts, a maker of motocross equipment. This box is solid construction, have quality drawers, and injection molded grab handles built in. Many mechanics refer to the activity of working with tools as "wrenching."

Top Suppliers: Craftsman™, Matrix Concepts™

PRO TIPS

A carefully crafted toolbox serves essentially as a handheld traveling workshop in a box — no need for hundreds upon hundreds of tools to get the job done! At a bare minumum, use rubber shelf liners to prevent tools from shifting around or 'migrating' around in sliding drawers. For next-level organization, cut out special foam liners to fit each individually shaped / sized tool — this facilitates ease and speed of storage and retrieval.

Below: An expanding level tackle box is great for storing supplies and small hand tools.

Below: My personal favorite portable toolboxes for on-the-go use, or workshops with limited space: **1)** Craftsman tote style toolbox. **2)** Sliding drawer style toolbox from Matrix Concepts **3)** Expanding level tackle box for various supplies.

1

2

3

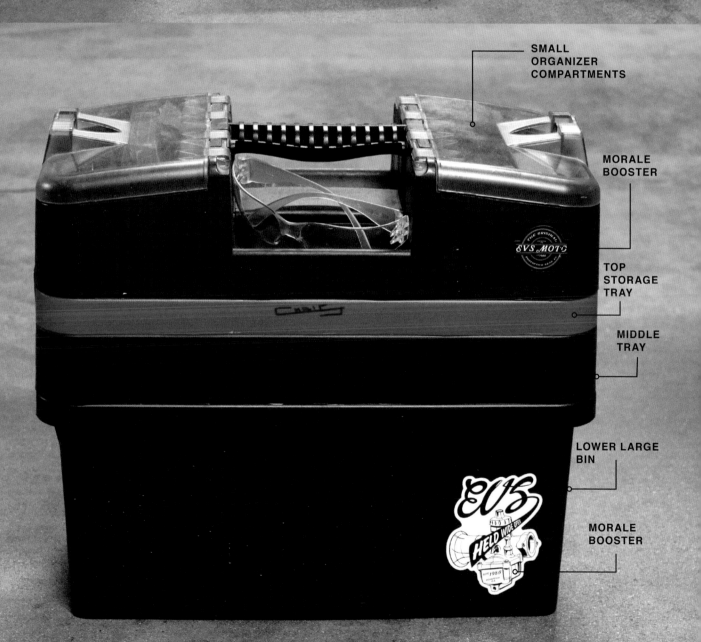

SMALL ORGANIZER COMPARTMENTS

MORALE BOOSTER

TOP STORAGE TRAY

MIDDLE TRAY

LOWER LARGE BIN

MORALE BOOSTER

Above: Usually one solid toolbox is all I need for traveling to remote workshops or makerspaces. It also saves space at home.

Below: One large, a few medium, and a handful of smaller compartments.

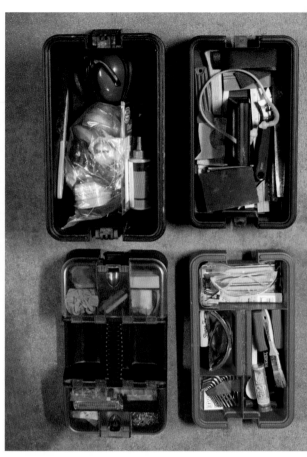

Storage: This Craftsman style toolboxes is my absolute go-to. What a solid toolbox needs is one large compartment for earmuffs and respirator, one or two medium sized compartments for various tools, and tiny organizer compartments for loose sandpapers, sanding sponges, and gloves.

Stickers: I don't know of one pro machinist or mechanic who doesn't have a set of stickers on his toolbox. The custom die cut stickers here are from Redbubble — you can get them in an infinite variety of custom designs from indie artists worldwide. In the military, soldiers wear all sorts of funky, often times comical and / or tongue-in-cheek velcro patches on their gear (yes, *even* the battle-hardened ones) — these are affectionately known as "morale boosters."

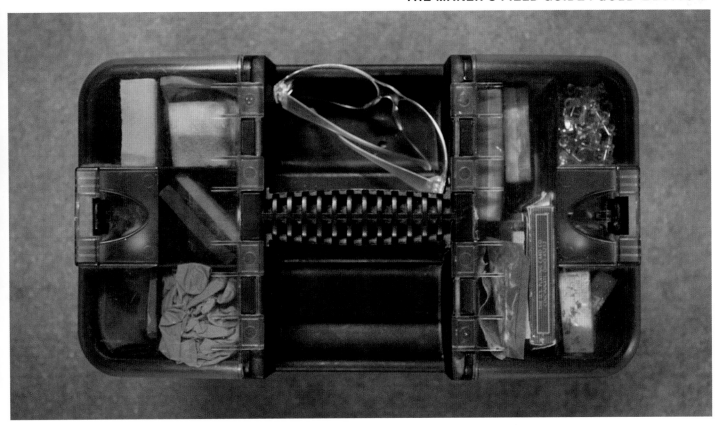

Organization: These see-through tiny organizer compartments are extremely useful for loose sandpapers, sanding sponges, and gloves. I will cut up sandpaper into tiny squares, and will usually re-use them, since it's a pain making a trip to the hardware store every time it needs to be replaced — It's also good for the environment!

Essentials: 1) Nitrile gloves, sanding blocks, sanding sponges, and spare paper clips for creating hanger hooks for spray painting oddly shaped models. **2)** An upright toolbox with sliding drawers is the way to go if you're in need of more space. Shown here is a wheeled, portable cart style version — but stationary standing or tabletop boxes also exist.

Power Drill

TOOL BASICS

The power drill is an absolute essential in any work shop, but unfortunately due to the rise of video games, most younger generations nowadays don't even know how to use one! Most power drills use battery packs charged with an external charger. Use slow drill speeds settings for screw driving, and faster speeds for drilling holes. Most commercial-grade drills also feature a hammer drill mode, useful for driving carbide screws into harder materials like concrete. There are hundreds of different bits available for the drill — keep in mind, the same bits used for the hand drill can also be used on the drill press. So go crazy.

Top Suppliers: DeWalt™, Craftsman™, Milwaukee™, Makita™, RIGID™, Hitachi™, Bosch™

SAFETY TIPS

Wear eye protection — especially when using the hammer drill!

PRO TIPS

Buy the best drill you can afford, period. This is one of those tools you'll be using all the time, so don't skimp on quality. A high quality drill will give more power, reliability, and will last decades if properly cared for. A used, quality name-brand drill is still leagues ahead of a new, sub-par or off-brand drill. Also, it is a good idea to invest in and keep at least one extra backup battery on hand. This fully charged backup battery will save two or more hours in charging time (at least), waiting for your active battery to re-charge after it dies.

Below: Hammer drill, high speed drill, and screw modes. Not all drills come standard with a hammer drill mode, but this function does come in handy when needing to create holes in extremely hard materials, such as concrete.

DRILL MODES

TIGHTENING COLLAR

DRILL CHUCK

SPEED SWITCH

EXHAUST FAN

POWER TRIGGER

BATTERY

Shop Vacuum

TOOL BASICS

The shop vacuum (or simply 'shop vac') is a must have piece of equipment for every serious shop owner. You may not need it all the time, but you'll notice not having one around on a particularly productive (aka messy) work day. A shop vac is essentially an industrial strength vacuum cleaner, which can suck up scraps that a traditional vacuum cleaner cannot with ease — making quick work of everything from sawdust and liquids, to nuts, bolts, scrap material, and metal tool shavings with ease. Some vacs also double as a blower, which is useful for clearing spaces quickly.

Many different sizes of shop vacs are available, however most important of all is to choose the right size unit for the size of your work space (a 10-16 gallon size should work for most spaces). Most vacs come stock with an assortment of various hose-ends and attachments, some with differently sized and shaped nozzles for different applications — including wet or dry cleanup.

Top Suppliers: Craftsman™, Milwaukee™, RIGID™

SAFETY TIPS

If your hearing is sensitive, you may want to wear hearing protection around the more powerful vacs.

PRO TIPS

Some shop vacs like the one shown on the facing page can double for use as a standing work surface for other machines like the tabletop belt sander. Be sure to empty out the shop vac when it starts to get full with waste, or else you will start to lose suction power.

Below: A battery-powered handheld shop vac. This model from Milwaukee™ conveniently uses the same battery from a power drill, and is useful for worksite jobs.

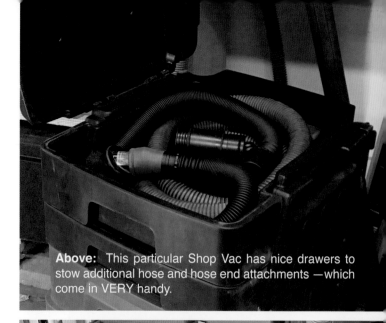

Above: This particular Shop Vac has nice drawers to stow additional hose and hose end attachments —which come in VERY handy.

HOSE-END
ATTACHMENTS

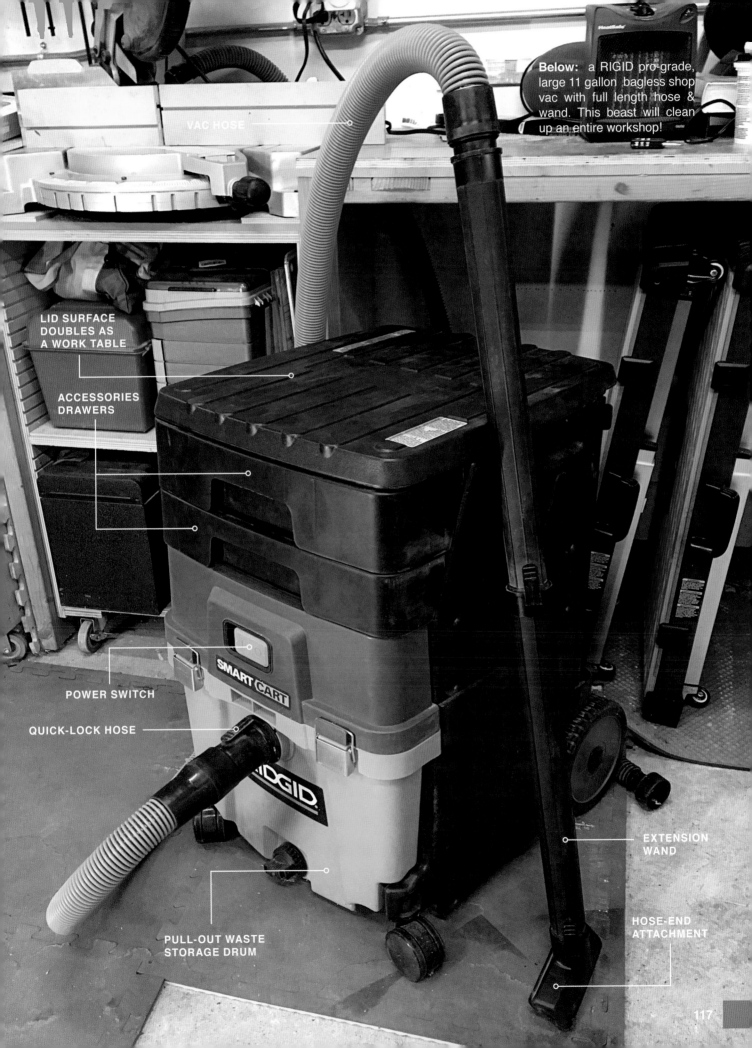

VAC HOSE

Below: a RIGID pro-grade, large 11 gallon bagless shop vac with full length hose & wand. This beast will clean up an entire workshop!

LID SURFACE DOUBLES AS A WORK TABLE

ACCESSORIES DRAWERS

POWER SWITCH

QUICK-LOCK HOSE

SMART CART

RIDGID

EXTENSION WAND

PULL-OUT WASTE STORAGE DRUM

HOSE-END ATTACHMENT

Rotary Tool (Dremel™)

TOOL BASICS

The rotary tool (aka Dremel) is one of the core staples in every serious model maker's toolkit, and is essentially a warp-speed power drill. The RPM speed can be adjusted using the dial located in the handle. Faster speeds are better for drilling or cutting. Slower speeds are better when using a polishing wheel, since higher speeds will melt the material. Most Dremel tools come standard with a set of attachment bits right out of the box. Many upgrades and expansion parts are also available (like the extension wand shown below). The Dremel works well on plastics, woods, tooling foams, and rubbers.

Top Suppliers: Dremel™

SAFETY TIPS

Do not cover the exhaust vents, or the tool will overheat.

PRO TIPS

A wide variety of different attachments, jigs, and wand extenders make the Dremel an extremely versatile tool — especially when expert-level precision, control or detail are needed.

Below: a special extender wand can be attached for greater control — especially in hard to reach places.

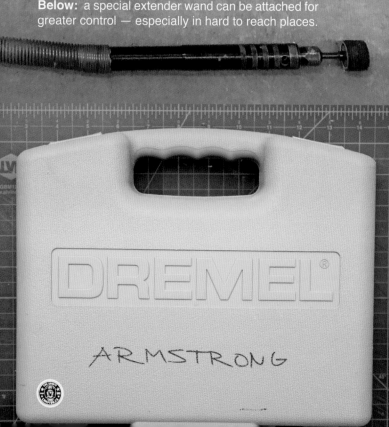

SANDING
BIT

CHUCK

CHUCK
LOCK

EXHAUST
VENTS

SPEED
DIAL

DREMEL

Hot Glue Gun

TOOL BASICS

The glue gun (aka hot melt) is a staple tool of model making. The gun features an internal heating element that melts glue sticks into liquid form. Once the glue hardens, it creates a bond between materials. In general, the bond is quite weak compared to white glue, and pales in comparison to CA glue and especially epoxy. However, hot glue still has its place for its incredibly rapid bonding capabilities, compared to epoxies which could take up to 5 minutes or more. Also, most hobby model kits are tailored specifically to be bonded together with hot glue. Also, hot glue is superior for use on fabrics or organic materials (i.e. plants / flowers for scrapbooking, etc.)

Glue Sticks - low temp, medium temp (all-purpose), and high temp formulas are available. Hot temp glue will melt at much higher temperature, will take longer to melt, and will require a high temp gun, but will create the strongest bond of all. Make sure to use the right glue for your project, however all-purpose formulas should work for most projects. Mini or full sizes available, anywhere from 4-10" in the full size range.

Mini vs. Full-Size - mini glue guns use mini sticks, and are most common. Full-size guns use larger or "full-size" glue sticks, and are a must for a pro-level workshop. Larger guns which use full size glue sticks will make your life much easier compared to the puny small sticks which you'll go through like water — especially on larger projects.

Top Suppliers: PROklebër™, Fiskars™

SAFETY TIPS

NEVER touch the glue while it is molten or still hot, and NEVER touch the tip of the gun while it is in operation!

PRO TIPS

Buy glue sticks in bulk to save costs and on trips to the store.

Above: This gun is a high wattage industrial strength version with two differnt power settings, up to 300W for high temp glue sticks.

Right: This gun has a protective collar around the nozzle to shield it from burns.

Below: Wattage can be adjusted with a switch. The higher wattage setting should be reserved for high temp glue formulas only.

Below: Glue will drip out of the gun's nozzle when it gets hot.

Above: To catch dripping glue, I'll typically place a scrap material such as this post-it note under the nozzle, to protect the table or work surface.

Below: I've used quite a few different glue guns, and the full-size gun below is my personal favorite. It's an affordable option, comes with its own carrying case, and is pre-packaged along with a starter set of glue sticks. Simple household guns operate at 40w-100w. "Industrial" grade guns like the one on the facing page operate at 150w-300w. The gun below operates at 100w — which I find to be perfectly adequate for almost any job you'd ever use it for. Higher wattage guns may speed up the melting of the glue, but can be overkill and harder to control — causing the glue to drip much more as a result, and thereby using up more glue unneccessarily. Another downside of the adjustable temp guns is that the fuse can blow out, so in my experience it's much better to have just one solid tool that's relliable, rather than one that's a Swiss Army Knife with multiple different settings.

INTERNALHEATING ELEMENT

BRASS NOZZLE

FULL SIZE 8"GLUE STICKS (ALL PURPOSE / MEDIUM TEMP)

PROklebër

WIRE FLIP STAND

POWER INDICATOR LIGHT

FLOW TRIGGER

POWER SWITCH

121

Circular Saw

TOOL BASICS

The circular saw is essentially a miniaturized, handheld version of the table saw, using the same basic function of a rotational disk cutting blade. Saw blades are interchangeable, with different tooth formations used to cut different types of material. A blade shroud works much like the safety switch on a rifle, and will not expose the cutting blade unless the switch is fully depressed (red lever). This saw is most useful for cutting larger panels into smaller sized parts, typically in outdoor applications where access to a shop is not available. Common uses are construction, furniture making, custom cabinetry.

SAFETY TIPS

Safety glasses and hearing protection are a must. Always make sure to cut along flat pieces only.

PRO TIPS

If you don't have space for (or else don't want to invest money into) a table saw or chop saw, do yourself a big favor and pick up a circular saw.

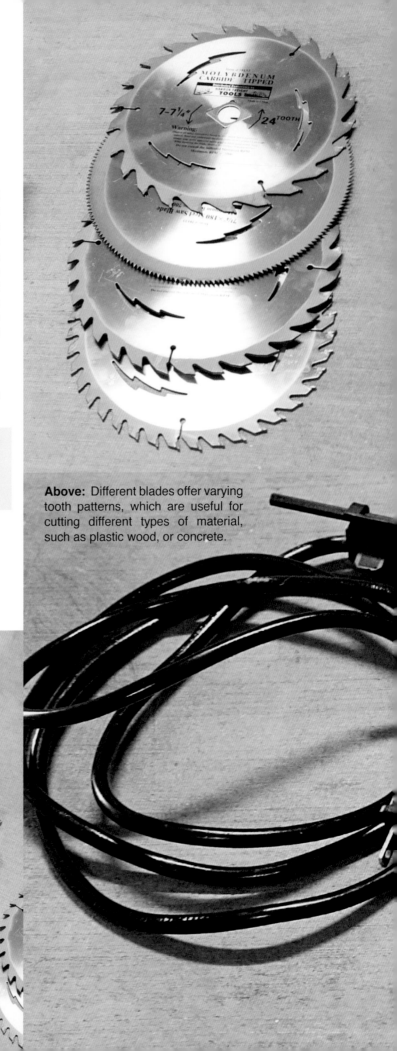

Above: Different blades offer varying tooth patterns, which are useful for cutting different types of material, such as plastic wood, or concrete.

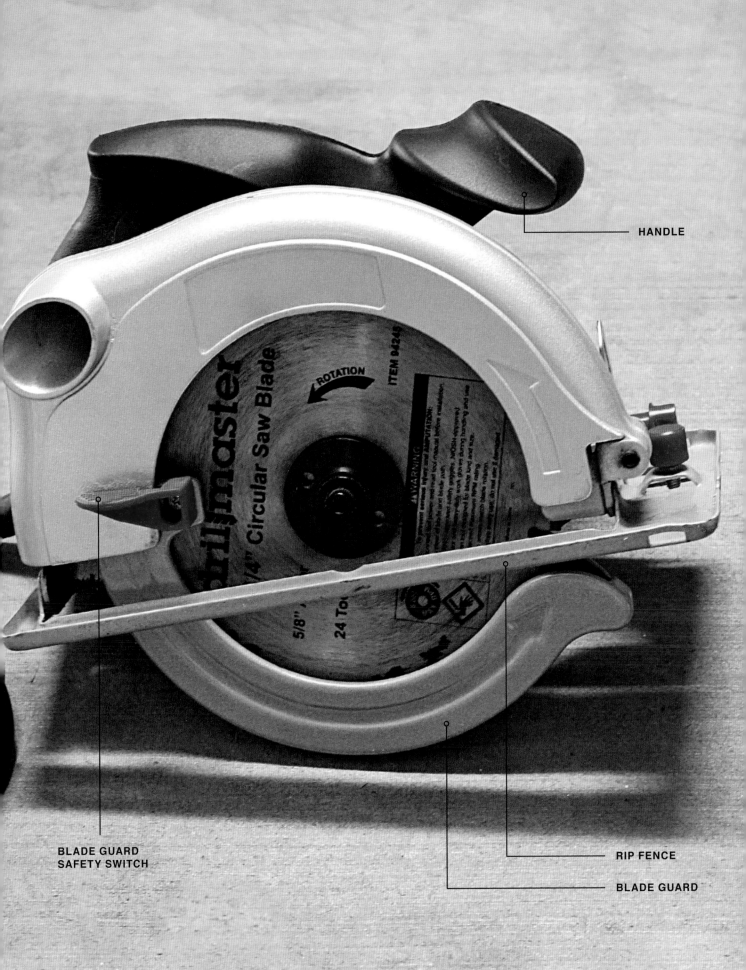

HANDLE

Drillmaster ¾" Circular Saw Blade

ROTATION

ITEM 94245

⚠ WARNING

5/8"

24 Too

BLADE GUARD
SAFETY SWITCH

RIP FENCE

BLADE GUARD

Clay Tools

TOOL BASICS

Clay Wire Tools ("Wires") - special round or square loop tool, made from steel wire fixed into a wood handle. Tool edges can be sharpened or serrated with a file, to give either a or shaving or raking effect.

Clay Finisher Tools - used to finesse and polish a clay surface. One type of finisher is a wooden handle with a flat metal wedge shape. Keep tool edges as sharp as possible, since sharp edges will cut cleanly.

Clay Finishing Steels - or "blue steels" are available in different thicknesses, from .006 to .020 gauge stainless or blue spring steel. Thicker gauge steel will be stiffer and more robust, better for removing more material. Custom shapes can either be pre-bought, or custom made on the foot shear.

Surform Rasp - handheld rasp to remove most material. This is the perfect hand-held size rasp and also works great shaving tooling foam, and the blade is replaceable.

Top Suppliers: Chavant™ Clay Tools are the tools of the trade among professional automotive clay studios (flat rake and round loop tool at far right). Kemper Tools are fine for Sculpey or Klean Clay mold box construction. Stanley™ is the preferred brand of Surform among industry pros.

PRO TIPS

A "rake" tooth can be added to the edge of any wire tool using a metal file, which will help to cut the clay vs. smudge the surface. True clay masters will oftentimes create their own tools so they can fine-tune them to meet their exact specifications — such as masonite wood knife edge and blue steel cutters below.

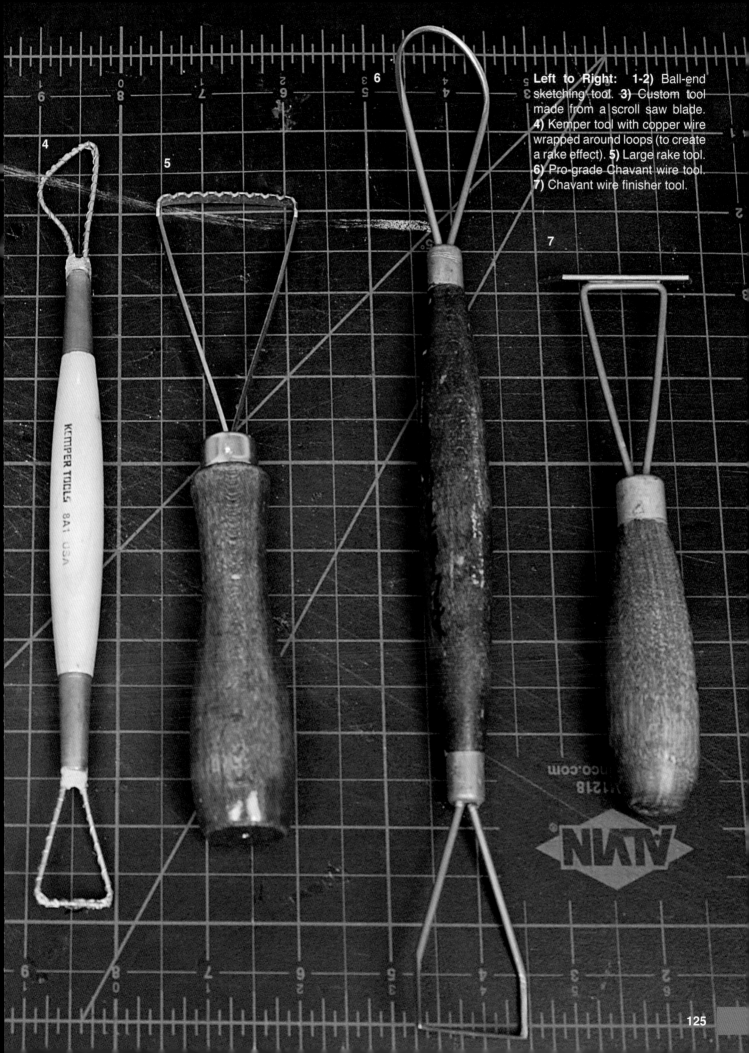

Left to Right: 1-2) Ball-end sketching tool. 3) Custom tool made from a scroll saw blade. 4) Kemper tool with copper wire wrapped around loops (to create a rake effect). 5) Large rake tool. 6) Pro-grade Chavant wire tool. 7) Chavant wire finisher tool.

Lathe Cutting Tools

TOOL BASICS

Lathe cutting tools come in a wide variety, with different blade tips available for different applications. Pointed spear-shaped tips are great for cutting grooves and parting lines, flat tips work well for flatwork, and rounded tips are best for general shaping and rounding. The lathe chuck wrench is used to tighten a part in place. The tool rest helps to steady a tool and allow for detail work.

SAFETY

Use a tool rest when possible, and hold the tool like a wand with an overhand grip — resting the index finger on the metal shaft portion.

PRO TIPS

Keep blade edges as sharp as possible. Dull blades will not cut as cleanly, and cause rough frays in material.

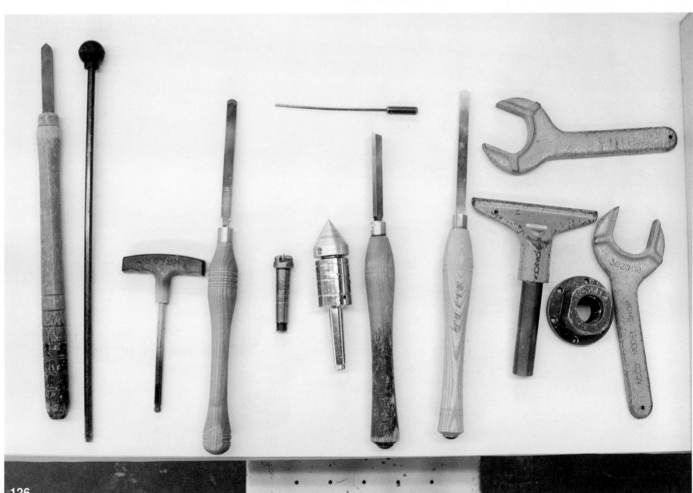

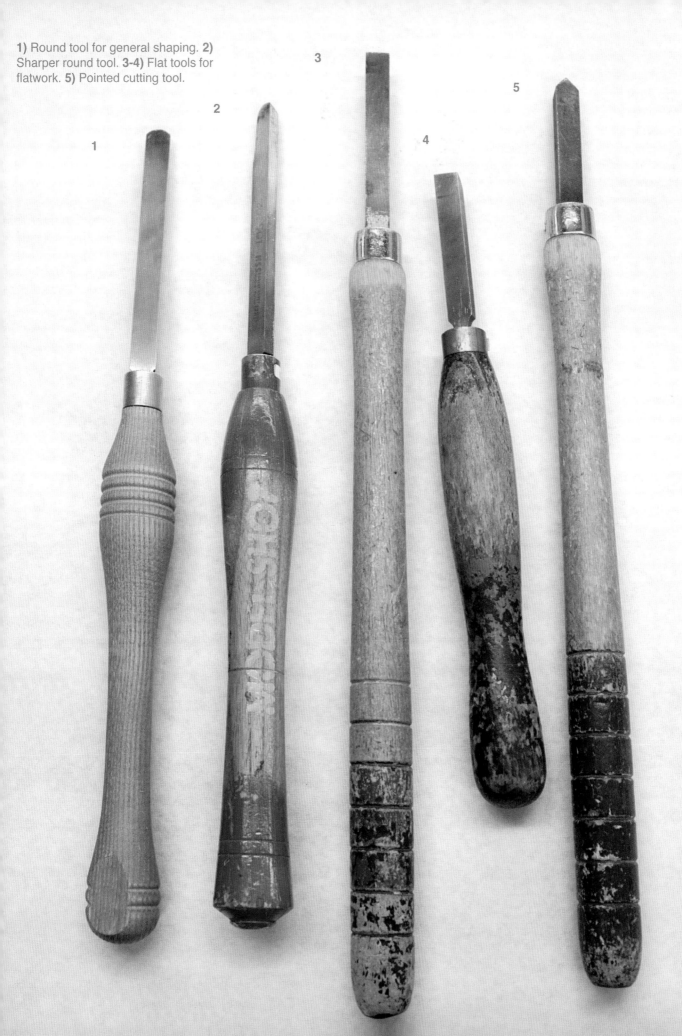

1) Round tool for general shaping. **2)** Sharper round tool. **3-4)** Flat tools for flatwork. **5)** Pointed cutting tool.

Cutting Tools

TOOL BASICS

X-Acto Knife - one of the EDC ("everyday carry") tools for general cutting and model making. #11 Blades are industry-standard in industrial design and architectural design. Blades are replaceable, so make sure to keep the blade as fresh and sharp as possible — otherwise your cut will be raggedly and/or frayed (especially when cutting foamcore). Because of the triangle point tip, X-Acto knife tips are perfect for cutting curves and wavy organic shapes.

Olfa Knife - another standard tool used by professionals, the Olfa knife is essentially a pen shaped, precision hand-held box cutter. It can be used for much deeper cuts vs. the shorter X-Acto blade. I've personally found the Olfa is much more stable and easier to control during straight-line cuts, vs. the X-Acto which is prone to wobbling or twisting mid-cut. Olfa blades have pre-scored break points, which can be broken off to reveal a fresh, perfectly sharp blade when the front edge gets dull. Replaceable blades are also available, making this a very versatile tool.

Olfa Circle Cutter - great for circular cutting and scoring. A needle tip keeps the tool stationary (much like a compass), while the adjustable blade tip cuts in a circular formation.

SAFETY

I've witnessed quite a handful of beginning architecture school students have to be hauled out by ambulance, after they cut themselves badly with an X-Acto (most of them running on little or no sleep). Do not be ham-handed when handling these tools, since they are basically surgical scalpels, after all!

PRO TIPS

For precise straight-line cuts, use a steel straight edge ruler as an edge to cut against only (do NOT use scissors here!) Steel is much harder than aluminum, making it much more robust to withstand the blade's edge, which produces more accurate, straighter cuts — and unlike aluminum does not shear off over time. I personally flip my straight edge upside-down (cork-side up like the picture on facing page), so I can keep the straight edge as close to the material's surface as possible when cutting. The cork also works like a grip. Another great tip is to flip your X-Acto blades upside down (with the blade tip stored back into the collar of the shaft handle). The plastic blade covers that come with the X-Acto's often fall off or get lost, so this makes storing them without a blade cover much safer.

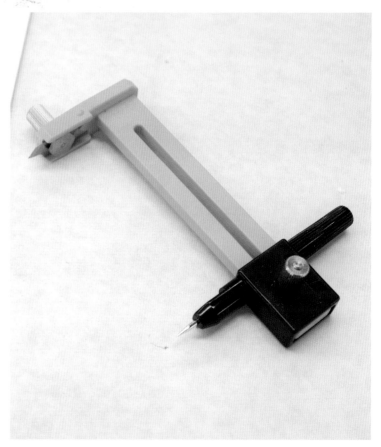

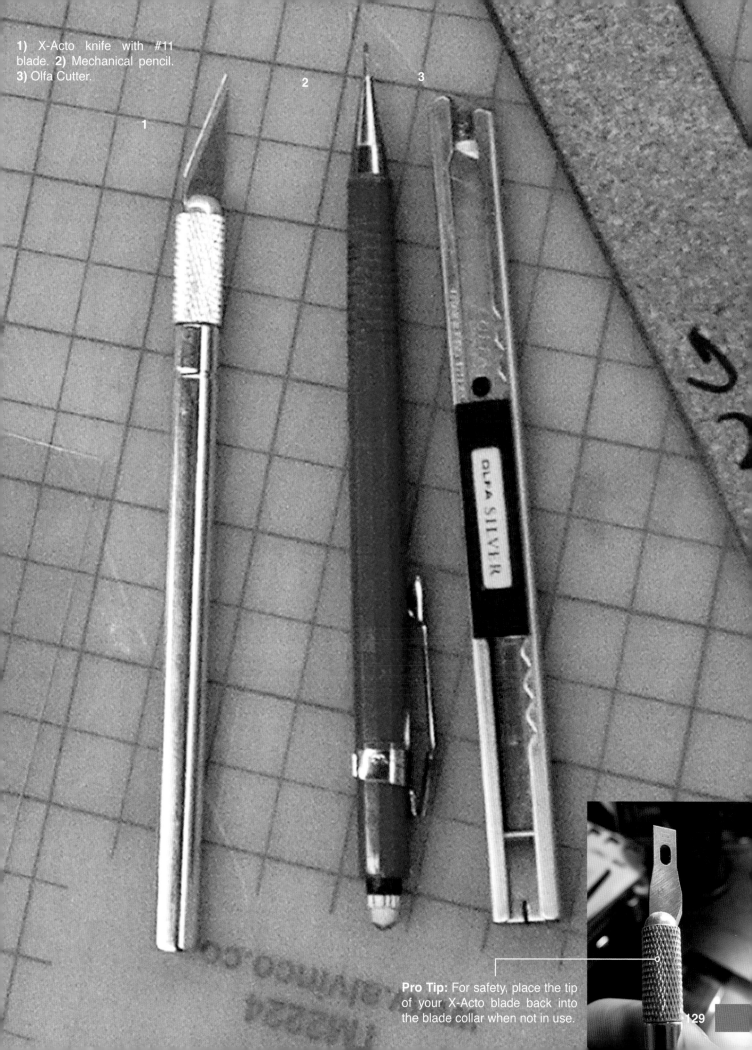

1) X-Acto knife with #11 blade. **2)** Mechanical pencil. **3)** Olfa Cutter.

Pro Tip: For safety, place the tip of your X-Acto blade back into the blade collar when not in use.

129

Marking Tools

TOOL BASICS

Dry Erase / Whiteboard Marker - non-permanent ink markers available in a rainbow of colors, used to write on whiteboards, windows or glass. "Whiteboarding" lends itself for creative idea flow, since it is difficult to over-develop or to fall in love with any one idea / design prematurely.

Copic Marker - the professional standard within the design industry. Photoshop has largely replaced the need to by hundreds of colored markers, but it is still good to have a small set around. A set of light, medium and dark Toner Gray with a few colors for accents is more than enough. Full grayscale sets for gradient blends are also available, if you're looking to take your sketching game to the next level.

Mechnical Pencil - good to have around for making non-permanent notes on materials such as wood. 0.5mm and 0.7mm are the go-to sizes here, in H (hard), HB (medium), or B (soft) graphite hardnesses. Whichever you select, make sure to get a set of graphite refills.

Pens & Pencils - pick a pen that fits your own personal preference. Usually when selecting a pen, it's very important to find one that doesn't clog up and leave ink residue everywhere. I'll try to find one that I can buy inexpensively in a pack. I'll also break off the annoying pocket clip, which makes it easier to rotate around in the hand while sketching. Currently my favorite sketching tool is a ballpoint pen called Bic Atlantis.

Sharpie Marker - permanent oil-based markers that should be a staple in every maker's toolbox or work bench. Sharpies have unlimited uses and are available in a variety of different tip widths, from standard round point, to chisel tip, to ultrafine. There's even an industrial or "super permanent ink" version, although I haven't found a dramatic differnece between the two. You're not a serious product developer or designer without a silver metallic Sharpie — which is perfect for marking up product samples, and is especially great for use on dark surfaces (even fabrics). This and gold metallic sharpies are go-to tools in the world of product development. Get yourself a set of each — you'll thank me later.

White or Red Gel Pens - white pens are useful for marking precise lines on dark surfaces. Red is good for making document revision markups or "red lines." Great brands are Uni-Ball Signo, Gelly Roll, and Pilot G-Tec.

White Prismacolor Pencil - great for marking lines on certain surfaces, including fabrics. Prismacolor Verithin pencils can hold a sharper edge than the standard Prismacolor pencils.

SAFETY

Stay away from Chartpak markers, as their fumes are toxic.

PRO TIPS

Make sure to splurge and buy quality, rather than an off-brand. There's simply no comparison between the two.The Mecca of exotic / specialty pen selection can be found at a Japanese stationary store called Kinokuniya. The Japanese don't mess around, and take their pens very seriously. When you find a certain brand of writing instrument, make sure to stock up on extras. Through experience, I've found models of pens can come and go quickly — so it's a bummer finally finding a dream pen only for it to be pulled from production a year or two later.

Below: Marking sample changes with Sharpie markers. Typically, the silver markers show up well on dark surfaces, while the black markers are best for light surfaces.

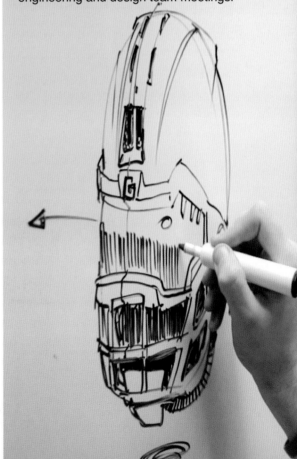

Below: Dry-erase markers are useful for "whiteboarding" or communicating design ideas in engineering and design team meetings.

Above & Below: A hit-list of some my personal favorite
writing instruments for use in design and development.

Sanding & Finishing Tools

TOOL BASICS

Sandpaper - paper with a textured tooth "grit" used to roughen or polish surfaces. Grit ranges from coarse (40-240 grit) to fine (320-2000 grit). General buff is around 180 grit —> Primer —> 320 grit —> paint. If a glass smooth surface is required, 600 Grit wet-sanding should be adequate. I've found that anything above 800 grit sandpaper to be overkill for most typical sanding applications

Sanding Stick / Sanding Block - custom wood "sanding sticks," or sanding blocks can be made by gluing sandpaper to a wooden block, dowel rod, or PVC tubes. Almost anything can be used as a sanding stick — many times I've used a plastic credit card wrapped in sandpaper for better control.

Sanding Sponge - 3M™ sanding sponges are also available in different grits. Sponges have much better control vs. standard sandpaper, and are especially useful for curved or rounded parts. Motor Guard™ makes useful sponges in single or dual-densities. Use these also as a base to wrap sand paper around when dry/wet sanding, buffing, and polishing. Dura-Block, Motor Guard, 3M WetorDry, and even rubber erasers can be used.

Sanding File / Rasp - large metal file with different file and rasp patterns throughout. Use this tool when heavier sanding is needed, before hitting with sandpaper or a sanding sponge.

Rubbing / Polishing Compound - special compound for removing scratches in surfaces. Different levels of compound are available, from fine (rubbing) to ultra fine (polishing), and can restore the clear quality of acrylic. Can be applied with a buffing machine.

SAFETY

Wear a dust mask when working with coarse grit papers and sanding files — especially when working with fiberglass or carbon fiber, since the glass fibers will turn into sharp microscopic shards of dust that can cause internal lung scarring if inhaled.

PRO TIPS

Build custom sanding jigs in curved or rounded shapes. Super 77 spray adhesive or double-stick tape is useful to attaching sandpaper to a custom shape. Always work with fresh sandpaper, instead of paper that is dull. Buying sandpaper costs money, but is not as costly as your time.

Left to Right: 3M sanding sponge, dual-density Motor Guard sanding sponges (cut to size) and rubber eraser for wrapping sandpaper around, heavy-duty sanding file/rasp.

40	60	80	100	180
240	320	400	600	
800	1000	1200	1500	2000

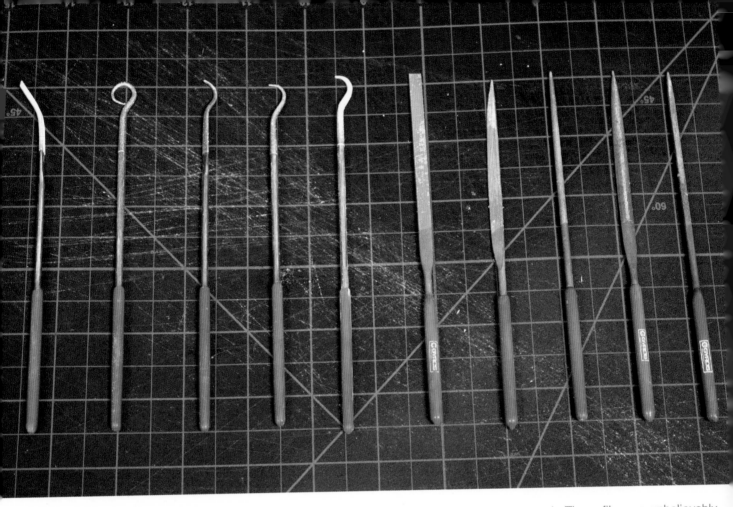

Sanding Files: A collection of dental tools and small files and for fine detail model making work. These files are unbelievably handy for small detail work, so get a set and hang onto them!

Below: 1) The Gyros brand small files and have been my personal favorite and have been my go-to for model building and making for years. A Surform rasp also pictured. **2)** Close-up detail of a hook dental tool with rough texture. Fine sculptors and craftsman swear by the unique dental tool shapes for their unique feel for intricate detail work — especially in hard to reach places.

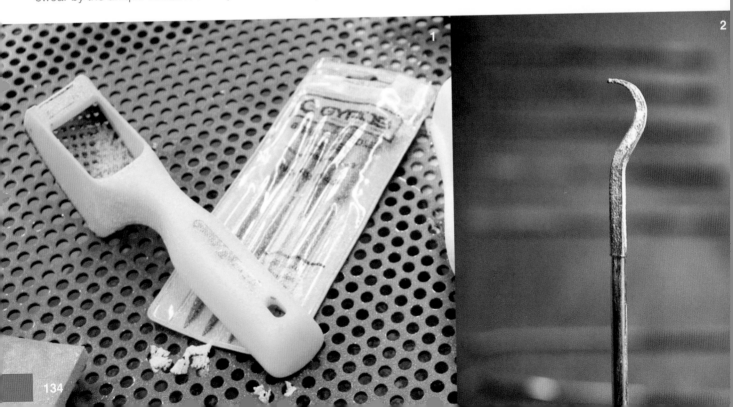

Rubbing / Polishing Compounds: Have the consistency of hand lotion or sun-block. Just like sandpaper, they are used in sequential order from **#1** roughest, to **#2** fine, and **#3** ultra-fine. The ratings on the bottle show 1-10, with 1 being roughest to 10 being finest. **#3** is specifically formulated for use on clear plastics & acrylics.

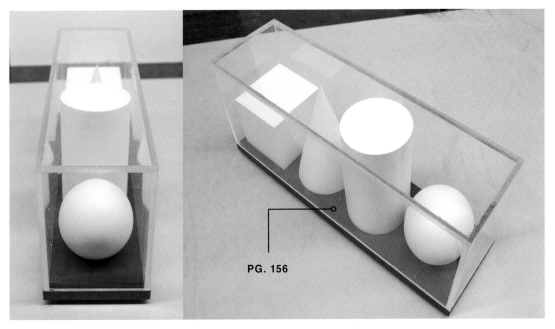

PG. 156

Left: The acrylic case shown here was bonded together with Weld Bond adhesive. Adhesive run-offs are inevitable, and must be buffed our with rubbing compound, then polished with the Maguire's Mirror Glaze polishing compound to restore crystal clarity with no cloudiness or scratches.

Precision Measuring Tools

TOOL BASICS

Straight Edge "Ruler" - the most basic tool of measurement, available with both imperial and metric units. Steel straight edges double as an edge guide to cut against using a blade (do NOT use aluminum).

Surface Contour Gauge - takes an accurate measurement of a surface's depth and curvature. This is one of the staple measurement tools in Industrial design, mechanical engineering, and automotive design. Plastic contour surface gauges work well with clay models, since they will not damage or leave an indentation in the clay's surface (unlike the harder steel gauges).

Dial Calipers - used to take a precise measurement of the height, width, or inner depth of a surface volume. Measures both in metric and imperial. Professional engineers & designers across the world almost always work in metric (millimeters and centimeters), since it is a far more accurate measurement system and can be fractioned easily. A plastic set of dial calipers work fine for most jobs — however, if ultra high precision is needed, a set of either precision metal or digital calipers is recommended. High-end calipers will have features like a measurement stop, where the precise dimension can be locked into place. Choosing between manual or digital ultimately comes down to personal preference, however many professional machinists and model makers swear by the manual kind, since a dead battery in the middle of a project can be cause for a huge annoyance and a trip to the store.

Combination Square - useful for establishing right angles, or checking things are "square."

Durometer Tester - used to check the hardness of any rubber or plastic. Density is measured in lbs per square foot. Shore A is for softer rubbers, Shore D is for harder plastics.

Digital Scale - a digital pocket or kitchen scale with an LCD readout is useful when needing to weigh material volume ratios for molding & casting.

Top Suppliers: Harbor Freight™, Pittsburgh™, Empire™, Kobalt™

PRO TIPS

Industry-standard for most product developers and engineers using dial calipers is 1/4mm (or 0.25mm) fractional measurement increments. Fractional increments more granular than 1/4mm increments are typically reserved for high precision devices like consumer electronics — where the tolerances need to be more precise, and fighting for fractions of a millimeter is a very real thing.

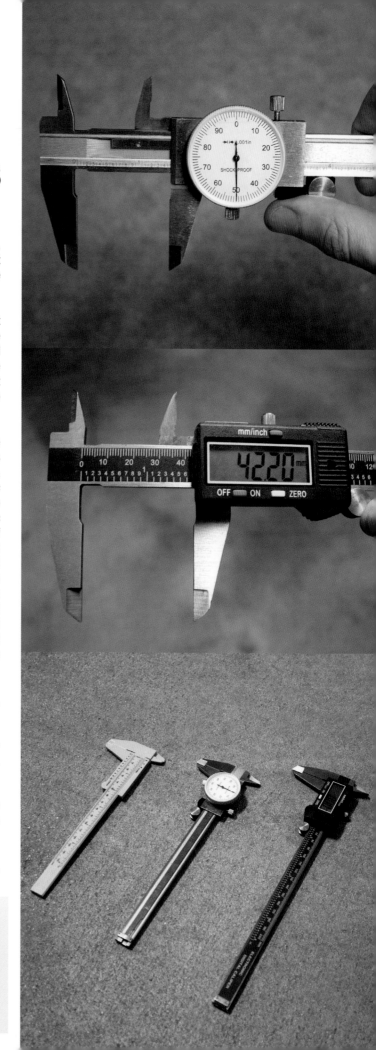

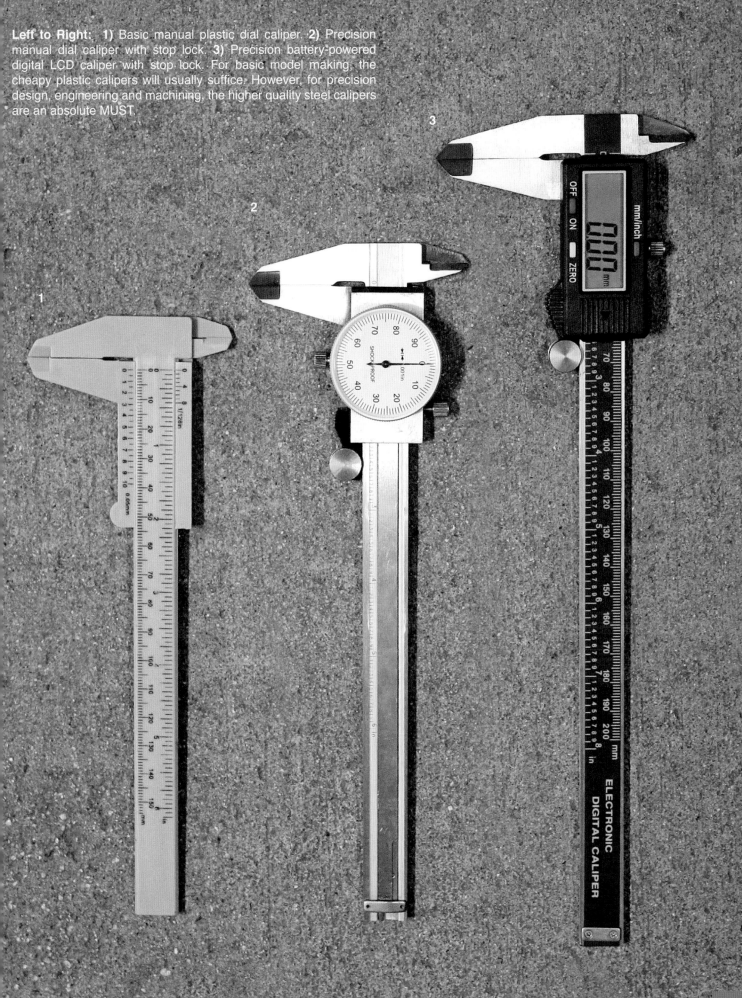

Left to Right: **1)** Basic manual plastic dial caliper. **2)** Precision manual dial caliper with stop lock. **3)** Precision battery-powered digital LCD caliper with stop lock. For basic model making, the cheapy plastic calipers will usually suffice. However, for precision design, engineering and machining, the higher quality steel calipers are an absolute MUST.

Right & Facing Page: Low-tech plastic dial calipers have gotten me through many a project and are suitable in many scenarios. **1)** Taking outside measurements with front of tool, **2)** Taking inside measurements with back of tool **3)** depth measurements can be made with the same tool. Notice the tiny steel rod that lowers from the bottom end of the caliper — this is for taking inside depth measurements in hard to reach places.

Below: Using manual dial calipers in a professional machine shop. Machining deals with high tolerances and precise measurements, which requires a quality dial caliper. Inches are fine for visual models only — but for serious manufacturing or engineering needs, metric (mm, cm) is a superior system and is industry standard.

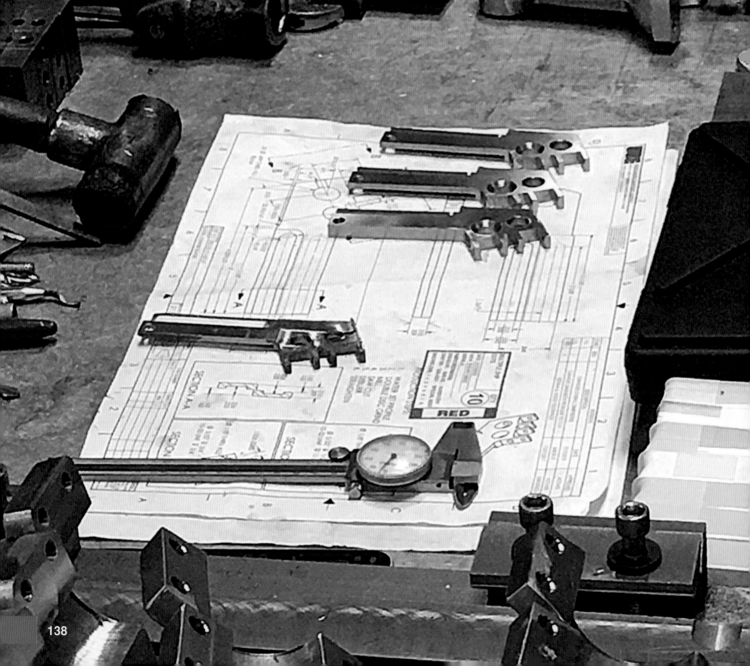

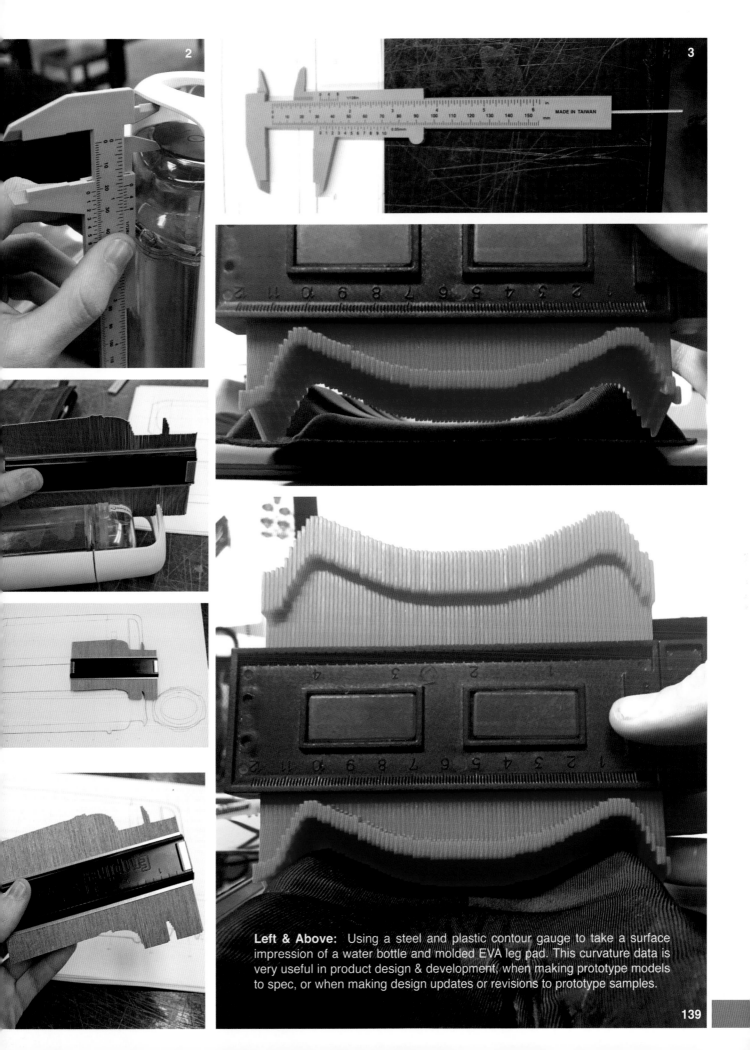

Left & Above: Using a steel and plastic contour gauge to take a surface impression of a water bottle and molded EVA leg pad. This curvature data is very useful in product design & development, when making prototype models to spec, or when making design updates or revisions to prototype samples.

HVLP Automotive Spray Paint Gun

TOOL BASICS

High Velocity, Low Pressure (HVLP) - these "gravity feed" spray guns are the top choice in commercial / industrial finishing applications, such as bicycle frame and automotive painting. HVLP uses an air compressor to propel highly concentrated paint fluids. Two major types are available — gravity feed (paint cup on top) or siphon feed (paint cup on bottom). Each gun has adjustment dials which can adjust the amount of air pressure, paint flow, and size / shape of spray (round, horizontal flat, vertical flat). Primer has a much higher solids content vs. paint. Paints and primers need to be thinned with a solvent like Acetone before they can be of sprayable consistency. Use specially formulated Catalyzed Automotive Primer, base coat and top coat only — in this order. LVLP (Low Velocity, Low Pressure) guns also exist.

Top Suppliers: Professional brands used by expert automotive painters are SATA, DeVilbiss, and Iwata — these guns have precision machined stainless steel components and can run upwards of $1,000 a pop. They are quality built and will last a lifetime if properly cared for. Most pros prefer gravity feed guns vs. siphon feed (an older technology). Harbor Freight offers low-end spray gun packages for around $45, which are decent enough for a handful of uses — however, parts are made of brass and are much lower quality.

PRO TIPS

Clean guns thoroughly after every use. If not, components will become clogged and the gun will need to be replaced. In 90% of scenarios, HVLP is superior to Siphon Feed guns.

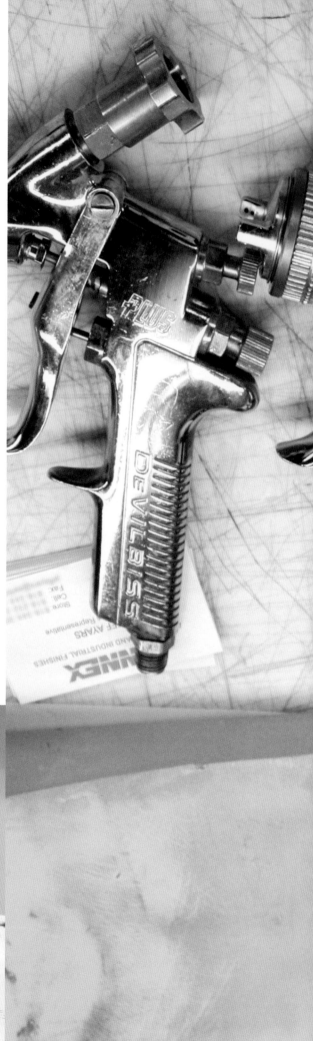

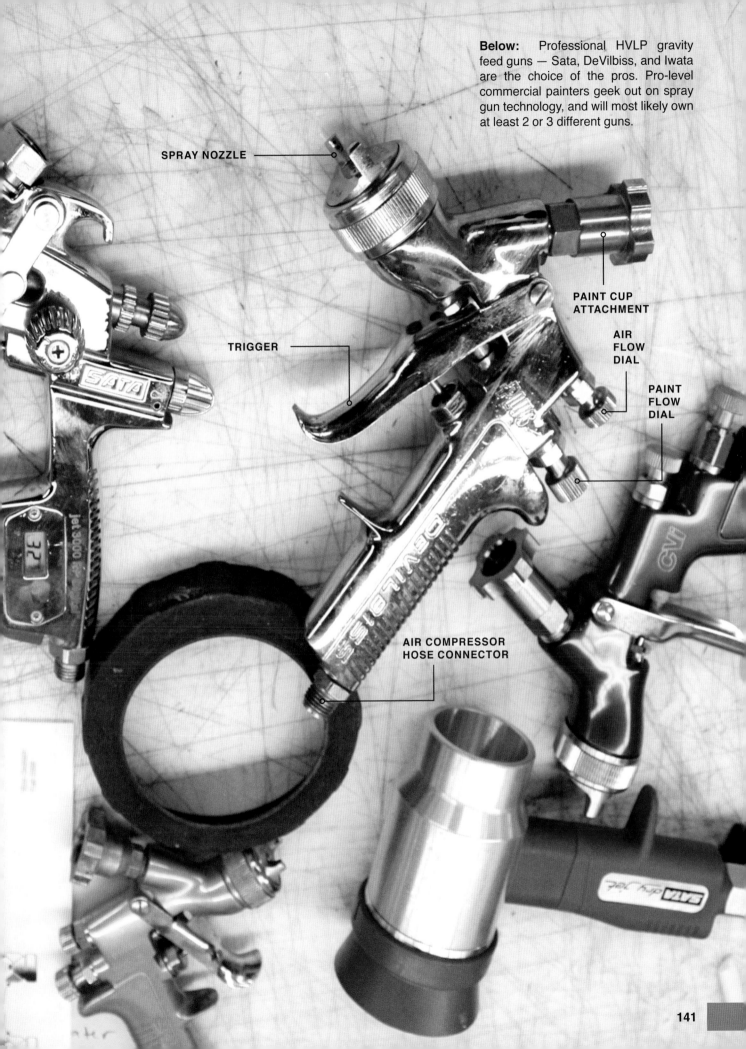

SPRAY NOZZLE

Below: Professional HVLP gravity feed guns — Sata, DeVilbiss, and Iwata are the choice of the pros. Pro-level commercial painters geek out on spray gun technology, and will most likely own at least 2 or 3 different guns.

PAINT CUP ATTACHMENT

AIR FLOW DIAL

PAINT FLOW DIAL

TRIGGER

AIR COMPRESSOR HOSE CONNECTOR

Left: A SATA handheld air blow gun. A blow gun is used for larger paint applications, such as in professional bodyshops (car body paint shop) — where water-based paints are increasingly used and take longer to cure, versus solvent-based paints. The blow gun uses a continuous high-volume air flow, and uses the same compressed air attachment as the HVLP or LVLP guns. This pressurized air essentially forces out all air from the paint surface, leaving behind only the pigmented paint solids — ultimately speeding up the paint drying process, and ensuring that re-coats will adhere much more evenly and consistently to the paint coat underneath. This has the benefit of reduced cycle times (recoat times) in the spray booth, which increases the overall efficiency of a paint job — especially in colder climates or in the wintertime, which will both adversely effect the paint drying process (and, will sometimes require that parts be placed in a large oven or that the entire spray booth be heated, in order to evaporate all water content).

Right: Proper distance of a heat gun above a model should be roughly 8"-10" from the surface of the model (the same distance as a rattle can spray paint or spray gun), and sprayed in sweeping, overlapping strokes. Shown is a professional body shop painter drying a metallic top coat in between coats, and before final clear coat. Be very careful not to hold the heat gun too close to the paint surface, or **1)** the compressed air may cause the paint start to may wrinkle, and **2)** the paint may start to bubble up from overheating.

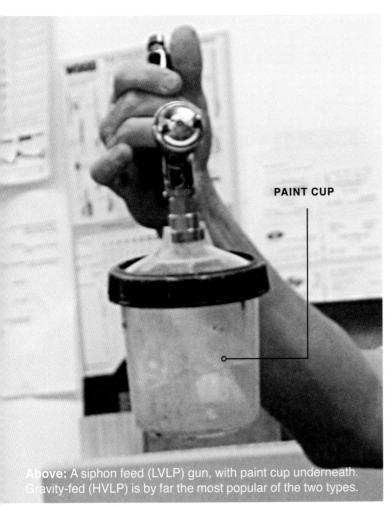

PAINT CUP

Above: A siphon feed (LVLP) gun, with paint cup underneath. Gravity-fed (HVLP) is by far the most popular of the two types.

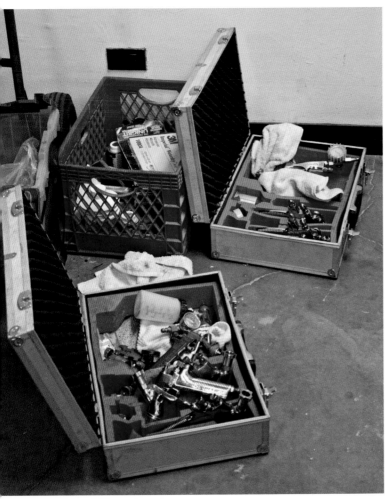

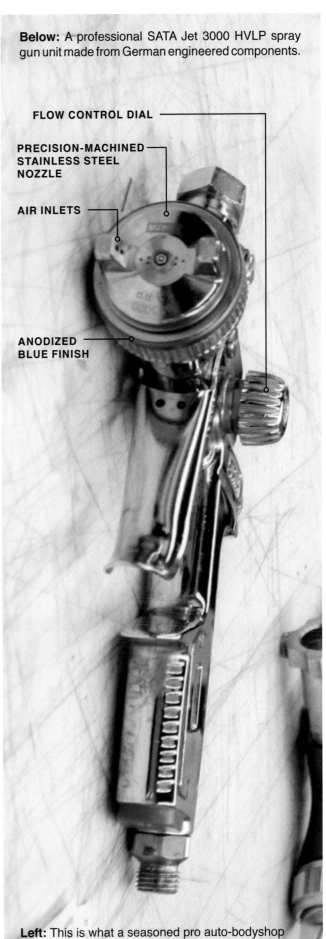

Below: A professional SATA Jet 3000 HVLP spray gun unit made from German engineered components.

FLOW CONTROL DIAL

PRECISION-MACHINED STAINLESS STEEL NOZZLE

AIR INLETS

ANODIZED BLUE FINISH

Left: This is what a seasoned pro auto-bodyshop painters' spray gun kit looks like. Each of the different guns has its own unique feel — just like a finely tuned tennis raquet or artist's instrument.

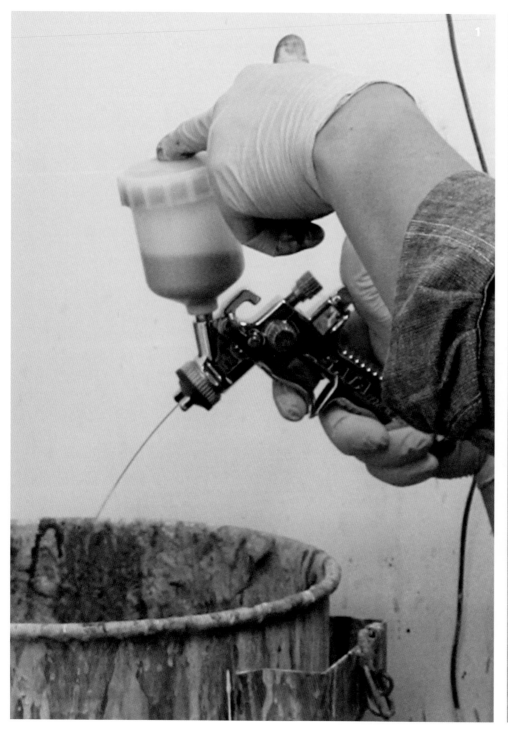

HVLP Gun Clean-up Process: 1) Fill paint reservoir with Acetone or other strong solvent, then depress the trigger to purge the solvent out through the spray nozzle. This will start to wash through the internal mechanical gun parts.

2) Disassemble the spray nozzle, air / paint valve adjustments, and spring components one by one. Once disassembled, clean the inside of the gun with a small wire brush (included with most spray gun kits).

3) After thorough brushing, leave the disassembled parts in a measuring cup filled with Acetone or Paint Thinner, then leave to soak for an hour or more. It's impossible to be too clean here, since any primer or paint buildup inside the gun can cause clogging. If clogged, the entire unit will need to be replaced — so put forth the extra effort to clean all parts properly!

"

[Bowerman] subsequently commandeered the family waffle iron and substituted melted urethane for batter. Unfortunately, he forgot to grease the iron with an anti-stick agent and it glued shut. Despite this setback, he persevered and fashioned a flexible, springy and lightweight rubber material with a raised, gridded pattern and grip traction...The first iterations were crude, but runners liked the feel and traction of the waffle sole and word of the invention quickly spread. Bowerman further refined the concept and developed the iconic Waffle Trainer in 1974.

On Bill Bowerman

NIKE CO-FOUNDER / LEGENDARY
TRACK & FIELD COACH

Chapter 4 — Materials

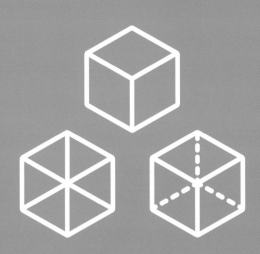

 1 SHOP OVERVIEW

 2 MACHINES

 3 HAND TOOLS

 4 MATERIALS

 5 APPLICATION

 6 ADV. PROJECTS

Spray Paints & Solvents

MATERIAL TYPES

Spray paint consists of a mixture of colorful paint solids and a chemical solvent thinner, which are propelled by a compressed air. Spray paint cans are referred to as "rattle cans" in the industry.

"Rattle Can" Spray Primer - automobile primer is a favorite in the design industry. The mid-gray color shows off details very well. Automobile "filler primer" is also available, which is thicker and has a higher solids content, which is better to fill in tiny pinholes. I've found the automobile primers to be superior quality to other types of primers on the market.

"Rattle Can" Spray Paint - most commonly available in either enamel or acrylic. Montana offers hundreds of high-quality, vibrant colors — with a versatile spray cap system for different spray effects (i.e. skinny to fat, round, flat, etc.).

HVLP Spray Primer / Paint - catalyzed primer, or "Cat" primer, hardens with an MEKP chemical catalyst. Color base coats are available in a wide variety of colors, and can be precisely color-matched by special order automotive paint shops.

Solvent - strong chemical used to temporarily thin, or remove paint from a surface (similar to nail polish remover). Acetone, lacquer thinner, and mineral spirits are the most common solvents. The strongest / most corrosive of all is acetone by far.

Top Suppliers: Rust-Oleum™, Dupli-Color™, Seymour Spruce™, Montana Cans™, SEM™, Krylon™, PPG™, DuPont Nason™, House of Kolor™, Klean Strip™, Evercoat™, PCL Poly Primer™, Tamiya™, Testors™, Plasti-Dip™

COMMON USES

Model making, custom airplane / car models, prototypes, DIY crafts, and everything in between. Rattle can paint quality can't come close to HVLP (especially when painting larger objects), but is much more convenient — and doesn't require the use of an air compressor.

SAFETY

Always work in a well-ventilated space or spray booth. Solvents are toxic and can be dangerous, so handle with extreme care and always wear a pair of nitrile gloves at bare minimum.

PRO TIPS

I've found (the hard way) that many major spray paint brands are based in California, and are formulated for California's dry humidity and warm temperatures. Damply humid locations like Houston will make paint drying much more difficult for some brands (especially in winter). Use the right materials to avoid the frustration of paint formulas not curing properly.

Above: Degreasers and "Rattle Can" spray paints shown in process order: Prep —> Primer —> Paint. Through experience, I've found the Rust-Oleum automobile primers to be far superior to other types of primers on the market. Don't hesitate to splurge a few extra bucks on quality primer — it will make a big difference in both drying times and finish quality. Montana acrylic enamels are a favorite in design circles, since they are available in a wide variety of high-quality vibrant colors — and dry much more quickly than other paints. They are also a favorite among sign painters, graffiti artists, and hobby model makers.

Above: 1) With new advancements in modern paint mixing technology, many crazy paint colors are coming out constantly — like the metallic paints pictured. **2)** Other popular "industry standard" primer brands. Always stick with the light gray, no matter the brand, as this will show off surfaces the best. **3)** The "Filler Primer" is useful for filling in small pinholes, but will not achieve anything near the results of a professional, HVLP catalyzed primer (and will dry much slower). This particular can was purchased from an auto parts store. SEM is also an industry favorite brand of filler primer, and possibly the thickest formula (meaning highest solids content) available.

Above: Testors is one of the most popular brand of acrylic enamels, and for good reason — the paints are very high quality, mix easily, are relatively inexpensive, and are available in a wide variety of colors. I typically use a flat horse-hair brush with acrylic enamel paints, for applying details and highlight colors to design models (see kitbash mech on pages 299 & 301).

Below: A well stocked wall of rattle can spray paint. The Montana™ brand is famous for their impressive range of colors available.

Above: The Montana™ cap system is tailored especially for discerning creators, designers, and model makers — and is meant to rival the variable spray / flow pattern of an HVLP spray gun or handheld airbrush. The caps are available individually, are replaceable, and produce a wide range of different spray widths — with the most common being "ultra skinny" (superfine), "skinny" (fine), "original" (medium width), "fat" (wide), and "ultra fat" (extra wide). I personally have found the standard cap to suffice for most projects. The cap system seems quite povpular for graffiti / mural artists however.

Left: To rival the Pantone® color matching system, Montana™ has their own standard color books available, called "True Tone." If you are a discerning painter but don't quite have access to an full air compressor and HVLP gun or airbrush setup— or, you simply want to avoid the hassle of mixing your own special paint colors or formulas — perhaps this is your next best option!

Adhesives

MATERIAL TYPES

2-Part Epoxy or Epoxy Putty- A liquid or putty mixed at 1:1 ratio. Epoxy is by far the best all-around glue for most scenarios. Different formulas set at different times, but the five-minute does well for most jobs. Mix with a popsicle stick or plastic utensil, whipping the mixture together liberally to ensure the two parts cure correctly. Coat both part surfaces with glue before holding in place under pressure.

Super 77™ - an aerosol sprayable adhesive, perfect for decals and mounting graphics / images onto foam core for presentations.

Hot Glue - low-temp, med-temp, and high-temp formulas are available. High temp glue is stronger but takes longer to melt, requires a higher wattage gun, and is black in color. I've found the all purpose / medium temp glue to be suitable for most projects, and is either clear or white in color. Use for foam core, plastic model kits, kit-bashed models, and quick study models that don't need much structural strength.

PVA Glue (White Glue, Elmer's Glue™, Tacky Glue, Wood Glue) - Polyvinyl acetate is a water based rubbery synthetic adhesive, which creates strong bonds between paper, chip board, wood, and foam core. Can be mixed with sawdust to create a paste for filling in small holes or cracks.

CA Glue (Cyanoacrylate) - aka "Super Glue", "Crazy Glue", or "Zap Glue" — good for bonding small parts quickly, since it sets almost instantly. Tends to leave chemical fog marks depending on the type of material (especially clear parts).

Weld Bond (Solvent Bond) - for joining plastics together. Specially formulations are available depending on the plastic types, from acrylic, ABS, PVC, etc. Weld-On 3 is a thin Acrylic bonding cement. Weld-On 6 is a thicker consistency and is better for filling in gaps.

Contact Cement - flexible adhesive, best for rubber parts.

SAFETY

Work in a well-ventilated area and wear nitrile gloves. Use a respirator mask when working with aerosol spray glues.

PRO TIPS

CA glue drying time can be sped up to cure almost instantly by use of an accelerator, or baking soda also does the trick.

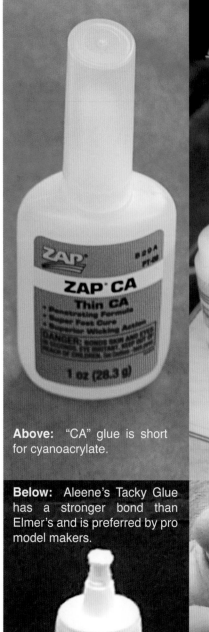

Above: "CA" glue is short for cyanoacrylate.

Above & Below: 2-part epoxy mixed at a 1:1 ratio.

Below: Aleene's Tacky Glue has a stronger bond than Elmer's and is preferred by pro model makers.

Below: Two of the most popular brands of spray adhesives (fun fact: the popular industrial design blog website / forum Core77 takes its name from Super 77).

3M
Super
77
Multipurpose Adhesive
Multiuso Adhesivo

Bonds many foils, plastics, papers, foams, metals and cardboard. Low mist formula.

Adhiere muchas láminas de metal, plasticos, papeles, espumas, metales y cartón. Fórmula de poco rocío.

DANGER! EXTREMELY FLAMMABLE LIQUID AND VAPOR. MAY CAUSE FLASH FIRE. CONTENTS UNDER PRESSURE. MAY CAUSE EYE AND SKIN IRRITATION. VAPOR OVEREXPOSURE MAY CAUSE RESPIRATORY TRACT IRRITATION AND CENTRAL NERVOUS SYSTEM DEPRESSION.

¡PELIGRO! LÍQUIDO Y VAPOR EXTREMADAMENTE COMBUSTIBLES. PUEDEN CAUSAR IGNICIÓN RÁPIDA. CONTENIDO BAJO PRESIÓN. PUEDE CAUSAR IRRITACIÓN DE LOS OJOS Y LA PIEL. LA EXPOSICIÓN EXCESIVA A LOS VAPORES PUEDE CAUSAR IRRITACIÓN DE LAS VÍAS RESPIRATORIAS Y DEPRESIÓN DEL SISTEMA NERVIOSO CENTRAL.

NET WT. 7 1/3 OZ / 207g
PESO NETO 7 1/3 ONZAS / 207g

SHAKE WELL! AFTER USE PRESS TIP OFF

3M
Spray
Mount™

Covers up to 20 sq. ft.

Spray Adhesive

For mounting art prints, posters and more!

• Repositionable on many surfaces
• Resists bleed through
• pH Neutral, photo safe

DANGER! EXTREMELY FLAMMABLE LIQUID AND VAPOR. VAPORS MAY CAUSE FLASH FIRE. CONTENTS UNDER PRESSURE. MAY CAUSE EYE AND SKIN IRRITATION. Read carefully other cautions on the side/back panel.

NET WT. 10.22 OZ (290 g)

Above: 1) Acrylic solvent bond (Weld Bond) is much stronger than regular glue, because the two surfaces actually fuse together in a chemical process. Only a tiny bit of glue is necessary, and is applied with a syringe. **2)** Make sure to have a jig set-up for gluing together parts at exact angles — like the 90° gluing jig above. Here, two clear acrylic panels are bonded together. The glue will fuse both acrylic surfaces together by melting the sheets through a chemical process. This is how clear museum display boxes are commonly made.

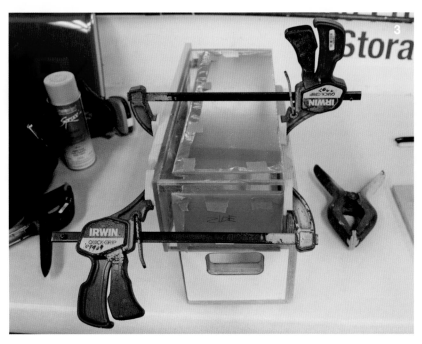

Above: 3-4) Once glued, set parts into place by tightly clamping together using C-clamps. A custom clamping jig is being used here to apply pressure evenly. Proper gluing and clamping methods will eliminate air bubbles, for museum-quality displays. These parts can then be routered to give different edge treatments. Notice the blue protective film — typically raw clear acrylic sheets come this way. A pro tip is to leave the film on thoughout the entire bonding process, then and ONLY then to remove it after the glue has set. This will help to protect from any errant glue marks which will require polishing out.

Above: 1) Wood glue is a type of waterproof PVA glue that creates a rock-solid bond and is extremely effective at holding wood parts together — no nails or screws needed. Here, a 1/2" (7 ply) plywood box is held together glued together with wood glue. **2)** A rabbet cut edge, which is common in furniture and box construction. Glue is coated evenly on both surfaces to be glued together, which will produce the strongest bond.

Above: 3) A close-up view of a rabbet joint coated with a generous amount of wood glue. **4)** Parts are held into orientation with tape before clamping under pressure. **5)** In general, you want to apply enough glue to allow it to "squeeze out" through the edges of the parts. This ensures an even bond, where any excess glue can be wiped clean before it is allowed to fully cure. Parts are held together with tape, then are clamped under pressure for an hour or more to allow the glue to set completely — using the same process as the acrylic box on the previous page.

Tapes

MATERIAL TYPES

Double-Stick Tape - 3M is a popular over the counter brand you'll be able to find at most hardware stores. This is the holy grail of all tapes in a professional model maker's toolkit!

Painter's Tape / Masking Tape (off-white or blue) - Look at the tape sculptures of Tapigami, who has elevated this kind of tape to an art form. I'm not a fan of the off white stuff, which has a bad name being used in middle/high school arts & crafts classes. The adhesive is very unpredictable, and has a short shelf life. Old tape dries out (becomes stale), cracks, and is virtually useless since it will ruin the underlying surface you're adhering it to. Stick with (pun intended) the blue stuff instead! Tapigami art form Danny Schieble.

Frog Tape - This is a favorite within the specialty automotive custom painting & paint & body shops, for it's unique ability to maintain a crisp edge while being easy to remove from a surface after the paint has dried. This is because of the special formula adhesive, which is not as strong as other tapes like the blue painters tape or black vinyl tape.

Gaffer's Tape - this is a medium strength adhesive black cloth canvas tape, and a trusted favorite in the film and special effects industry. Used by gaffers to rig up props, lighting and sound equipment, etc.

Duct Tape - best for strong paper, chip board, and foam core bonds.

Vinyl Tape - usually black in color, this tape is usually strong

Striping Tape - mostly black in color, a specific category of vinyl plastic tape that's used for striping or scale tape drawings (typically done at 1:4 or 1:1) in the automotive design industry (a technique that, despite being low-tech is still being used today). Thicknesses can vary from 1/2", 1/4", 3/8", all the way down to 1/32" (1mm).

Chrome, Metallics, or Specialty Tapes - for joining Gorilla tape is a strong black tape. Several differnt tapes exist for different effects or creating decorative wraps (similar to patterned wall paper).

Packaging Tape - this is a clear vinyl tape made with extra sticky adhesive for providing a strong line of protective defense while taping up boxes and packages. I've found infinite uses for this tape.

Scotch™ Tape - this is the standard tape that comes in a roll. Commonly referred to as Scotch™ tape, which is the most popular brand of this particular kind of tape.

COMMON USES

Tape drawings (automotive design), packaging, film & TV, paint masking, quick mock-ups, footwear "shell patterns", model making.

PRO TIPS

Have at least a few different types of tapes in different thicknesses around, since you'll never know when they'll come in handy.

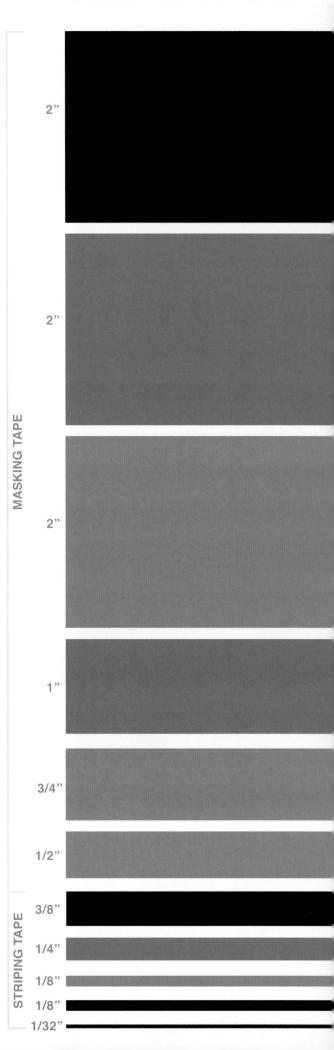

MASKING TAPE

2"

2"

2"

1"

3/4"

1/2"

STRIPING TAPE

3/8"

1/4"

1/8"

1/8"

1/32"

Below: There's many different types of tapes for different purposes. Choose the best tape that suits your individual project's needs. Below are blue vinyl striping tape and green 'Frog tape' — a favorite among professional painters.

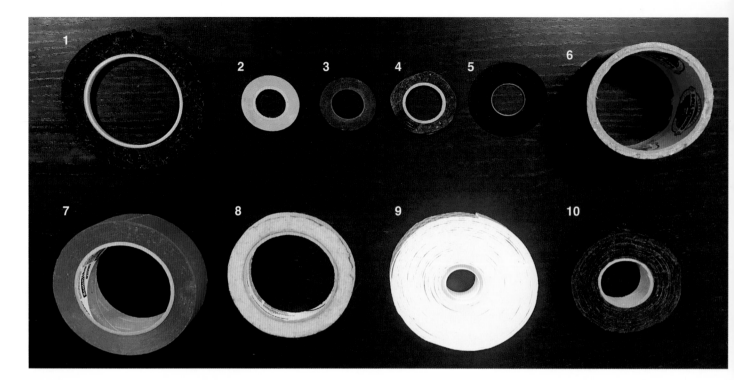

Above: There's almost an infinite variety of different tapes available, each one suited for a unique application. Pictured above are a few of my favorite tapes for model making / design: **1)** 1/4" (6mm) black vinyl striping tape, **2)** 1/8" (3mm) green striping tape, **3)** 1/8" (3mm) black striping tape, **4)** 1/8" (3mm) black striping tape, **5)** 1/32" (1mm) black striping tape, **6)** 2" (5cm) Gorilla™ tape, **7)** 1 1/2" (3.5cm) blue painter's tape, **8)** 3/4" (2cm) masking tape, **9)** 3/4" (2cm) 3M double stick tape, **10)** 3/4" (2cm) gaffer's tape.

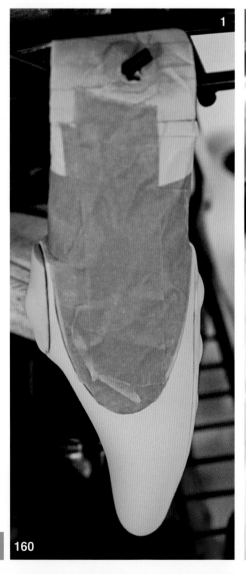

Left: 1) Areas masked off with frog tape, to apply a clear rubberized plasti-dip spray coating to the handle sections of this model. **2)** After the tape has been removed. Showing the effect of the rubberized plasti-dip coated handle vs. the gloss yellow body.

Below: Frog tape used again, to mask off areas before applying a clear coat (Krylon crystal clear) to the body section of this model.

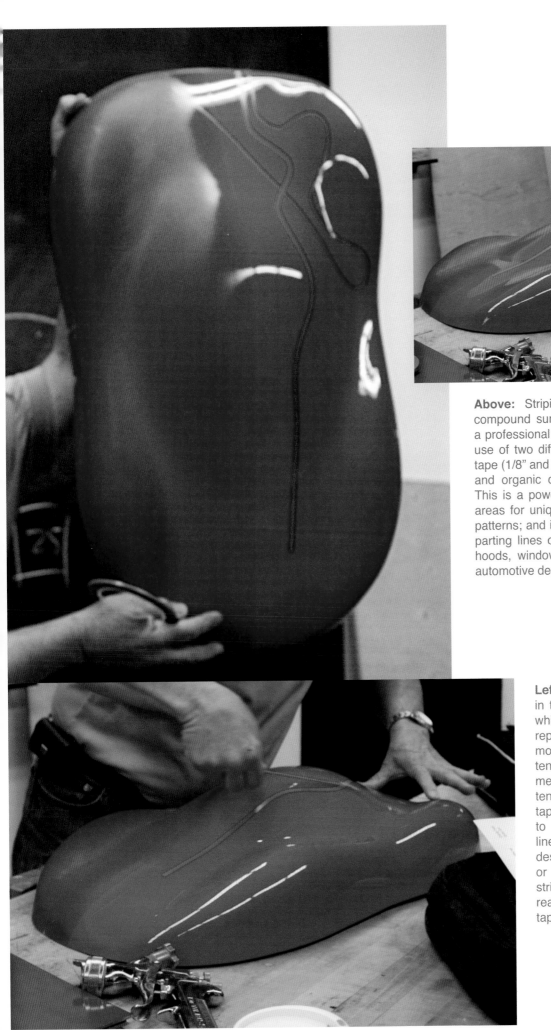

Above: Striping tape is used for tight compound surface curvature bends. Here, a professional bodyshop painter demos the use of two different thicknesses of striping tape (1/8" and 1/4") to show how tight bends and organic curvatures can be achieved. This is a powerful way to mask off certain areas for unique paint designs or complex patterns; and is also often used for creating parting lines or "cut lines" (such as doors, hoods, windows, trunks, etc.) in 1/4 scale automotive design models.

Left: To create an organic bend in the tape, hold one end down while using the free side to move, reposition, and pull down to the model's surface under constant tension. This is the exact same method used for creating tight line tension or "snap" in automotive tape drawings — which are used to establish the bold character lines and proportions of a new design, before moving into clay or 3D CAD (usually black vinyl striping tape is used for easy readability, instead of the blue tape here).

Above & Facing: Artist Danny Schieble (Tapigami) has turned tape origami into an art form, and has created a newfound appreciation for DIY culture & philosophy. Just one of the millions of wildly creative uses of tape!

PLEASE TAKE PHOTOS, BUT DON'T EAT or Touch♡

Modeling Clays & Polymers

MATERIAL TYPES

Industrial / Automotive Modeling Clay - or "hard styling clay," is commonly referred to as "Chavant Clay" — one of the more popular brands of industrial design clays, around since 1892. This professional styling clay comes in cylindrical blocks called "billets," which melt down in a special clay oven — then hardens to be rock-solid at room temperature. The hardened clay can then be sculpted, cut, and buffed to a final glass-like finish. Chavant clay has a darker brown color compared to Faber Light — a German clay by Staedler,™ favored in the automotive design industry for its light color & buttery smooth consistency. Industrial clay can be primed and painted for finished presentation models. It is still used widely in top automotive design firms and advanced R&D studios worldwide.

Super Sculpey™ - is not actually a clay, but a polyester based polymer compound which hardens in the oven. The gray Sculpey Firm is popular in the model making industry, for it's uniform gray color. It's the clay of choice of the dynamic brotherly sculpting duo known as Plastic Cell — two brothers who are famous for their minatiure celebrity figures, such as Joe Rogan and others. Some sculptures mix Sculpey Firm with regular Sculpey (beige flesh tone color) at a 1:1 ratio — giving the material a softer, more pliable consistency.

Klean Clay - doesn't dry out, useful for construction of mold boxes in RTV mold making.

Plasticine - this is a favorite within the toy design and special effects industry, for it's ability to take on very good detail in miniature maquettes or creature sculptures. One of clays of choice used by McFarlane Toys' sculptors.

COMMON USES

Automotive, motorcycle / bicycle helmets, special FX props/creatures/vehicles, toy making for the toy industry, sculptural installations.

SAFETY

Be careful when using Sculpey in the family oven (trust me, I know from experience). The chemicals will evaporate and the smell will stain the inside of the oven, and can possibly be transmitted to food. If you're going to bake Sculpey in a kitchen oven, wrap the sculpture in a turkey baking bag.

PRO TIPS

Using the right type of clay for the job is key. DO NOT mix clay types, since formulas and consistencies differ from brand to brand.

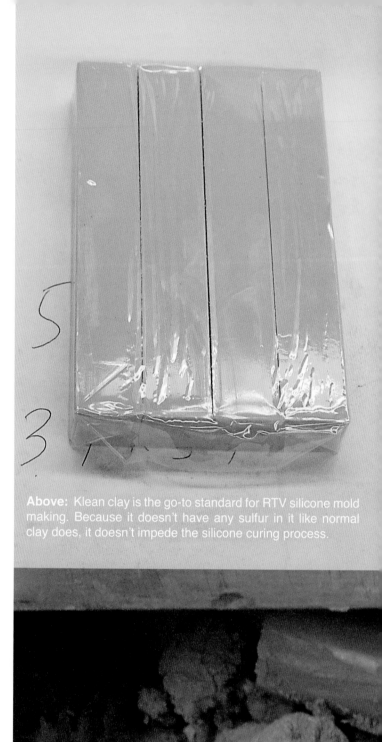

Above: Klean clay is the go-to standard for RTV silicone mold making. Because it doesn't have any sulfur in it like normal clay does, it doesn't impede the silicone curing process.

Below: Two very popular clay types used by the professional toy design and model making industries are Super Sculpey (firm is gray color, normal Sculpey is flesh tone) and Klean Klay.

SuperSculpey FIRM
oven-bake clay
pâte à modeler
pasta de modelar

Extra-Firm Gray Sculpting Compound
Firm texture is perfect for sculpting fine details
Gray color makes clay easy to photograph
Shatter and chip resistant

Mélange gris pour sculpture, extra-ferme
La texture ferme est idéale pour sculpter de petits détails
La couleur grise de la pâte à modeler la rend facile à photographier
Résiste aux chocs et aux éclats

Compuesto extra firme de color gris para esculturas
Su textura firme es ideal para esculpir finos detalles
Su color gris es fácilmente fotografiable
Resistente a golpes y astillado

Gray / Gris / Gris

454 g (1 lb)

Klean Klay

NON - DRYING

AP

NON-TOXIC
CONFORMS TO ASTM D-4236

NET WT. 16 OZ.

MODELING CLAY
THIS PACKAGE CONTAINS FOUR STICKS MODELING CLAY

GBM1218
www.alvinco.com

ALVIN

Above: Faber Light (a favorite in automotive design) clay billets are softened in a clay oven. When warmed, the clay has the consistency of a form-able, soft putty — then turns rock hard after allowed to cool at room temperature. 165

Modeling Foams

MATERIAL TYPES

Polyurethane (PU) Foam — also known as Urethane Foam, Ren Foam, Renshape, Tooling Foam, Tooling Board or Modeling Board — ranges from soft (10lb, low density) to harder (75lb+, high density). The foam's density depends on the air-to-material ratio, where softer material will have larger "air bubble" pores. Harder foam pores are so small that they are almost microscopic. PU foam has a more uniform consistency versus wood, MDF, or fiber board, making it much easier to sand.

Blue "Insulation Foam", Styrofoam, Fun Foam — blue / pink insulation foam and styrofoam are typically used for "bucks" or underlying bulk volume of models, and cut easily with a hot wire knife. Fun foam is a type of sheet foam that can be cut by an X-Acto or laser.

Top Suppliers: Renshape™, Modulon™

COMMON USES

Commonly used in the footwear industry to CNC cut a "wooden model" of a shoe's outsole, and also for 1:4 scale automotive design models before final production tooling is cut, . In these examples, a very hard foam (such as 40 lb+) can achieve finite details like embossed or debossed logos, thin panels, and tread patterns. The large foam stacked at lower right (facing page) are from a BMW advanced R&D lab facility, and is used to mill full-size concept cars. Some designers still prefer the tactile feedback of foam to the digital 3D printing alternative.

SAFETY

Use a dust mask to avoid inhaling airborne crystallized sanding dust.

PRO TIPS

Selecting a foam that's best for the project at hand is crucial. Softer foams shape easier, but will need to be sealed with Shellac or catalyzed primer if a painted model is needed.

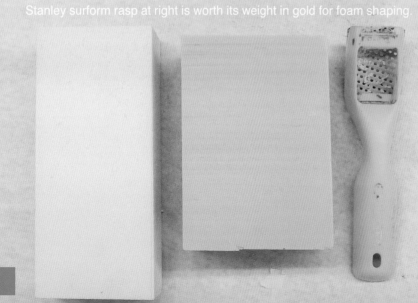

Below: At left is a 10 LB low density foam, where the air bubbles are still visible. In the middle is 20 LB foam with no visible air bubbles. The Stanley surform rasp at right is worth its weight in gold for foam shaping.

Above: Blocks tooling foam in different densitites from Modulan. 30lb, 15lb, 40lb, and 50lb pictured. Selecting the right density will ultimately depend on the type.

Below: Large stacks of PU tooling foam (20LB), which have a similar density to wood, but with much more uniform in consistency — making it perfect for CNC milling of large-scale models and/or prototypes (including 1:1 concept cars).

MODULAN 652*******
SRT 800-645-5766

40 LB

50 LB

Automotive Body Filler (Bondo™)

MATERIAL TYPES

Automotive Body Filler, more commonly known as Bondo™ (one of the most popular manufacturers of auto body filler), was formulated by chemical company 3M originally to fill and restore dents in car body panels after accidents. Since it's original purpose, it has been adapted for use by professional model-makers and designers alike, both for surface preparation and as a free-form sculpting material.

Bondo™ - is a thick 2-part polyester paste-like compound, which hardens to be rock-hard after mixing with a chemical hardener (catalyst). When mixing, make sure to "fold" the material over on itself with a popsicle stick or plastic utensil, instead of "whipping" air bubbles into the mixture — as air bubbles will start to show and create inconsistencies when filed down or sanded. Although mix ratios vary, typically one drop of catalyst per golf-ball size of body filler is a good rule of thumb.

Metal Glaze™ - "glazing putty" is a more fluid, less clumpy material. It is a thinner paste-like material and is preferred in the industry for filling surface pinholes. It is much smoother to sand, unlike rock-hard Bondo. Metal Glaze is much more expensive than standard Bondo, however was a favorite among Art Center transportation design students building 1:4 scale car models.

Filler Putty - a thinner form of bondo, which cures entirely on it's own (no catalyst needed). Used primarily for filling in pinhole surfaces — as it never really cures rock-hard like the 2-part formula with catalyst. One dries through stronger chemical reaction, the other air dries.

Top suppliers: 3M, Bondo™, Evercoat™, Dynatron™

COMMON USES

Most commonly, Bondo is used to fill valleys, small pinholes, gaps, or cracks in a part. However, as a modeling tool I've seen it used for designing everything from stylized motorcycle helmet chin bars/visors, to prototype Motocross boot buckles. These parts are then 3D scanned and cleaned up in CAD to create highly sculptural, manufacturable parts.

SAFETY

Bondo™ is one of the harshest chemicals covered in this book, with a very strong smell. Always work in a well ventilated area, and wear a NIOSH respirator mask accordingly.

PRO TIPS

Use less hardener to slow down the chemical hardening process, or more to speed it up. Careful not to use to little, or the mixture will not fully cure. Add too much, and it will harden and become clumpy during an application.

STAGE
PASO 2

bondo® *Brand*

BODY FILLER
RELLENADOR PARA CARROCERIA

Original formula for fast, easy repair and restoration of your vehicle
Fórmula original para una rápida y fácil reparación y restauración de su vehículo

WARNING! OXIDIZER. FLAMMABLE LIQUID AND VAPOR. CAUSES EYE IRRITATION. MAY CAUSE ALLERGIC SKIN REACTION. Read carefully other cautions on the side/back panel.

¡ADVERTENCIA! OXIDANTE. LÍQUIDO I INFLAMABLES. PROVOCA IRRITACIÓN EN LOS PUEDE CAUSAR REACCIÓN ALÉRGICA EN LA P cuidadosamente otras precauciones e instrucciones de panel lateral/posterior.

Filler/Rellenador: Net Wt./Cont. Neto 1.75 lb / 793 g
Hardener/Endurecedor: Net Wt./Cont. Neto .75 oz / 21 g

262 3M

RTV Silicones & Urethanes

MATERIAL TYPES

Room temperature vulcanization, or "RTV" is a process where a 2-Part liquid silicone or urethane resin mixes with a hardener (or "catalyst"). The material then solidifies in a chemical reaction known as thermosetting, where thermal heat is given off (hence the name "thermo." Resin casting is an inexpensive way to approximate injection molded parts for product development & manufacturing.

RTV Silicone - most commonly used as a molding material — since by nature, it does not stick to any material other than itself. Available in a range of hardnesses.

Urethane Resin - a thermosetting plastic or rubber casting material. Available in a wide range of colors and densities (durometers), ranging from soft flexible rubber (Shore A, 50-95) to hard plastic resins (Shore D, 60-75).

Urethane or Latex Foam - a 2-part thermoset foam, works similar to resin except expands to fill a mold cavity. Christian Bale's Batsuits were made of foam latex to save weight and allow for more flexibility in the neck cowling.

Dye Pigments - can be used to give color to molds or castings (much like a concentrated food coloring). The amount of dye pigment used will determine the color and opacity of the part.

Fillers - metallic or ceramic powders can be mixed into the casting resin, in a process known as "cold casting."

Top Suppliers: Smooth on™, Silpak™, BJB Enterprises™, Polytek™, Monster Makers™

COMMON USES

Special FX movie props, museum and historic building restoration, prototyping, and countless other use cases. A Pour-cast or rotational cast, is commonly used for larger museum / restoration pieces. RTV casts can be used for low-temperature or "cold casting" only — differing from high-temperature parts like casted aluminum, which requires a sand mold (i.e. car engine blocks).

SAFETY

Wear gloves and work in a well-ventilated space. Each material comes with its own MSDS (Material Safety Data Sheet), which will cover everything from mixing ratios, curing times, as well as proper safety and disposal.

PRO TIPS

Silicone is a relatively expensive material, so try to design molds in a way that minimizes material usage.

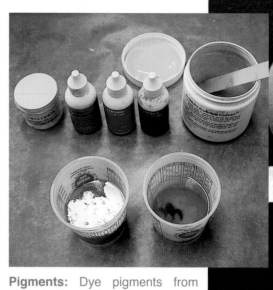

Pigments: Dye pigments from Smooth-On, and metallic powder from Alumilite.

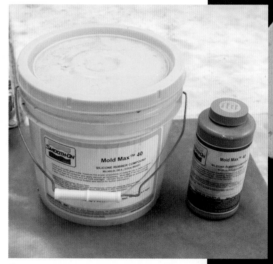

Silicone: A gallon-sized pale of silicone and catalyst from Smooth-On (1:10 mixing ratio by weight).

BJB TC-2?

FLEXI

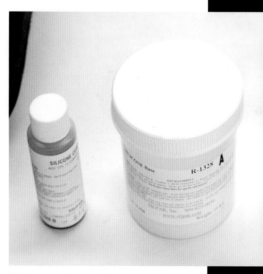

Silicone: A small portion size of silicone and catalyst from Sil-Pak.

BJB F-2

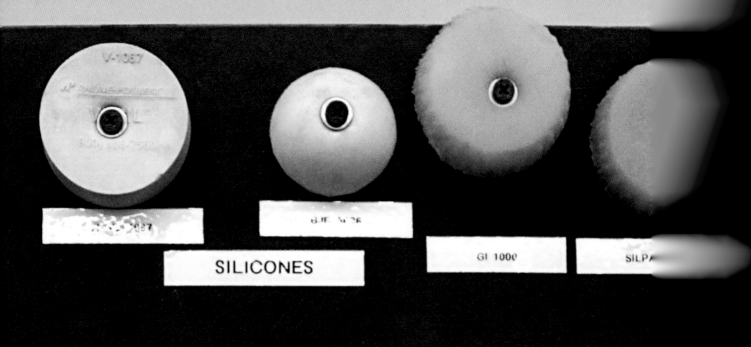

SILICONES

GI 1000 SILPA...

RIGID URETHANES

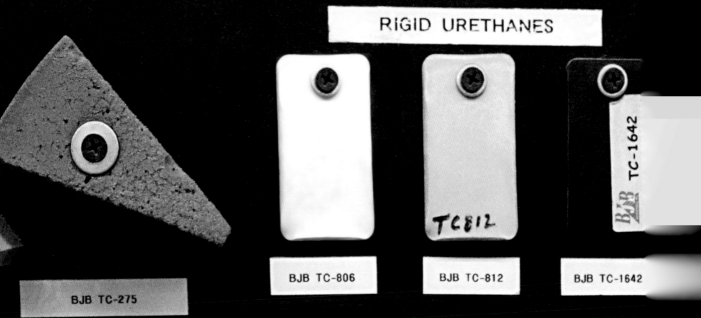

BJB TC-806   BJB TC-812   BJB TC-1642

TC812   TC-1642

BJB TC-275

RETHANE FOAMS

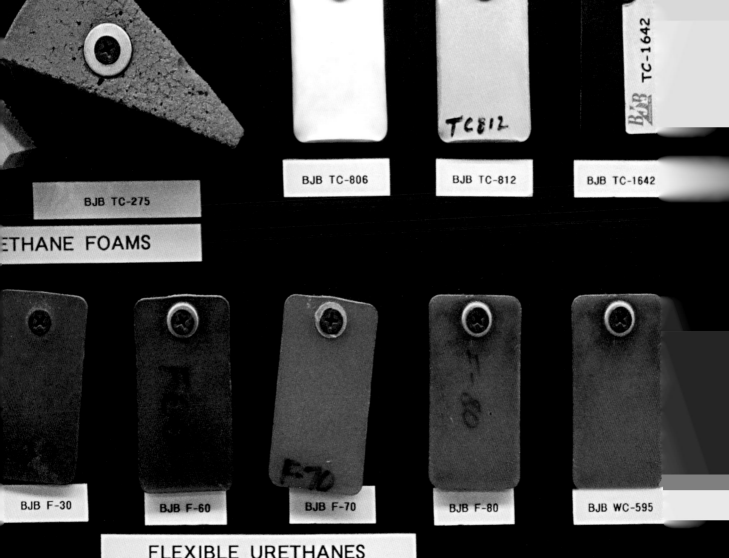

BJB F-30   BJB F-60   BJB F-70   BJB F-80   BJB WC-595

FLEXIBLE URETHANES

Molding: Silicone comes in a variety in different colors and durometers, which will vary by brand. Unmixed silicone is milky white in color, until the catalyst is added (small green vial at left, typically mixed at 1:10 by weight). This will activate the chemical reaction process, whereby the silicone will fully cure after 16 hours.

Casting: Below is a collection of urethane resin sample swatches, arranged by different hardness and setting times (where Shore A = softer, and Shore D = harder). Most resins will naturally cure either as a solid white or amber color, but in my experience the white resin is much easier to work with — as it cures much more uniformly and reliably (even in high-humidity climates) and is very easy to pigment and / or finish afterward.

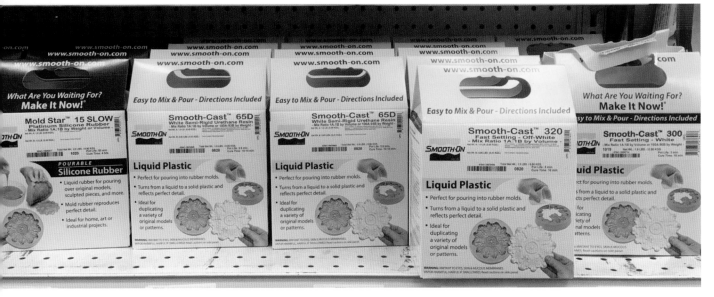

Above: A selection of Smooth-On 2-part urethane casting resins. Each formulation has different setting times — some cure as quickly as 30 seconds, to five minutes, to some up to half an hour or more.

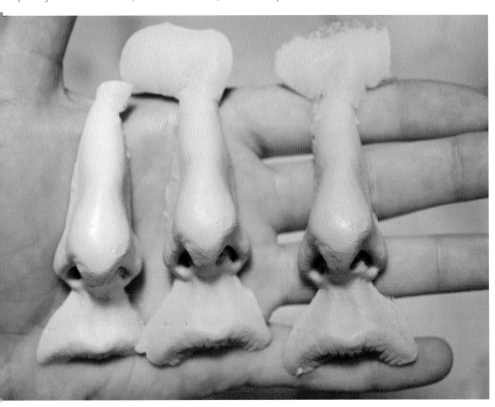

Left: Flexible urethane resin life-castings made from a silicone mold. Expanding urethane foam can also be cast in this same way, but is much more difficult to handle. Pigments can be added to the resin material while it is being mixed. Here, a flesh-tone color from Sil-Pak has been used.

Below: Each cast part demolding creates micro-tears in the soft mold's surface. If sprayable mold release isn't available, petroleum jelly can be used to prolong the life of a mold.

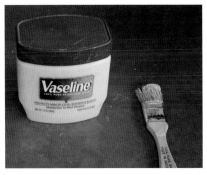

Below: In addition to pigments, many different cast powder effects are available. These powders are either mixed into the 2-part liquid resin mixture or dusted onto the inner surfaces of the mold, before the casted part is allowed to fully cure. Shown here is a range of different metallic powders from Smooth-On.

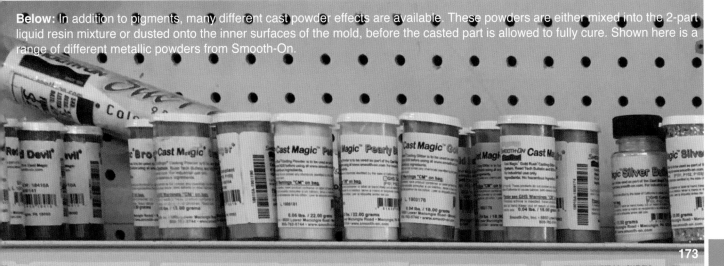

Alginate (Lifecasting)

MATERIAL TYPES

Alginate is a non-toxic mold making compound derived from seaweed. When alginate powder is mixed 1:1 with water, it hardens within 15 minutes into a silicone-like flexible mold. Molds are good for single use only. Originally developed for use in the dental industry to make molds of teeth for custom dentures and braces, Alginate has seen widespread use in the special effects, cosmetics, and prosthetics industries. The material will pick up every last detail — down to microscopic fingerprints and skin pores.

Top suppliers: Silpak™, Monster Makers™

COMMON USES

Most commonly used first in the dental industry, for taking precise molds of teeth for custom fitted braces and dentures. Over time the material became adapted for use by the Hollywood Special Effects industry and later prosthetics, for taking detailed life casts of an actor's body parts — for use later when making body form molds, costumes, and hair & makeup.

SAFETY

Alginate is non-toxic, however be careful not to splash plaster in your eyes during the casting mixing process.

PRO TIPS

Use gypsum bandages to create a reinforcement backer layer or "mother mold," to hold the structure of the alginate — since the material by itself tends to be quite soft and flexible.

Below: Alginate comes in different colors depending on the brand. Shown below is a "headcast" alginate mold, with gypsum bandages added to hold the shape of the soft mold (known as a mother mold). A permanent silicone mold is often made from this temporary mold, which will dry out and crack within hours.

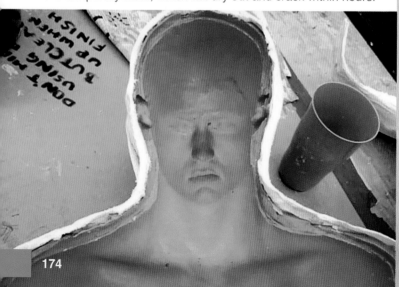

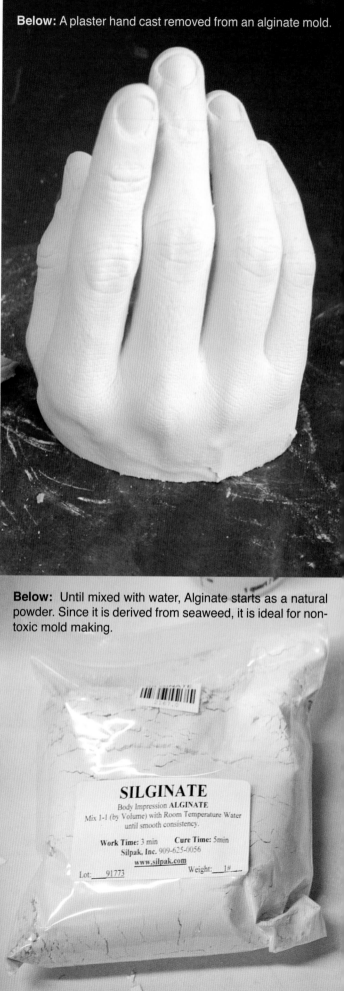

Below: A plaster hand cast removed from an alginate mold.

Below: Until mixed with water, Alginate starts as a natural powder. Since it is derived from seaweed, it is ideal for non-toxic mold making.

SILGINATE
Body Impression ALGINATE
Mix 1-1 (by Volume) with Room Temperature Water until smooth consistency.

Work Time: 3 min   Cure Time: 5min
Silpak, Inc. 909-625-0056
www.silpak.com
Lot:____91773_____   Weight:____1#____

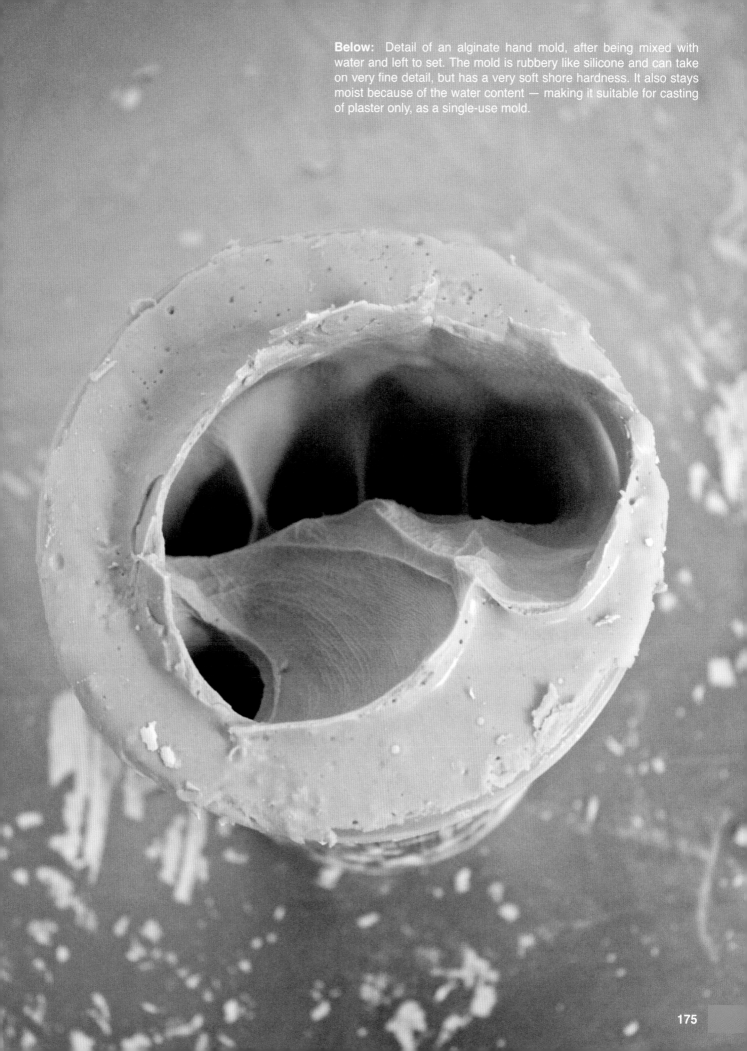

Below: Detail of an alginate hand mold, after being mixed with water and left to set. The mold is rubbery like silicone and can take on very fine detail, but has a very soft shore hardness. It also stays moist because of the water content — making it suitable for casting of plaster only, as a single-use mold.

Woods

MATERIAL TYPES

Wood is one of the oldest and most fundamental building materials — it is also one of the most common materials you will find in every standard work shop.

Natural Wood - cut from natural tree forests, the grain will vary widely depending on the type of species. The natural wood grain contributes to the beauty of the wood, and is preferred when the final surface of the wood will be shown — for example, to give warmth and character to hand-made custom furniture. The two major types of natural wood are hardwood and softwood. Hardwood has more dense fibers and is cut from dicot trees such as oak, cherry, maple, or mahogany. Softwood has less dense fibers and is cut from coniferous trees such as fir or pine, and makes up about 80% of the world's production timber. Balsa wood is a softwood common in scale models (pg. 175, 181).

Man-Made Wood - most commonly plywood, fiber board, particle board, LDF (low density fiberboard), and MDF (medium density fiberboard). The natural chopped wood fibers, or sawdust, is mixed together with adhesive binders. These engineered materials can be made to be stiffer and lighter (i.e. plywood), or to make more inexpensive (i.e. IKEA furniture) vs. wood from nature. Man-made woods are preferred when the surface of the wood will not be shown — such as after being painted. Wood glue & MDF board works similarly to large sheets of paper, and can be glued, stacked, and sandwiched in the same way.

Wood Finishes & Treatments - stains (dark, medium, light colored), wax, varnishes, shellac, lacquers and sealants can enhance the resistant qualities of wood and also give an attractive look to the natural wood grain. Protective coatings such as shellac and polyurethane based lacquers are commonly used to seal the pores of the wood in order to make the surface weather and water resistant.

COMMON USES

Architectural design & engineering, construction, structural building, custom furniture, custom cabinetry, custom display fixtures, functional storage solutions.

SAFETY

Some woods cause splinters. While natural sawdust is not inherently toxic, it is still a good idea to wear a dust mask when shaving off large amounts of dust. MDF and fiberboard contain the chemical Formaldehyde, so it's advised to wear a mask when working with these materials.

PRO TIPS

There are many woods for different looks. There are entire books on the subject of wood species used for woodworking, which will not be covered here. Man-made woods like masonite, plywood, and MDF should be suitable for most structural design or model making applications.

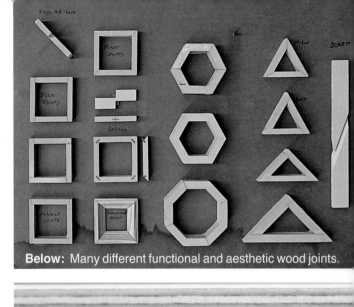

Below: Many different functional and aesthetic wood joints.

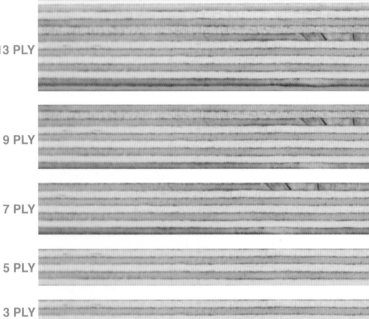

13 PLY

9 PLY

7 PLY

5 PLY

3 PLY

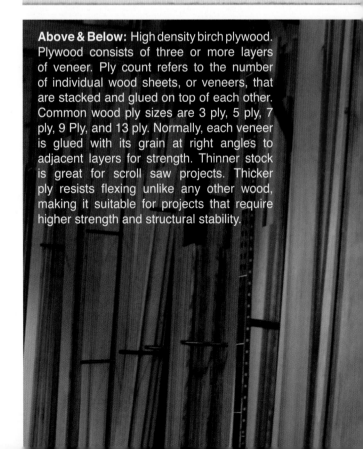

Above & Below: High density birch plywood. Plywood consists of three or more layers of veneer. Ply count refers to the number of individual wood sheets, or veneers, that are stacked and glued on top of each other. Common wood ply sizes are 3 ply, 5 ply, 7 ply, 9 Ply, and 13 ply. Normally, each veneer is glued with its grain at right angles to adjacent layers for strength. Thinner stock is great for scroll saw projects. Thicker ply resists flexing unlike any other wood, making it suitable for projects that require higher strength and structural stability.

1/8 MASONITE

1/8 ITALIAN POP

SUGAR PINE

1/4 MASONITE

1/8 PLY WOOD

GELUTONG

1/4 MDF

1/4 PLY WOOD

RED RENSHAPE

1/2 MDF

3/8 PLY WOOD

BLUE RENSHAPE

3/4 MDF

1/4 WIGGLE BOARD

Above: An assortment of some of the most common types of wood used in professional model making. Renshape foam is softer and has a much smoother consistency than wood.

177

Above & Below: A laser cut accordion hinge effect created by a process known as siping.

Above: Thin sheets of veneer laser cut into an interlocking "flat pack" form to give three-dimentionality.

Below: A traditional carved wood relief at the historic Queen Mary ship in Long Beach. Note the wood stain added for color, and gloss shellac or laquer varnish added for protection. Laquers or sealants can also have stains built-in.

Above & Below : 1) A filler putty can be created by mixing sawdust with wood glue. **2)** Bare Juletong wood bowl **3)** Wax applied.

1

2

3

178

Micro Scale : A 3D wall relief texture milled by CNC from plywood. Simple effects like this can drastically heighten the perceived experience or ambiance of an interior design. Notice the layers of wood ply or "veneer" are visible — this wall was likely milled from 13 ply.

Macro Scale : Wood is typically added to give a sense of warmth and texture to a space. Here, a vinyl wood "look-alike" was used instead, to provide a point of visual interest and to heighten the experience at this shopping mall.

Below: Traditional japanese-style architecture uses either tongue and groove, or mortise and tenon style construction. Both are held together by a mechnical pressure fit only, rather than by a chemical adhesive bond or by using fasteners such as screws or nails.

Below: Wood is known for its warmth and is a natural design choice for architectural projects, like this modern home design in BC, Canada.

Macro Scale: Wood is still the most common building material because of it's low cost. Large-scale infrastructure development projects like this one are what's known as urban design or urban planning. Often, miniature scale models made by architects share very close resemblance this full scale build. This is one of the big reasons why, even in the advanced age of CAD today, balsa wood and chipboard models are still used — as they simulate the actual production materials, and serve as a proof-of-concept test of a design's load-bearing structure (pg. 189).

Molded Plywood: A molded plywood propellor. This process is perhaps most famous in the Eames Lounge Chair, which involves pressing a stack of sheet wood plys under high pressure, during an epoxy lamination process. Hard steel male and female "forms" hold the wood plys into shape while it cures. This is also how skateboard decks and snowboards are made.

Steam Bending / Molding Wood: Like molded plywood, but instead of using a man-made ply laminate, natural hardwood is used instead. The wood is "bent" or molded into a 3D shape using a combination of heat and moisture. This relaxes the wood's fibers and allows it to conform to a pre-defined shape or hard "form." Once cooled and dried, the shape becomes permanent.

Below: Scale hardwood aerodynamic aircraft models, used to test the drag of a new aircraft prototype. A coat of clear wax or laquer gives the wood a high gloss finish and protects its surface from scratches and stains.

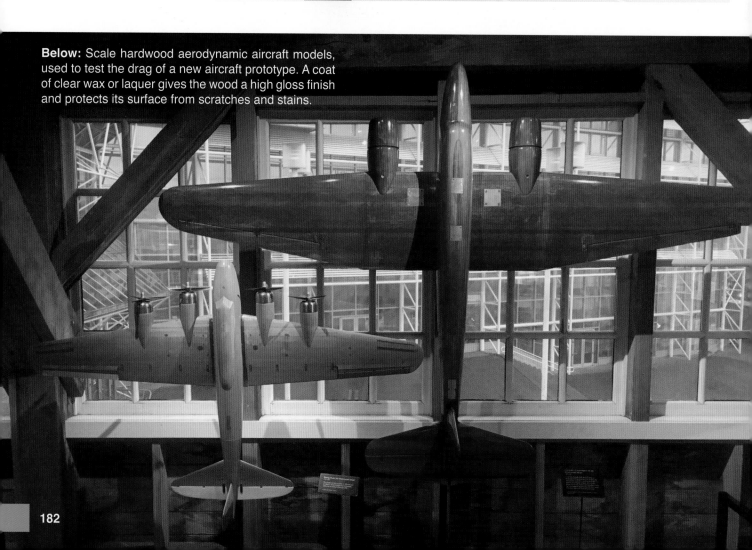

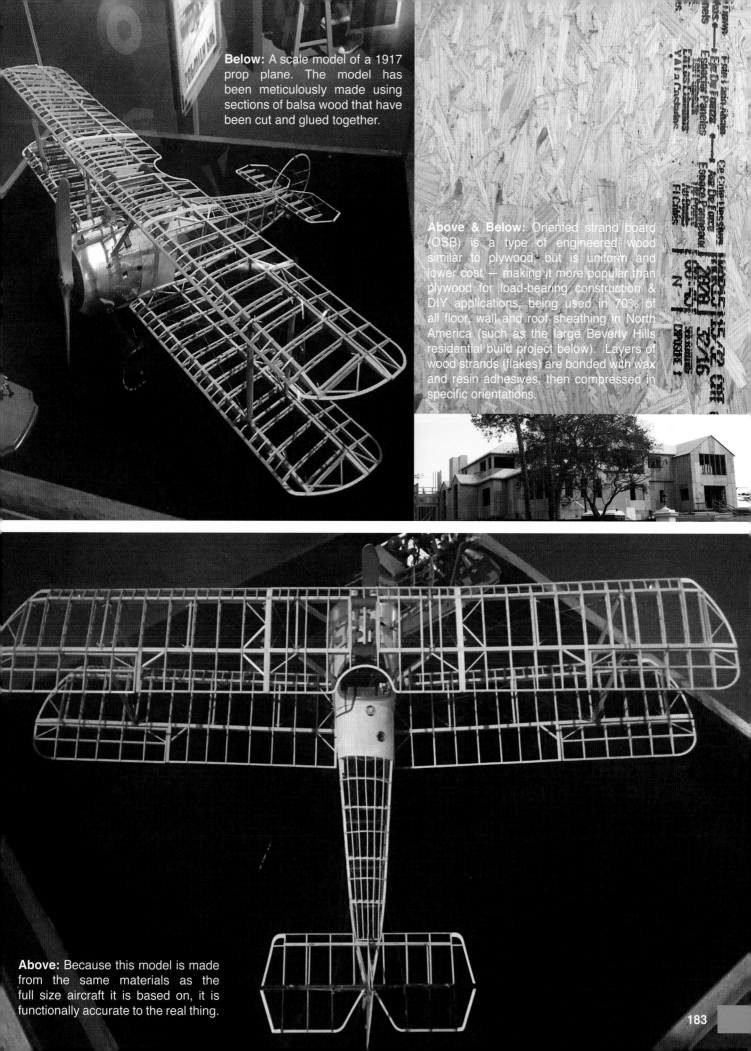

Below: A scale model of a 1917 prop plane. The model has been meticulously made using sections of balsa wood that have been cut and glued together.

Above & Below: Oriented strand board (OSB) is a type of engineered wood similar to plywood, but is uniform and lower cost — making it more popular than plywood for load-bearing construction & DIY applications, being used in 70% of all floor, wall and roof sheathing in North America (such as the large Beverly Hills residential build project below). Layers of wood strands (flakes) are bonded with wax and resin adhesives, then compressed in specific orientations.

Above: Because this model is made from the same materials as the full size aircraft it is based on, it is functionally accurate to the real thing.

Plastics & Acrylics

MATERIAL TYPES

Acrylic, styrene and polyethylene (PE) sheet plastics are most commonly used in model making, with polycarbonate (PC) and polypropylene (PP) and ABS are used in injection molded manufacturing. "Nylon" is an umbrella term for injection plastics.

Acrylic - a stiff plastic, making it brittle. Acrylic will need to be cut on the table saw, band saw, or laser cutter. Acrylic is better suited as a structural material vs. styrene. Many colors are available, including opaque, transparent, or clear.

Styrene - is flexible and pliable and can be scored and snapped with a knife. Is less structural than acrylic, and most commonly white color.

Polyethelyne (PE) - is a non-stick, flexible, milky-white color material that can be scored and snapped with a knife.

Acetate - a clear or transparent, flexbile plastic. Can be score cut with a kife, and is useful for making templates. Warby Parker makes their prescription eyeglass frames out of this material.

COMMON USES

Professional architectural / interior design / environmental design scale models, laser-cut corporate logos and graphics, clear acrylic museum / showroom displays.

SAFETY

Acrylic is brittle and can become chipped when flexed or stressed, so be careful when handling.

PRO TIPS

There are many different types, thicknesses, and colors of plastics available — make sure to choose the characteristics depending on the job at hand. The strongest bond between plastics will be a solvent bond or "weld bond", where the two parts are fused or "welded" together in a chemical process.

Above: Styrene comes in different textures & thicknesses.

1/4 BLUE ACRYLIC	1/16 ACRYLIC CLEAR	.060 PETG	.020 STYRENE
1/4 RED ACRYLIC	1/8 ACRYLIC CLEAR	.060 PETG	.060 STYRENE
1/4 WHITE ACRYLIC	1/4 ACRYLIC CLEAR	.060 POLYETHYLENE	.090 STYRENE
3/8 WHITE ACRYLIC	3/8 ACRYLIC CLEAR	1/8 POLYETHYLENE	1/8 STYRENE
1/4 ACRYLIC ROD	1/8 MIRRORED ACRYLIC	1/4 POLYETHYLENE	1/4 STYRENE
1/2 ACRYLIC ROD			

Above: A range of common plastics used for model making and rapid prototypes.

187

Below: Plastic sheet samples in a variety of colors from the acrylic supplier Acrylite. These acrylic sheets are great for making laser cut tactile signage. Rowmark's laser and rotary engraving product sample book is known as the bible for laser cutting pros, and includes physical touch-and-feel samples of almost every single type of sheet plastic and exotic effect under the sun.

Below: A scale urban planning model on display an industry tradeshow. These buildings were most likely precision cut using thin sheets of white styrene plastic and weld bond glue.

Above: 1:4 scale, CNC milled car display at the LA Auto Show — made from a raw block of clear acrylic plastic material known as a billet.

Left: A miniature scale cruise ship model made from vacuum cast white styrene plastic, that has been painted to give a realistic effect. The clear "glass" window areas are made from thin sheets of acetate.

Foam Core / Chip Board & Corrugated Board

MATERIAL TYPES

Foam Core Board - a foam "core" sandwiched between two large pieces of laminated paper "skins". Available in black or white with different core thicknesses, typically in 1/8", 1/4", 3/8", 1/2", 3/4", 1".

Chip Board & Museum Board (Boxboard or Paperboard) - a solid sheet of stiff paper. Chip board is a combination of paper pulp fibers that are held together with adhesive binders. Boxboard, chip board and and museum board are all available in a variety of thicknesses. Chip board is primarily available in natural cardboard color only. Museum board is available in different colors and has a smoother finish (without the visible paper pulp like chip board). Both board types can be painted with acrylic enamel paint and brush. Apple™ commonly uses boxboard packaging, which has the advantage of having a perfectly flat surface which is suitable for direct printed or laminating of the printed paper skins.

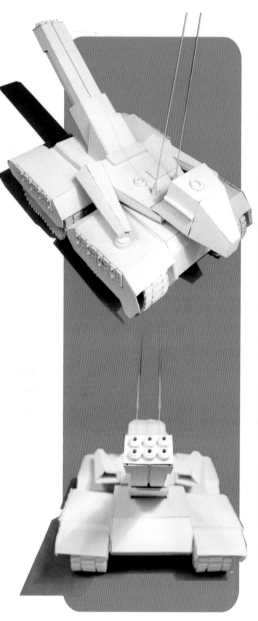

Corrugated Cardboard (Fiberboard) - commonly known as "cardboard" — two pieces of particle chip board (inner skin laminate and outer skin laminate) sandwiched over a corrugated paper flute in the middle, which increases structural strength and stability with a reduced weight.

COMMON USES

Architectural & theme park scale models, urban design planning, scale models, interior design, environmental design, POP (point of purchase) and movie theater displays, prototype mock-ups, product packaging.

SAFETY

Keep your X-Acto or Olfa knife blade sharp or replace when worn out for the clean, non-raggedy cuts, but also for safety — a dull blade is a dangerous blade!

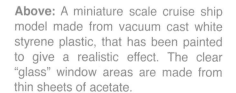

PRO TIPS

Aleene's Tacky Glue is by far the best glue to use for foam core and chip board — it is extremely robust, offering benefits like quicker drying times and more strength in comparison to standard Elmer's white glue. For much faster drying time, hot glue can be used, but the bond is not nearly as strong as with white glue.

Above: A miniature scale cruise ship model made from vacuum cast white styrene plastic, that has been painted to give a realistic effect. The clear "glass" window areas are made from thin sheets of acetate.

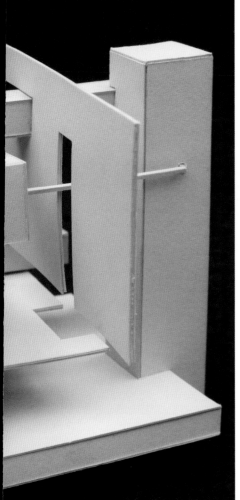

Above: A scale architectural model made from chipboard (base), museum board (walkways), and balsa wood (railings and structural overhangs — see page 173 for the real life application).

Above: A museum board study model held together with white glue. Museum board and chip board are both favorites in architectural scale models, and can be painted easily.

Above: Chip board can be glued in stacks to create a layered effect.

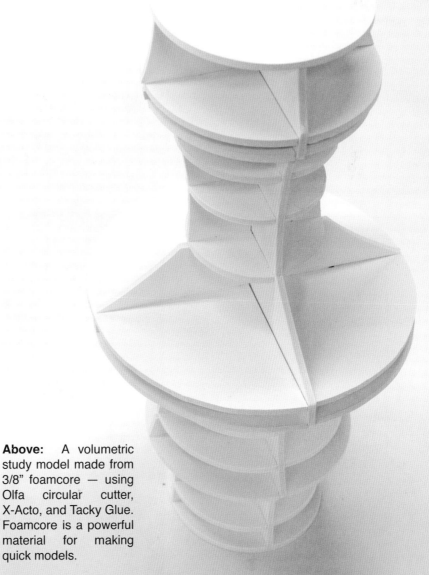

Above: A volumetric study model made from 3/8" foamcore — using Olfa circular cutter, X-Acto, and Tacky Glue. Foamcore is a powerful material for making quick models.

189

Right: A 3D volumetric T-Rex head that has been laser cut layer by layer out of corrugated cardboard, and glued together piece by piece. The T-Rex 3D model data was used to create a CAD file for cutting in 2D laser vector software.

Cardboard Specifications: Corrugated board is specified for by the weight of the skin papers and the size of the flute pattern. Packaging, transport and logistics is a huge indusry — and yes, there is such as a thing as a packaging engineer, who will stress test the strength of packaging — since protecting the inner contents from damage in shipping and transport can potentially save a company millions of dollars in damages or losses!

F FLUTE   0.9 to 1.2mm

E FLUTE   1.2mm to 2mm

B FLUTE   2.4mm to 3mm

C FLUTE   3.5mm to 4.2mm

Right: A freestanding 3D cardboard movie theater display. Many of these displays can get quite elaborate, and are commonly made from a cardboard substrate, with full color CYMK printed graphics that are adhered to the surface with spray adhesive.

Above: A life-size 3D flatpack cardboard T-Rex sculpture on display at the Maker Faire in San Mateo, California. This sculpture was also wired with electronics inside, for light effects and sounds.

Below & Right: Notice the 2D cardboard panels were joined together using clear zip ties, rather than glue, which allows for non-destructive assembly and re-assembly.

Metals

MATERIAL TYPES

Metal science and technology is known as metallurgy, and working with metals is known as processing. Metals are used anywhere high strength and durability are needed.

Aluminum, Steel (Stainless), Bronze, Brass, Nickel Silver, Copper, or Titanium - these are the most common metal alloys. Aluminum is much softer than steel or titanium, and is commonly used to create mold tooling (aircraft grade aluminum is the highest quality of all). Titanium has one of the strongest strength-to-weight ratios of any metal.

Die Cast or Foundry Cast (Lost Wax Process) - molten metal that is poured into a mold (often single-use sand molds). Commonly how engine blocks and jewelry items are made.

Machined - refers to CNC or manually milling of a raw metal billet, which is known as "subtractive manufacturing." Photo chemical machining is another process for small parts.

Extruded - forcing a metal material through a pre-formed die to create a thin-walled shape (i.e. aluminum iPod).

Sheet Metal Stamping (Die Cutting) and Bending - mass produced automotive body panels are made by die cutting of sheet metal, which are then bent into shape (handmade car bodies like those of a Jaguar are hand-hammered into shape). Die cutting is also used to create functional and / or decorative peforations in metal, or to shave weight.

Laser or Waterjet Cut - thin, low gauge sheet metal can be laser cut. Thicker, heavy gauge metal must be waterjet cut.

Hydroformed - similar to injection molding, but instead of pressurized air, this process uses pressurized water to force molten metal to form to the inner walls of a mold cavity.

Forged or Drop Forged - a process that entails "folding" red-hot heated metal in a large forge (oven), which strengthens the mollecular bond of the metal particles. This is how samurai katana swords are made.

Tempered - tempering a process of heat treating, which is used to increase the toughness of iron-based alloys.

Cold Cast - a process that entails mixing metal powder with a 2-part resin to create hybrid castings that give the appearance of solid metal without the functionality, and is much faster and much less expensive than foundry casting.

COMMON USES

Automotive panels, consumer electronics, luxury goods.

PRO TIPS

Heat treating or special coatings can strengthen a metal.

Below: Aluminum rims of a one-off concept car that have been either machined or die cast.

Above: hydrojet cut signage.

Above: Waterjet or laser cut perforation pattern on a machined aluminum C-pillar of a concept car. Unique perfing designs can lend alot to a product's originality, but functionally and aesthetically.

Below: A freestanding metal display in Whistler, Canada. The ring panels here were most likely waterjet cut from stainless steel, then welded together with the inner / outer cylindrical ring surfaces. The metal was also likely coated to protect it from the elements.

Above: Machined aluminum scale model of the Apple Park "spaceship" campus in Cupertino, California.

Waterjet Cutting: A "sanding block" is made by attaching a strip of sandpaper to a scrap wood block using strong double-stick tape. Shapes like these are useful for reaching areas which are harder to get a handle on by any other means — here, a strip of 150-Grit sandpaper is used to remove small table saw blade grooves from the inside of a countersunk dado cut.

Above: Fine detail and smooth curvature is achievable with machining, such as the curvature shown on the model above.

Above & Below: This Apple Park interactive model is made entirely from machined aluminum — just like Apple's desktop and laptop computer devices. Sitting in the lobby of the visitor's center, and designed by Apple's chief of design, Jonathan "Jony" Ive.

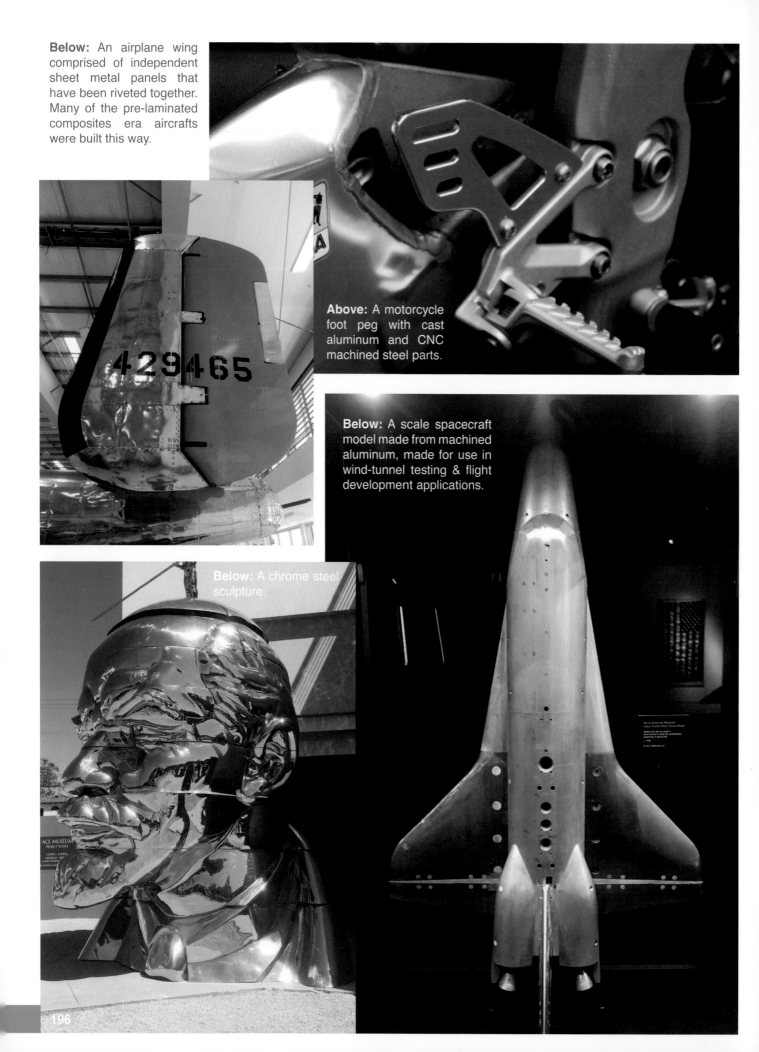

Below: An airplane wing comprised of independent sheet metal panels that have been riveted together. Many of the pre-laminated composites era aircrafts were built this way.

Above: A motorcycle foot peg with cast aluminum and CNC machined steel parts.

Below: A scale spacecraft model made from machined aluminum, made for use in wind-tunnel testing & flight development applications.

Below: A chrome steel sculpture.

Above: A cast bronze outdoor sculpture. Notice how some metals will develop a patina after exposed to the air and outside elements (known as oxidation), if left untreated.

Above: A machined titanium propusion thruster that was used in the mars rover. Titanium all is used here for its high strength properties.

Fiberglass & Carbon Fiber Composites

MATERIAL TYPES

Fiber composites entail a process where glass or carbon fibers are woven into a "cloth" or "mat." This soft fabric is then carefully placed into a negative mold, mixed with a resin binder — such as epoxy resin — which infuses with the mat fibers to then form into a hard shell shape through a process known as lamination. The two primary lamination types are hand "lay-up" and vaccum-bagged composites. Patterns need to be cut to ensure the woven fiber materials drape correctly over complex surfaces.

Fiberglass Reinforced Plastic (GFRP) - Glass-fiber reinforced plastic, where millions of glass fiber strands are woven into a quilted "mat" or "cloth", and then combined with an epoxy resin polymer.

Carbon Fiber (CFRP) - Carbon fiber reinforced plastic, or simply "Carbon," has the strength of steel but at a substantially reduced weight. CFRP uses graphite fibers and is superior in both strength and stiffness vs. fiberglass, but it is also many multiples times the cost.

COMMON USES

Anywhere where lightness, stiffness, and strength are needed. Fiberglass is most commonly used in boat hulls and sports car bodies — like the one at far right. Carbon Fiber is commonly used in exotic supercar bodies (i.e. Ferrari, Lamborghini, McLaren, Porsche), Formula 1 race car monocoques, fighter jets, bicycles, high-end sporting goods including helmets, golf shafts, ice hocky sticks, soccer sole cleat plates, aftermarket car body parts / motorcycle parts, and functional prosthetics.

SAFETY

Composites can be nasty to work with, so use a respirator mask and gloves when handling.

PRO TIPS

One of the paradoxes with carbon reinforcements and pre-preg is that the less something weighs, the more expensive it becomes. This is especially true for traditional woven cloths and unidirectional pre-pregs — meaning the mat comes pre-impregnated, or soaked in resin, and is typically stored in refrigerators to ensure freshness. Vacuum-bagging techniques ("vacuum-bag composites") suck out excess epoxy laminate material and results in much better precision, strength, layer uniformity, and a vastly reduced weight. 2D patterns can be cut on a large plotter for maximal precision.

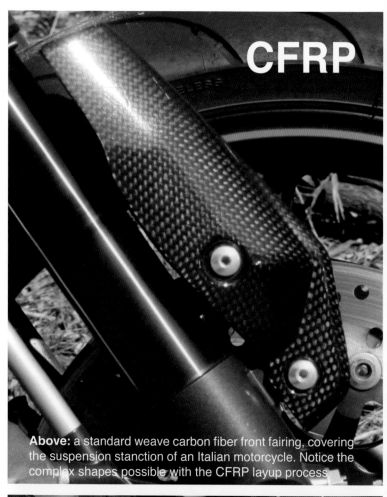

Above: a standard weave carbon fiber front fairing, covering the suspension stanction of an Italian motorcycle. Notice the complex shapes possible with the CFRP layup process.

Below: A raw, laminated fiberglass sportscar body. The Chevy Corvette is perhaps the most famous example of fiberglass body construction — which is a step down from higher-end (European) exotics and race cars.

GFRP

CFRP

Above: HYPED is an experimental Hyperloop transportation pod constructed from pre-preg / vacuum bagged carbon composites. Hyperloop is Space-X CEO Elon Musk's vision for the future of high-speed, mass transportation — with many corporate sponsors and global engineering teams racing to prove the technology's viability. Carbon fiber composite is chosen for its unrivaled lightweight, high-strength qualities. Credit: The University of Edinburgh Hyperloop Society.

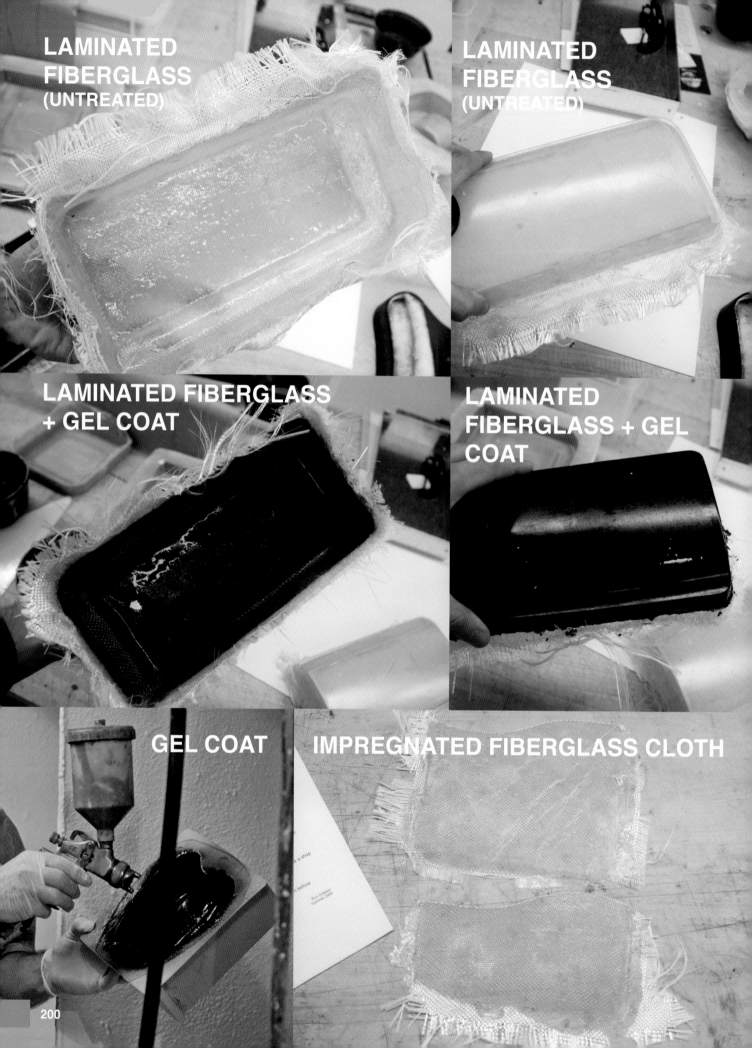

LAMINATED
FIBERGLASS
(UNTREATED)

LAMINATED
FIBERGLASS
(UNTREATED)

LAMINATED FIBERGLASS
+ GEL COAT

LAMINATED
FIBERGLASS + GEL
COAT

GEL COAT

IMPREGNATED FIBERGLASS CLOTH

2D PATTERN TEMPLATES

2D TEMPLATES FITTING

FIBERGLASS MAT

DE-BURRING

FIBERGLASS CLOTH

3K PLAIN WEAVE

12K PLAIN WEAVE

12K WEAVE SILVER

Above: Many different functional and decorative carbon fabric weaves exist, with the most common type being the plain weave pictured above. The larger weave patterns shown in middle and at right are close to full scale (each square or "tape" width is 20mm or 3/4", which is also refered to as tow size), and are from the same carbon manufacturer who supplies the carbon fiber 'spread tow' fabrics for Oracle's $10 million AC72 carbon / titanium racing "yacht" sailboats, used in the America's Cup (under the team management of eccentric tech titan Larry Ellison). The use of advanced materials — like composites that are vacuum-bagged and cooked in an oven over foam sandwich 'daggerboard' hulls, carbon hydrofoils, and rigid carbon air sails allow the boats to travel up to 50mph!

12K TWILL WEAVE

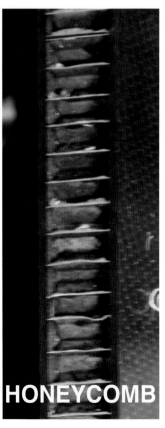

HONEYCOMB

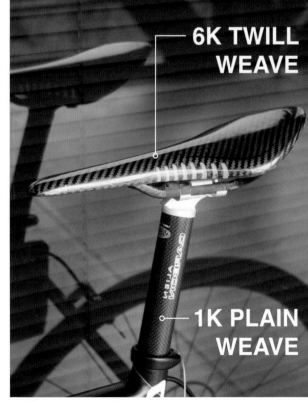

6K TWILL WEAVE

1K PLAIN WEAVE

Above: Large twill weave spread tow pattern (tape width = 20mm or 3/4"), and lightweight Nomex honeycomb sandwich core construction (pictured here is the carbon hull of the HYPED Hyperloop transport pod.

Above: Due to the functional the quest for lighter weight and stiffness, you'll typically find carbons used in all modes of transportation — including bicycles.

Above: Performance race car body made from twill weave CFRP left untreated and unpainted to save extra weight. This is a perfect example of the complexity of compound curvatures possible with carbon laminates. The clear epoxy "plastic" resin impregnated into the high strength carbon cloth fibers gives it its characteristic shine.

CFRP
TWILL WEAVE

Left: A raw finish carbon fiber interior cockpit and steering wheel. Carbon is used heavily in racing and transportation for it's superior torsional rigidity, and where grams of weight are relentlessly shaved in an effort to give the slightest competitive edge over the competition. There are also hydro-dipped fake carbon "look-alike" finishes avaialable — for those who want the decorative look, to try and "look" the part — but, who do not want to shell out the steep price to obtain the functionality of the real thing (these are the same folks who purchase fake Rolexes for their signaling properties alone, knowing full well that these timepieces are a far cry from their quality Swiss counterparts, and will often fall apart after only a few months of use). The look-alike carbons are usually easily distinguishable from the real thing, since what they are essentially is just printed pattern graphics applied to a surface.

CFRP
PLAIN WEAVE

Below: An aerodynamic and lightweight fiberglass monocoque cockpit. Notice the black gel coat finish.

GFRP
GEL COAT ADDED

Below: The same assembled zero emission gravity racing vehicle with paint coat and graphics applied.

GFRP

Below: An aerodynamic wing-shaped, lightweight and super stiff carbon fiber axle.

CFRP
PLAIN WEAVE

Leather & Fabric Textiles

MATERIAL TYPES

Soft goods or cut & sew is where 2D flat patterns are cut from cloth with heavy steel cutting dies, then sewn together. Cutting dies have sharp edges and are pressed under high force using a hydraulic press, which can cut cleanly through huge stacks of material at a time. Die cutting is similar to using a cookie cutter, only replacing soft cookie dough with sheets of fabric.

Natural - Leather comes from the skin or "hide" of an animal, through a curing process that consists of dehydration & petrification (very much like jerky) and tanning. Tanning is a nasty chemical process and requires large rolling tanning drums (these plants are known as "tanneries"). Leather will still retain a natural oil to it, so andy adornments must be sewn or riveted since adhesives or hot-melt used in bonding will eventually breakdown. Almost any skin you can think of can be turned into a leather — including cow (the most common), pig, goat, kangaroo, alligator / crocodile, snake (python), and even cod (Bill Bowerman of Nike fame was said to be obsessive about experimentation, and used with cod skin with the shoes of his track and field team, since he touted it to be fractions of an increment in weight lighter). Gradations of leather range from full grain and top grain (uppermost portion of hide), split leather and Nubuck (middle portion of hide) and suede (lowermost portion of hide). Can be die cut, de-bossed / embossed, laser engraved, tanned, dyed and stained to give different effects.

Synthetic - Synthetic textiles account for what's known as the textile industry, and it's a huge player in how the world's human population (and, a few pet canines) is clothed from the elements. Recent textiles can very closely simulate the look, feel, and texture of their natural counterparts — such as microfiber suede (replacing natural animal suede) and . The most common types are PU and Nylon. Can be die cut, heat cut, laser cut, sewn, bonded, silk screen or dye sublimation printed. The possibilites really are endless.

Stretch Fabrics (Two-Way / Four-Way) - Commonly known as Lycra Spandex. Two-way stretch fabric stretches in only two directions, while four-way stretches in all four directions. Used in technical performance apparel that needs to move with physical / athletic activity, often as stretch panels or as a full garment (i.e. Under Amour or LuluLemon compression garments).

COMMON USES

Apparel, car / vehicle interiors, outdoor clothing & gear, tactical / military gear, neoprene surfer wetsuits,

PRO TIPS

Start building a material library, which can be as simple as cutting up sample swatches yourself. This will come in handy later when selecting materials for a project. Be mindful of pattern design in order to maximize material consumption or "yield."

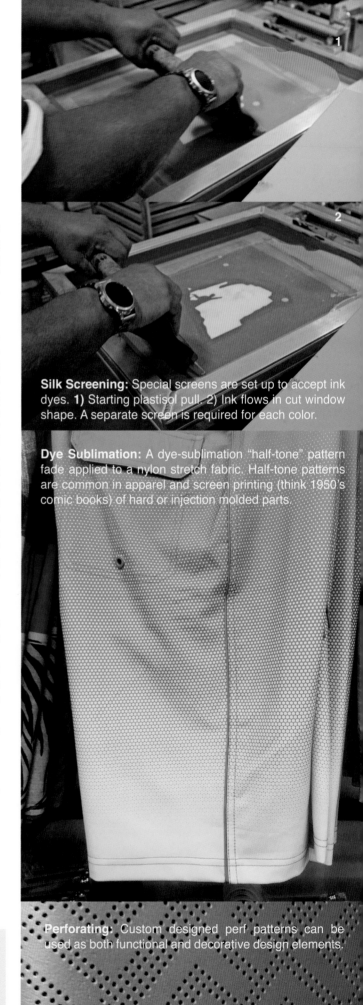

Silk Screening: Special screens are set up to accept ink dyes. **1)** Starting plastisol pull. 2) Ink flows in cut window shape. A separate screen is required for each color.

Dye Sublimation: A dye-sublimation "half-tone" pattern fade applied to a nylon stretch fabric. Half-tone patterns are common in apparel and screen printing (think 1950's comic books) of hard or injection molded parts.

Perforating: Custom designed perf patterns can be used as both functional and decorative design elements.

Below: An example color pallette used in an automotive interior. Color palletes can create a cohesive brand DNA or aesthetic across a seasonal product collection, and is used in everything from interior design, interior (automotive) design, fashion and apparel lines, etc. Each different material color will need to be dyed separately.

INTERIOR COLOR

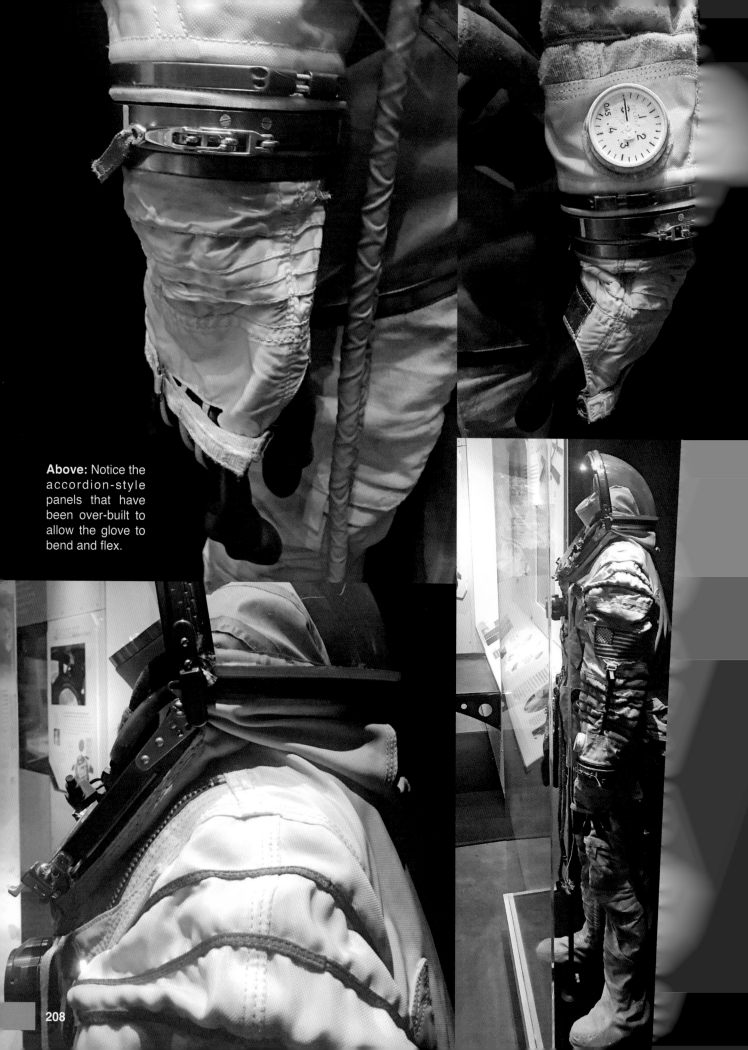

Above: Notice the accordion-style panels that have been over-built to allow the glove to bend and flex.

Below: An astronaut pressure suit, which served active duty in outer space. This is an example of an extremely robust, technical garment that has been constructed with heavy-duty features such as triple-stitched panel overlays, reinforced seams, and a heavy denier ballistic nylon main body.

"

It took me four and a half years and I built 5,127 prototypes until I got it right. That sounds tedious, in fact it was absolutely fascinating. Each failure — the 5,126 failures — taught me so much. Successes teach you nothing, failures teach you everything. Making mistakes is the most important thing you can do. I do think that schools get it wrong by marking people who give the correct answers. I think they should mark people who get the *wrong* answer, but *learn* something from it. But, we engineers know that you only learn things by making *mistakes*, you only learn things by going to the lab and to the work shop, building things and observing things, and seeing what's happened. You don't get it by sitting at a drawing board or lying in a bath. You only get it by building things.

James Dyson

FOUNDER/CEO & CHIEF ENGINEER,
DYSON, LTD.

Chapter 5 — Application

  1 SHOP OVERVIEW

  2 MACHINES

 **3** HAND TOOLS

  4 MATERIALS

  5 APPLICATION

6 ADV. PROJECTS

Sanding & Polishing

TIPS & TECHNIQUES

Anything can be used for sanding, including children's foam play mats — it all depends on the control and tactile feel you are looking for, so feel free to get creative.

Dry Sanding - used to sculpt a material, or to prepare the surface in pre-primer stage. Rougher, coarse grit sandpapers work best here for removing more material.

Wet Sanding - wet sanding is used as the last and final surface prep just before final painting — as the final paint will pick up the exact finish & quality of the underlying surface. Much finer grit quality is used for surface polishing — up to 600-grit in the post-primer stage — to create a glass-smooth surface ready for painting.

PRO TIPS

Add a few drops of liquid dish soap into the water when wet sanding for better results. The soap will help lift away the fine debris caused by sanding away the base material. Always use a backer when wet or dry sanding for better, more uniform control — NO FINGERS! It's also a good practice to keep a shop fan blowing in closed areas where ventilation is lacking.

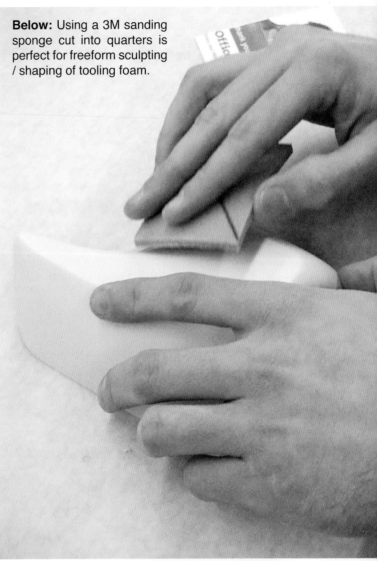

Below: Using a 3M sanding sponge cut into quarters is perfect for freeform sculpting / shaping of tooling foam.

Above: A variety of implements used as sanding blocks / sticks — including plastic spoons, wood dowels, children's play mats, and rubber erasers.

Above: Sanding blocks made using Super 77™ to adhere sandpaper to MDF (double stick tape can also be used).

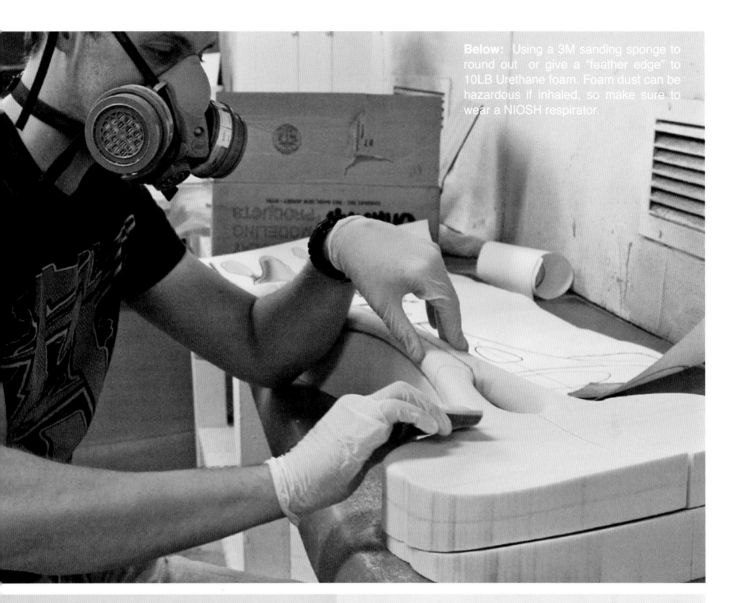

Below: Using a 3M sanding sponge to round out or give a "feather edge" to 10LB Urethane foam. Foam dust can be hazardous if inhaled, so make sure to wear a NIOSH respirator.

Left: Sanding blocks made using Super 77™ to adhere sandpaper to MDF (double stick tape can also be used).

Right & Facing: 1) A "sanding block" is made by attaching a strip of sandpaper to a scrap wood block using strong double-stick tape. Shapes like these are useful for reaching areas which are harder to get a handle on by any other means. **2)** here, a strip of 150-Grit sandpaper is used to remove small table saw blade grooves from the inside of a countersunk dado cut.

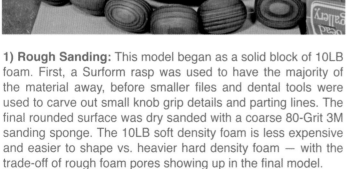

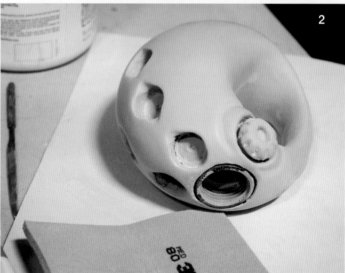

1) Rough Sanding: This model began as a solid block of 10LB foam. First, a Surform rasp was used to have the majority of the material away, before smaller files and dental tools were used to carve out small knob grip details and parting lines. The final rounded surface was dry sanded with a coarse 80-Grit 3M sanding sponge. The 10LB soft density foam is less expensive and easier to shape vs. heavier hard density foam — with the trade-off of rough foam pores showing up in the final model.

2) Fine Sanding: The foam model is coated with Shellac to seal the foam pores, before being primed. After primer, the model is sanded again with a coarse 80-Grit 3M sanding sponge and small files for detail work. Sanding sponges work best here, since the sponge's surface contours well with rounded curvature and complex shapes. The sponges are also perfect for either dry or wet sanding use.

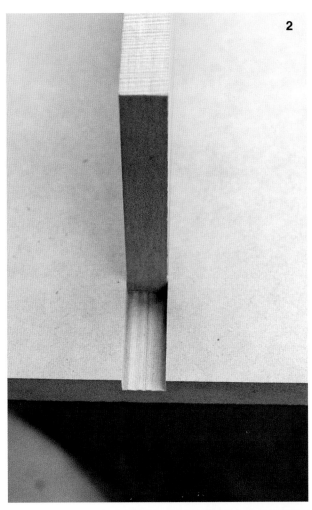

Above: "Sanding Jigs" can be made in an infinite variation of shapes and curvatures. Here, an MDF jig is cut on the band saw, where a strip of sandpaper is double-stick taped or glued onto the surface with spray adhesive. Shapes like these are useful for creating convex rounded sanding shapes.

3) Final Wet Sanding: After several thick coats of primer, a guide coat is lightly spritzed onto the surface — a contrast color (black here) is used so that it easily stands out against the primer. This guide coat is then wet sanded so that none of the color shows against the gray primer. **4)** In this example, the textured grip handle area is left rough, while the main surface body is sanded to a glass-smooth finish.

Automotive Clay Modeling

TIPS & TECHNIQUES

Modeling can be both additive or subtractive. Despite increasingly advanced & disruptive digital 3D CAD design technologies, clay is still (yes, STILL!) the top choice in the automotive design profession. Why is this? The major reason being that the design teams can see the model in 1:1 full scale to fine-tune every last line and surface detail. Also, because clay is both an additive & subtractive material, the exterior body shape designs can easily be changed "on the fly" — allowing for more advanced styling options. Once the clay model is complete, it can then be 3D scanned. By placing dots over the surface of the model, this CAD model can be cleaned up digitally in CAD, then re-formatted as a manufacturable, A-Class surface design — used later for sheet metal body panel stamping or composite fiber lay-up manufacturing. Automotive clay sculpting is said to be a "battle for line tension," or "snap" (the curve of two "theoretical tangencies," or points). A Spline — white styrene tool at lower right of facing page — can check your surface tension. The Spline makes a natural curve when bent — imagine a tight hanging clothesline.

PRO TIPS

Use the best quality of clay you can get your hands on. Better quality clay is more expensive, but will have a superior consistency and shape much better. Mixing clay brands is not recommended, since the consistencies are different. This will also cause uneven discoloration.

Below: 3D scanning a helmet with a handheld scanner. 3D scanning is commonly used in highly sculptural design work (i.e. motorcycle/cycling helmets, car exteriors), to translate a clay model into 3D CAD for production/manufacturing.

Above: Custom made blue steel finishers.

Below: A Chavant clay wire finisher is perfect for creating hard edges or smooth, flat curatures. A tooth can be added to the finisher or clay wire loop tools using a metal file — which helps to "cut" the surface of the clay instead of smudging.

Below: Using a blue steel "pickle" finisher.

Above: Checking surface tension (or "snap") with a styrene spline — the spline checks that contours are visually taught.

Spread: Rough clay modeling using surform rasp, Chavant wire tools, and paring knife.

Above: After overall surface details have been set in place, blue finishing steels are used to tighten-up and polish the clay surface to a glass-like finish. This final clay model can then be 3D scanned or spray primed & painted.

219

Foam Modeling

TIPS & TECHNIQUES

PU modeling foam (tooling foam) offers modeling by subtraction only (unlike clay, which can be used for both addition and subtraction). Foam be cut, sanded, turned on lathe, and painted — similar to just how wood can. A Surform "cheese grater" rasp with handle is by far the best tool for removing large amounts of material quickly (Stanley yellow handle tool pictured). With finer details, small sanding files, dental tools, or sanding sponges can be useful for creating compound curves, complex surface forms, and panel parting lines (or "cut lines") into a model. In many ways, tooling foam is a superior method for creating quick study models for evaluation — especially of hand-held products. Commonly used in product design for helmets, kitchenware, and handheld consumer electronics.

PRO TIPS

Foam under 20LB density will need to be sealed with either Shellac or Automotive Cat Primer before painting. Use a hard (dense) foam when making a painted presentation / appearance model, otherwise the paint will seep into the pores of the softer foam.

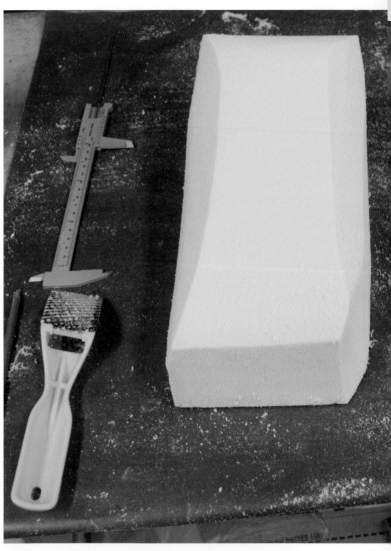

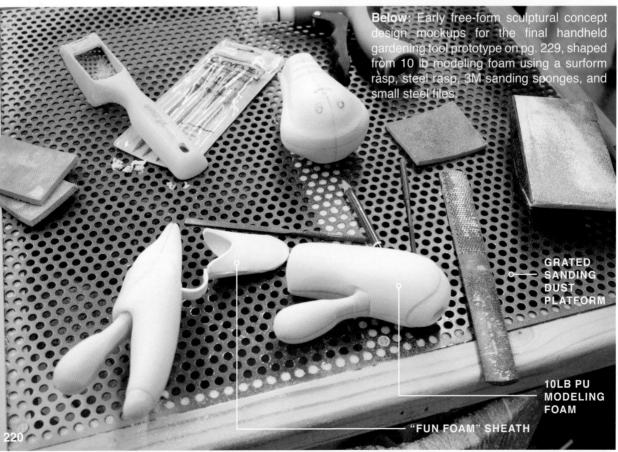

Below: Early free-form sculptural concept design mockups for the final handheld gardening tool prototype on pg. 229, shaped from 10 lb modeling foam using a surform rasp, steel rasp, 3M sanding sponges, and small steel files.

GRATED SANDING DUST PLATFORM

10LB PU MODELING FOAM

"FUN FOAM" SHEATH

Above: A 3M sanding sponge — cut into quarters for easier handling. Sanding sponges are useful for shaping free-form organic, curved, or compound surfaces.

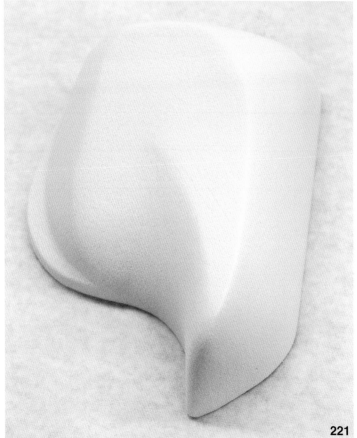

Full Prototype Development Process: 1) Concept Sketches: Quick sketches can be helpful to explore the look, feel, and functionality of a design before committing to 3D model making. Here, industrial designer Joey Zeledón begins with a round of hand sketches to explore different functions, ergonomics and styling details before moving into foam studies.

2) Rough Cutting: Once a few sketches are chosen to move forward, an initial orthographic side view is cut at 1:1 scale from a solid block of 15LB foam (RenShape). This piece looks crude, but will be very useful to give an overall three dimensional volume to the mixer.

3) File Sanding: Rounding out sharp edges with a small rasp file. Unlike clay, once foam is subtracted it can't be added again. Foam was used here instead of 3D modeling, since ergonomic handle shapes could be easily modified on-the-fly. Even in this advanced age of 3D printing technology, tactile touch & feel feedback like this simply cannot be replaced. Many designers still swear by using foam or clay to achieve results they feel they simply cannot get by using any other means.

4) Paper / Sponge Sanding: Modeling foam is the perfect material when quick study variations are needed. In the product design / R&D world, these quick study models are a compelling way to communicate concepts to internal design & business teams, a client, or outside investors — long before committing to final 3D CAD and / or costly manufacturing prototype development work & investment.

5 - 8) Final Details: A rounded sanding stick is useful for shaping interior curvatures (here, a wood dowel has been wrapped in sandpaper). Final panel lines are sketched in with a small file tool. Over a dozen iterations were explored, before the final design was chosen to move into 3D CAD, and later full production (image #8).

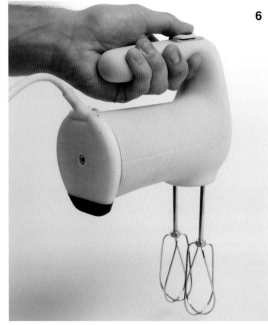

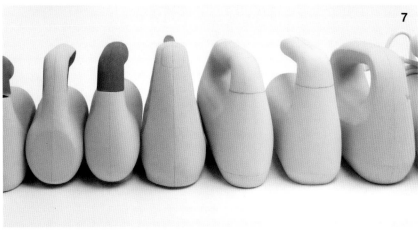

Oxo On hand mixer prototype process by Joey Zeledón. This product is part of a line of electric appliances painstakingly designed with simplicity and user needs in mind — instead of copious bells and whistles. Client: OXO International.

Bondo™ Modeling

TIPS & TECHNIQUES

Bondo™ body filler modeling can be both additive and subtractive. The filler compound is first added through spreading, then subtracted through carving, sanding, drilling, or cutting.

Mixing - although mixing ratios vary, typically one drop of catalyst per golf-ball size of body filler is a good rule of thumb.

Spreading & Sculpting - plastic spreaders, playing cards, or custom cut styrene templates are useful for smooth controlled Bondo spreading application. Custom templates increase the control over filler radius / fillet.

Sanding / Carving / Cutting - Bondo hardens within about 30min-1hour. It can then be sanded, cut, or carved just like wood — or, more material can be added.

PRO TIPS

Use painter's tape to create clean edges or to mask off parts of a model which you'll want to keep clean. It's a good idea to keep a fan blowing to disperse the Bondo™ fumes, when mixing and ESPECIALLY when sanding.

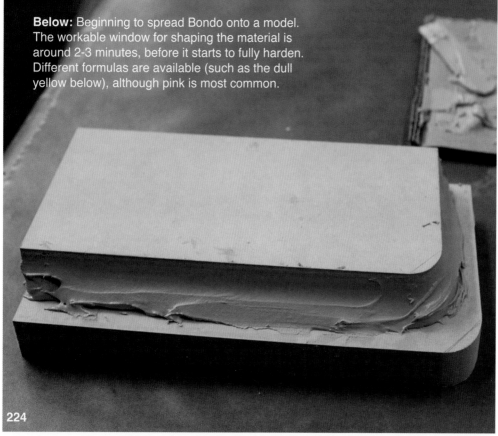

Below: Beginning to spread Bondo onto a model. The workable window for shaping the material is around 2-3 minutes, before it starts to fully harden. Different formulas are available (such as the dull yellow below), although pink is most common.

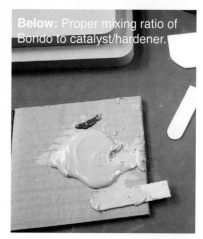

Below: Proper mixing ratio of Bondo to catalyst/hardener.

Above: A rounded plastic squeegee is used to apply Bondo to create a clean fillet transition. Once hardened, the Bondo surface can then be cut, drilled into, and sanded just like wood or foam.

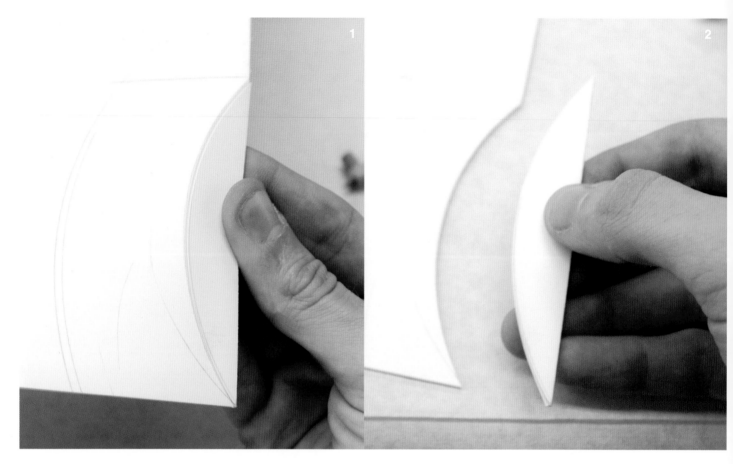

Above: Using a circle cutter to create a Bondo spreading template from Styrene. These templates are useful for spreading smooth, controlled applications in Bondo. 1) Use the blade to first score a cut. 2) After the Styrene is scored, it can be snapped off cleanly. Use templates like these for creating controlled filler radius / fillet.

Right: Metal Glazing putty (green) is a favorite for applying the final refined details and for filling pinholes in a model's surface, and is applied with a plastic squeegee. Repeat this process and primer as needed.

Below: Playing cards can also be used to spread body filler. You'll often seen pro paint / body shop specialists using this trick — also, since playing cards are disposable, they are a very cost effective method to use.

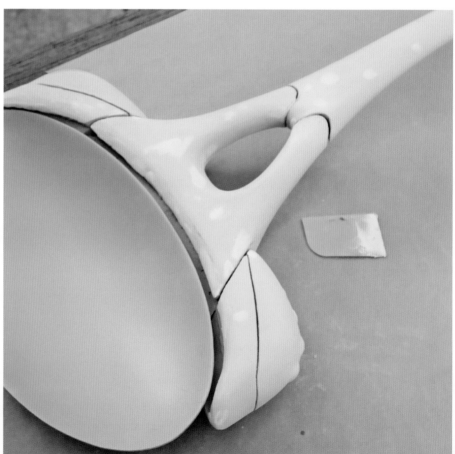

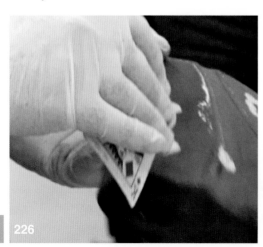

1) A raw fiberglass motorcycle tank pulled straight out of a mold is far from perfect. Notice the small pin holes and surface imperfections caused by irregularities on the inside of the mold.

2) After the first coat of primer, the surface still has unattractive surface "orange peel" and valleys. Bondo body filler is spread over these areas to fill the pinholes and surface gaps. Once hardened, this new layer is sanded with coarse-grit sanding sponges to even out with the primed surface below.

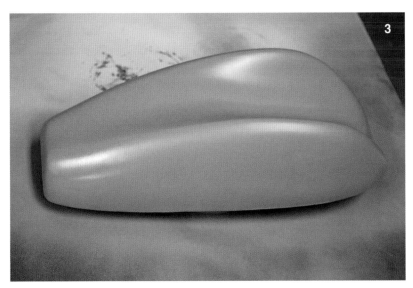
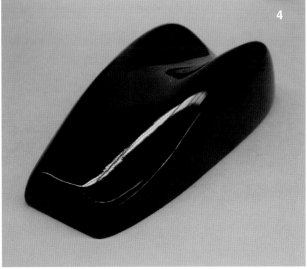

3 - 4) The primer / Bondo process is repeated until there are no longer any surface irregularities. Once the final primer coat dries, it is then wet sanded (600 grit) and painted with black rattle-can spray paint. Notice the professional level of paint quality that can be achieved with a simple, inexpensive can of $5 paint — given the surface has been finished properly beforehand (gloss black is the true test of a quality surface, as it will show any and every imperfection — no matter how slight).

CNC Milling & Machining

TIPS & TECHNIQUES

Like 3D printing, the part starts out as a 3D CAD file. The CAD file is then uploaded into 3D CAM software, which will translate the design's volumetric details into a manufacturable part. A toolpath is the programmable "path" of the end mill, assigned based on the part's geometry / finish requirements. Once a successful toolpath is created, this machine code can then be saved and repeated over and over again to create exact replica parts. Raw cutting material is referred to as a "blank". The blank material will determine the type of milling bit used, as well as the speed of the cutting operation. Harder materials like steel alloys require more time to machine. Plastics, foams, and softer metals require much less machining time — thus reducing overall costs of the machining operation.

PRO TIPS

Use the proper toolpaths and cutting bits depending on the job at hand. Larger bits will create a gradated / layered step effect, while use of progressively smaller bits and tighter toolpaths (more machining time) will create more smooth detail without steps.

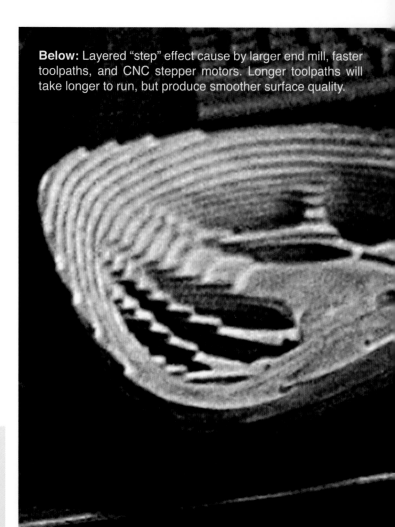

Below: Layered "step" effect cause by larger end mill, faster toolpaths, and CNC stepper motors. Longer toolpaths will take longer to run, but produce smoother surface quality.

Right: 1) A water bottle milled on a desktop Roland CNC machine from an acrylic "blank." Notice the clarity of the material — this would be impossible to 3D print, and would be difficult to resin cast without use of a pressure pot. **2)** This wooden tiki model is one more perfect example of the level of detail a tabletop CNC machine can achieve, using a natural non-man made material that would be impossible to 3D print and very difficult to simulate through molding & casting.

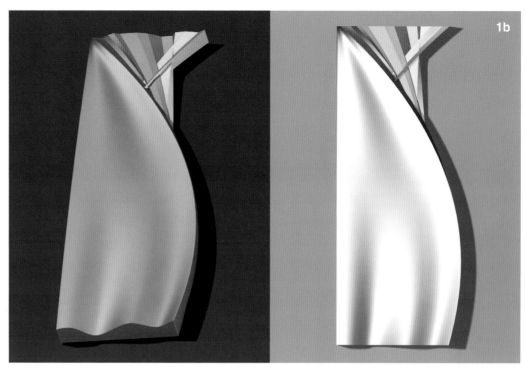

Above: 1b) 3D CAD trophy design modeled in SolidWorks. This 3D part geometry is uploaded into CAM software for CNC routering. Newer design & engineering software packages now have CAM features built-in.

Below: 2b) A "blank" made from three layers of MDF sandwiched together with wood glue. One side is cut first on a 2.5-Axis CNC, then **3b)** Flipped upside-down to cut the other side. **4b)** Notice the waves in the top part surface, showing the glue layers in between. Outer support posts around the part's perimeter hold the part into place, and can later be removed with a Japanese pull saw or hand saw.

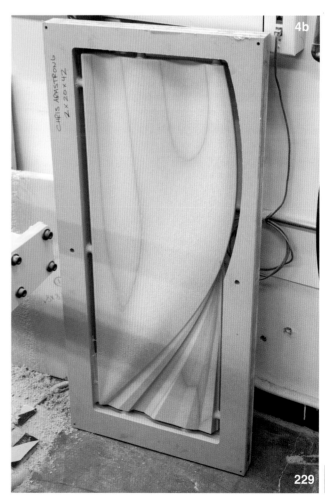

Above & Below: A DM brand CNC machine with LCD screen display for monitoring live progress of the cutting toothpaths, as well as other critical instrumentation that can be used to track the part progress and to prevent any errors or disruptions.

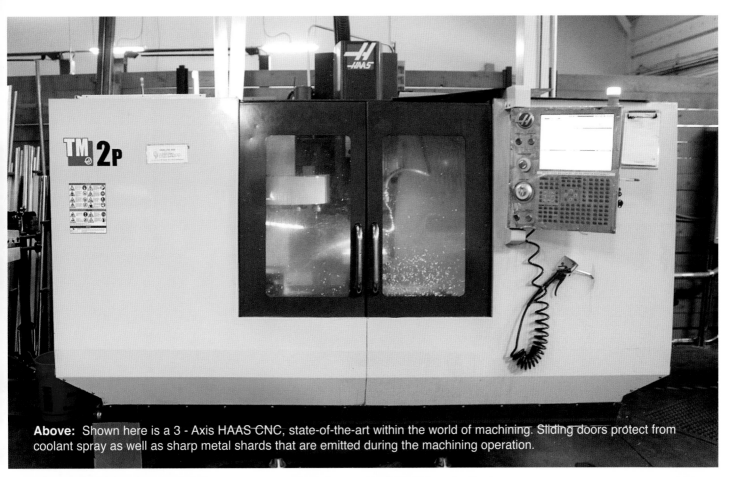

Above: Shown here is a 3 - Axis HAAS CNC, state-of-the-art within the world of machining. Sliding doors protect from coolant spray as well as sharp metal shards that are emitted during the machining operation.

Left & Above: An end mill machining a steel alloy blank using a water based "cutting fluid" — a type of a coolant/lubricant designed specifically to keep the workpiece at a stable operating temperature. Since metalworking produces a high amount of heat from friction, this cutting fluid maximizes the life of a cutting tip and prevents rust from forming on machine parts and cutters.

Facing Page: The type of toolpath and/or milling bit used will vary depending on the part's overall contours and complexity — multiple toolpath patterns can also be combined. CAM software packages can run toolpath simulations for verification, which will spot any potential production issues before the physical part is machined (called "cutting steel"). Step-over reduction (bottom) shows the process where the ridges or "scallops" left in a feature by the ball end mill can be reduced. The tool "steps over" more times, creating finer detail and increasing machining time.

PARALLEL 0°

PARALLEL 45°

PARALLEL 90°

CONTOUR

SCALLOP

HORIZONTAL AND PENCIL

SPIRAL AND RADIAL

MORPH AND FLOW

MORPHED SPIRAL
AND PROJECTION

STEPOVER REDUCTION

Above: CNC machined aluminum pivot linkage on a high-end mountain bike suspension assembly. The red anodized coating was added as a post production process. Because machining is much more expensive than standard die-casting of metal parts, you'll typically only see this technology used for high-end products — since machining is by far a superior process, and preferred because of its high strength-to-weight ratio, as well as extremely robust durability (for the "weight weanies" in the sport of MTB).

Below: A 2D graphical relief image that has been routered into flat panels of wood, using a 2.5 axis CNC router to cut into a specified depth. This routering effect is similar to the rastering effect produced by laser etching, but on a much larger scale.

3D Printing

TIPS & TECHNIQUES

FDM, SLA, SLS, or Polyjet process will need to be selected according to the printer and part requirements. Popular 3D programs used for 3D Print-ready files are SolidWorks, Rhino 3D, PTC Creo, Alias, and ProEngineer (*other file types can be used, but will need to be exported into a useable file type). Parts must be sanded and primed before painting. Mold supports will need to be carefully designed into the part, to be less visibility after they are removed (supports under the T-Rex shown).

PRO TIPS

Many 3rd-party services offer to print 3D parts without having to commit to purchasing an expensive 3D printer — however, the quality & affordability of desktop 3D printers are improving all the time. Large-format parts outside of the printer's printable bed area can be printed as separate parts, then pieced together using 2-Part epoxy or CA glue (a process known as "tiling"). Choose the printer and printing type based on your part at hand.

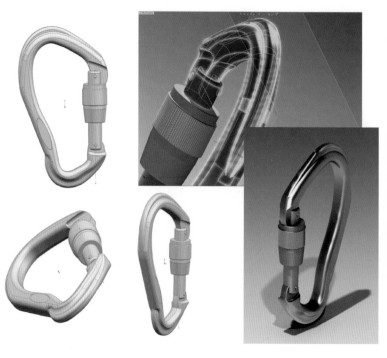

Above: All parts start as 3D CAD files. The 3D printer translates the CAD data into a physical object.

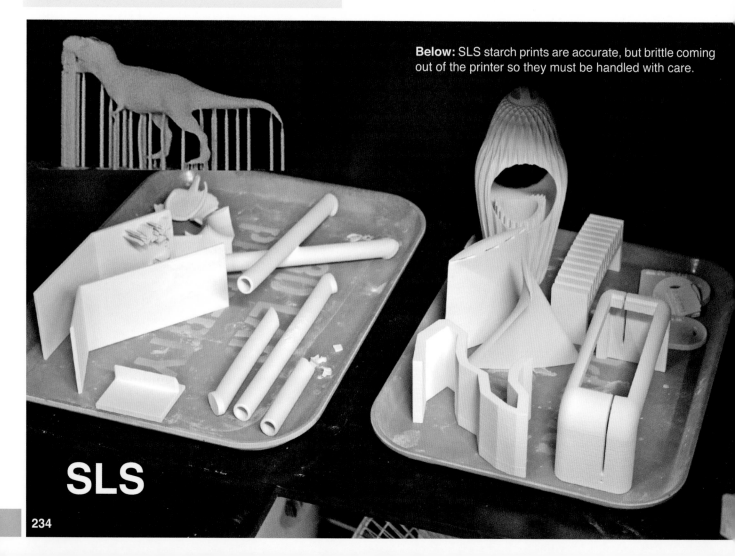

Below: SLS starch prints are accurate, but brittle coming out of the printer so they must be handled with care.

SLS

1) SolidWorks 3D CAD model, **2)** Materials & colors rendered in Keyshot, **3)** File exported as .STL geometry for 3D printing, **4)** SLS starch printed part before being infiltrated.

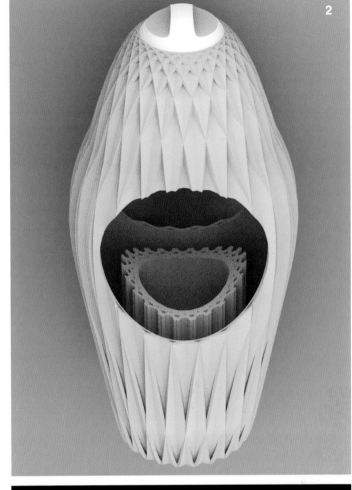

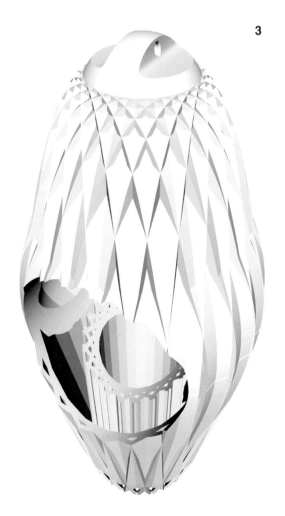

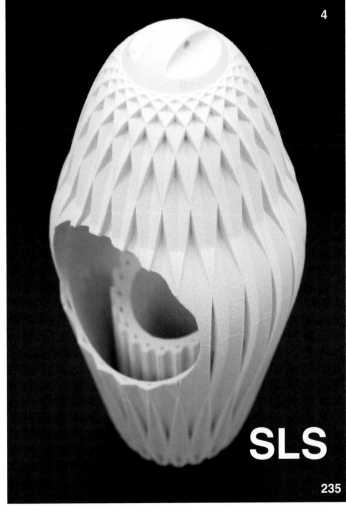

SLS

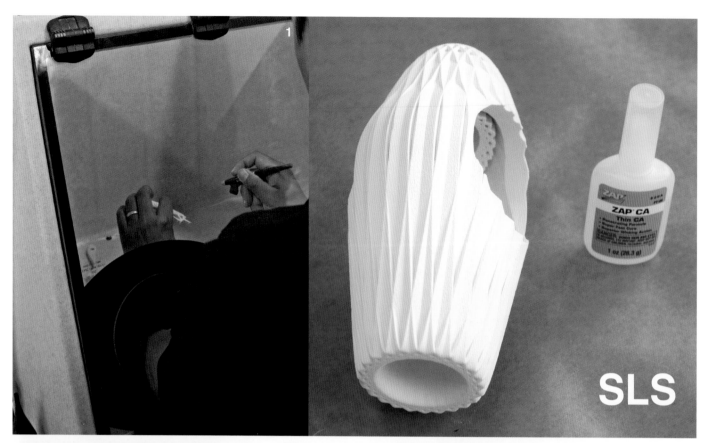

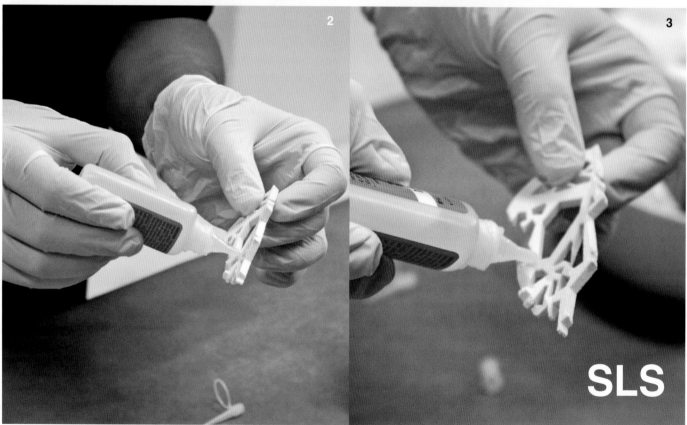

Infiltration Process: CA glue is used to harden SLS "starch print" parts in a process known as infiltration. Before SLS parts have been infiltrated, they are still brittle to the touch. **1)** First, the majority of the excess powder is blown off with compressed air — this will reveal the fine part details. **2-3)** Wearing gloves, CA glue is applied much like wet paint, and allowed to soak through the entire part. Once the part is infiltrated, it is ready to be sanded, primed and painted for a final appearance model.

Right: 1) 3D CAD model of a handheld gardening tool, built in SolidWorks. The model is subdivided into separate assembly parts by material type, which will make it easier to print and paint them separately — similar to how an injection molded & die cast product would be assembled.

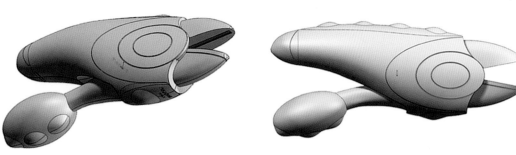

Below: 2) The final parts are SLS printed from the 3D CAD file. **3)** The starch printing process will pick up every fine detail of the 3D part — down to embossed text / logos. **4)** The parts are infiltrated, primed, sanded / wet sanded, then **5)** painted separately. **6-7)** Once the paint dries, the parts are then epoxy glued together to create a convincing appearance product model — shown at below right.

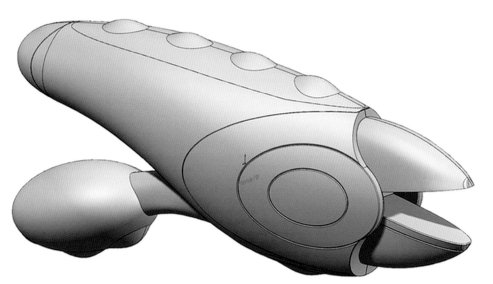

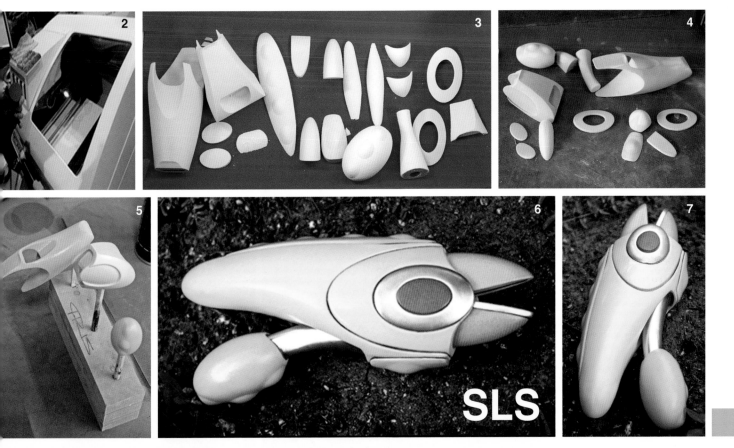

SLS

FDM
LOW RESOLUTION

FDM
MEDIUM RESOLUTION

SLA
HIGH RESOLUTION

Above: Surfboard fin prototypes printed using entirely different print methods, with noticeably different qualities and resolutions. FDM Nylon fin on left is strong and can be printed inexpensively on a homebuilt printing machine. The fin in the middle is a higher quality nylon. Finally, the fin right is printed in polyjet hi-resolution and is more suitable for aesthetic purposes.

Below: 3d printed metals is the latest revolution in printable materials. Since 3d printed metal has many strength characteristics rivaling that of standard cast or machined metal parts, it can be used for durable medical prosthetics — such as this metal jaw replacement shown. By the time this book makes it to print, there will be many more materials which can be printed!

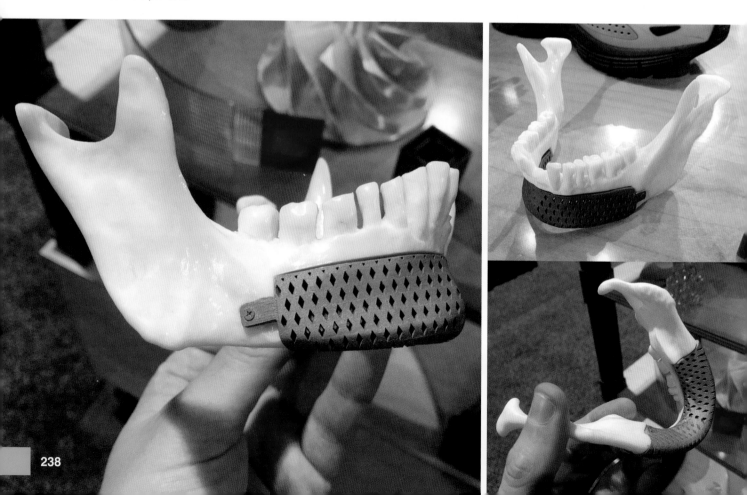

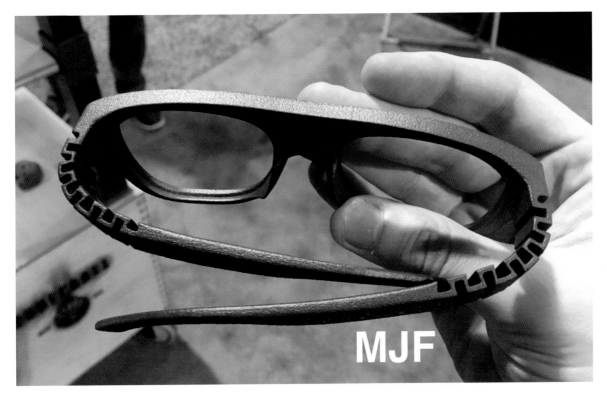

Multi-Jet Fusion (MJF) Technology: HP has innovated patented a printable, flexible material that rivals the robust quality of injection-molded nylon — as shown on the flexible earstems of these printed eyewear frames. The hammered texture finish is a charateristic surface quality of MJF. Typical 3D printing would be too brittle, and would crack and/or break under such stress put upon the material. 3D printing technologies are improving all the time, and one day we may live in a world where many products can be simply printed at home from a desktop printer, rather than being mass produced by expensive injection molding machines, and then need to be shipped from far distances to retail distributors and / or customers. This would truly be a revolution in decentratlized manufacturing like nothing before it!

Above & Below: Nylon filaments for use in FDM are available in a wide spectrum of colors, and avaialble from different suppliers. The quality of the filmament is very similar to the plastic wire used in weed trimmers (aka "weed wackers") and come rolled in a spool. A new spool will need to be loaded into the 3D printer each time a diffferent color is needed. Some filaments can simulate a matte metallic sheen — such as the large bullfrog printed below — but are a far cry from true metallic paints or finishes.

Above: Here a small sample Buddha model has been used to show the highlight, matte or gloss level, and translucency quality of the nylon filament material being printed. Notice that the layered steps or "striations" are clearly visible in each of these models — this is a signature look of low-resolution FDM technology. These lines can be sanded out, primered and painted over to produce a smooth finish, but is time consuming. So, bear this in mind when selecting the correct 3D printing technology for your project.

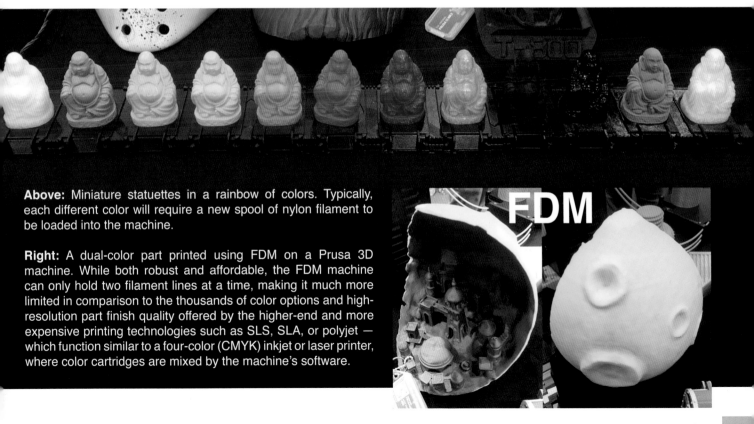

Above: Miniature statuettes in a rainbow of colors. Typically, each different color will require a new spool of nylon filament to be loaded into the machine.

Right: A dual-color part printed using FDM on a Prusa 3D machine. While both robust and affordable, the FDM machine can only hold two filament lines at a time, making it much more limited in comparison to the thousands of color options and high-resolution part finish quality offered by the higher-end and more expensive printing technologies such as SLS, SLA, or polyjet — which function similar to a four-color (CMYK) inkjet or laser printer, where color cartridges are mixed by the machine's software.

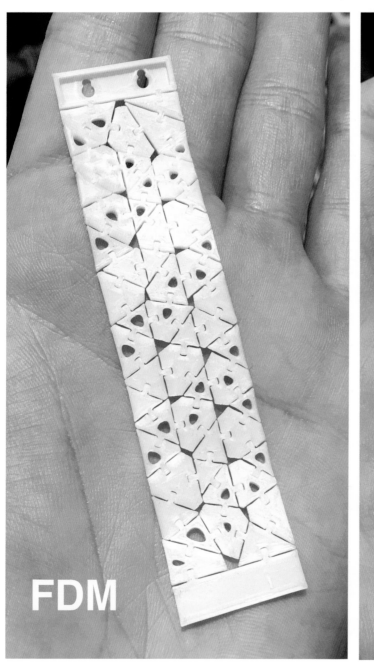

FDM

FDM

Above: One of the unique aspects of additive manufacturing is the ability to print highly precise, extremely high tolerance parts that are already pre-assembled straight out of machine. Here, a articulated wristwatch band is printed from nylon filament plastic, where the hinge joints are interlocked with one another. This unique polygonal hinge design allows the part to move and articulate in many different directions — which, would be extremely laborious, if not *downright impossible* to produce using almost any other manufacturing method!

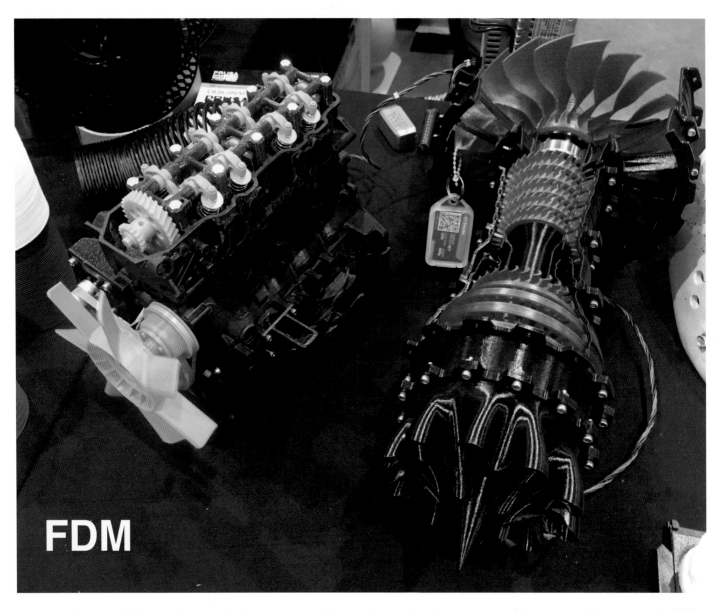

FDM

Above & Below: High-precision evaluation test parts for use in engineering are one of the many advantages of additive manufacturing. These functional prototype parts show the extremely intricate assemblies of a jet turbine and the inner workings of an internal combustion engine, that actually move like the real thing. The different colors were printed off as separate parts, which were then assembled later.

FDM

SLA

Above & Below: 1) These three SLA parts were printed using a typical process whereby the trellis structures underneath are known as "supports." These supports help to prop up the part while it is being printed, and then snapped off in post. Because they are located underneath the part, are generated by the 3D printing software, to best determine their shape and location. After their removal, the attachment areas are barely noticeable. This prevents large, unsightly areas and / or parting lines which would effect the aesthetic finish quality of the parts. **2)** Some of the supports have been broken here to reveal the figure's beard underneath. **3)** A close-up detail of the supports, and how they are attached to a base structure. This base holds the part firmly into place while the printing platform is being lowered down during the printing process.

SLA 2

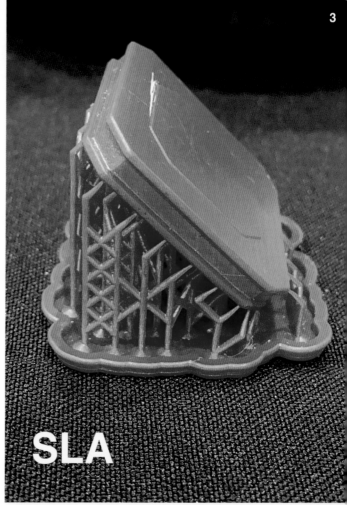

SLA 3

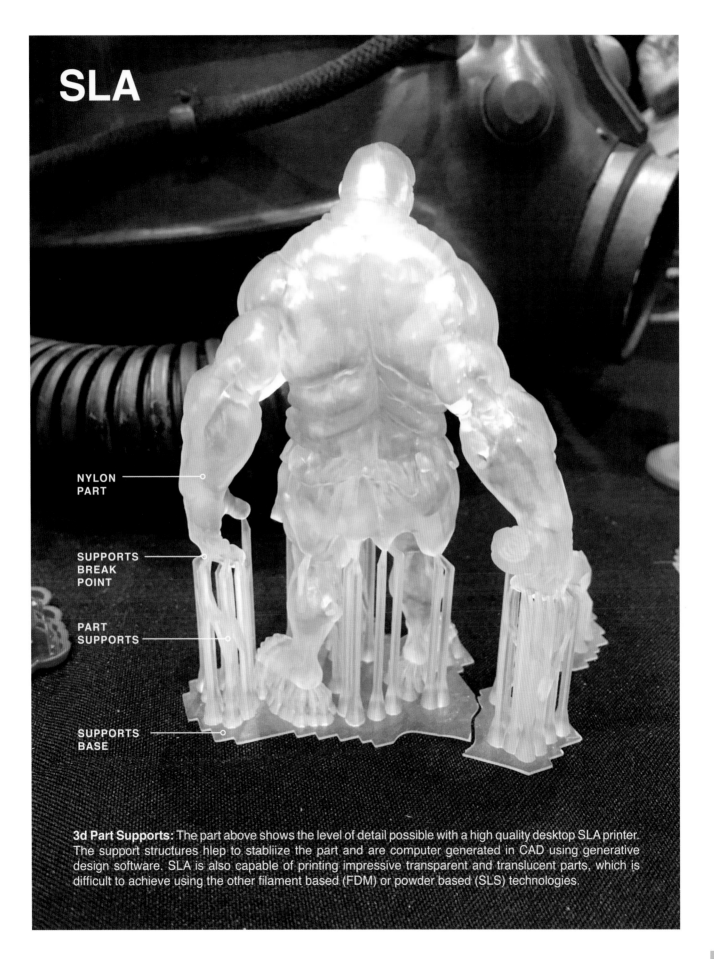

SLA

NYLON
PART

SUPPORTS
BREAK
POINT

PART
SUPPORTS

SUPPORTS
BASE

3d Part Supports: The part above shows the level of detail possible with a high quality desktop SLA printer. The support structures hlep to stabliize the part and are computer generated in CAD using generative design software. SLA is also capable of printing impressive transparent and translucent parts, which is difficult to achieve using the other filament based (FDM) or powder based (SLS) technologies.

Right: This whimsical little steamboat model is known as #3DBenchy, and has become *the* standard calibration part for testing and benchmarking 3D printers. By 3D printing this STL file, you will be able to benchmark your 3D printer and materials and compare the result to other users' prints and machines. The different surfaces of the #3DBenchy model reveal typical issues regarding surface finish, model accuracy, warping, etc. It may look like a simple part, but it is specifically designed to test a large array of challenging geometrical features for 3D printers, and touch on different issues related to additive manufacturing — such as smooth surfaces, symmetry, planar horizontal faces, tiny surface details, cylindrical shapes, overhang surfaces, low-slope-surfaces, large horizontal holes, small horizontal holes, slanted small holes, and first-layer-details. A high-resolution STL file is available for free at 3Dbenchy.com.

Below: A #3Dbenchy ship printed at 1:1 scale (15mm) on an FDM machine. The layer steps (striations) are much more visible in comparison to the high resolution SLA models above (which have been shrunken all the way down to 20% or 1:5 scale). The part at right was die cast in metal from a mold created from this printed model.

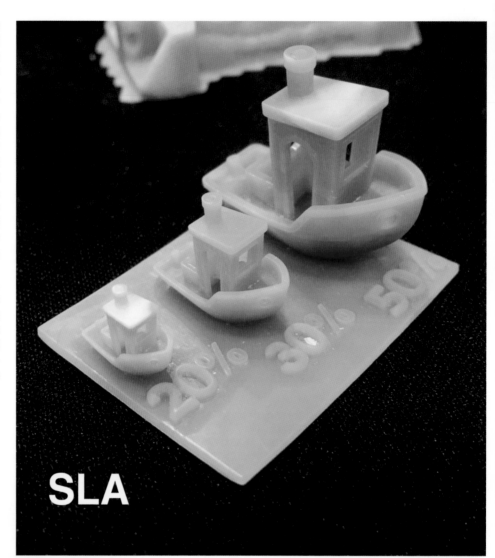

SLA

FDM

DIE CAST

Below: A hollow sculpture printed in SLA. This form's organic surface structure is similar that of generative design.

SLA

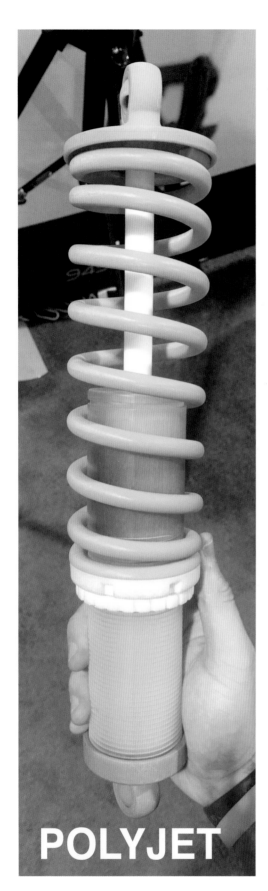

POLYJET

Polyjet Fusion Technology: The spring here was printed in softer, more flexible material than the white and semi-translucent internal compression damper part. Most importantly, all of the parts in this assembly were printed already assembled in one machine, in one sitting!

FLX4870
Shore70

FLX4860
Shore60

FLX4885
Shore85

FLX4850
Shore50

FLX4895
Shore95

Shore40

FLXA440
FLX980

TangoBlackPlus

Rigur RGD450

Above & Below: One of the more impressive developments in 3D printing technology is the powerful ability to print in different durometers. The softer the durometer the material is printed at, the more flexible and "rubber-like" it becomes. These polyjet samples from Stratasys show how both opaque (above) and translucent (below) materials can both be printed on the same machine and at variable hardnesses, ranging Shore 40 up to Shore 95 in durometer.

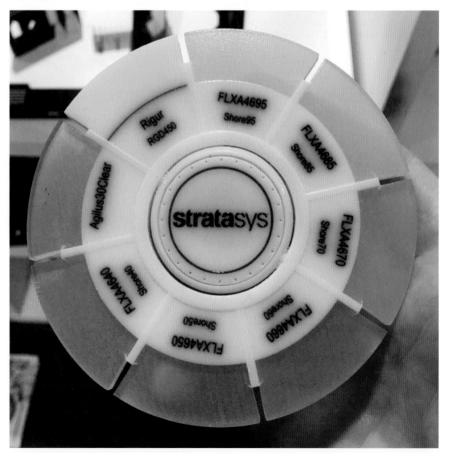

FLXA4695
Shore95

Rigur
RGD450

FLXA4895
Shore85

Agilus30Clear

stratasys

FLXA4670
Shore70

FLXA4840
Shore40

FLXA4650
Shore50

FLXA4660
Shore60

POLYJET

Above & Below: 1) A "rubber" shoe outsole from a 3D printer that isn't actually rubber at all — but instead is a simulated elastomer with a soft "rubber-like" feel to it.

POLYJET

POLYJET

Above: 2) The same is true for the tire below, where the interior hard rim portion was printed pre-assembled to the softer durometer black "tire" around it's outer perimeter. **3)** Some advanced 3D printers such as the Stratasys J750 can print different colors, simulated materials such as wood grain, stitches, transparent materials, and can even print to accuratelymatch Pantone® like this shifter knob.

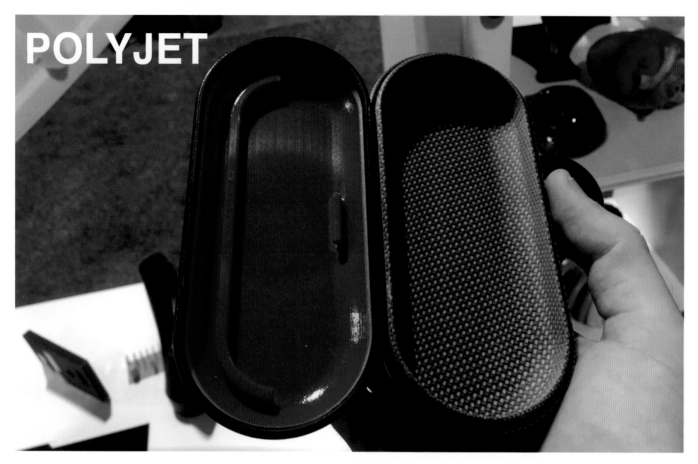

POLYJET

Above: Here is a good example of both the power and the ability to 3D print countless different material effects, paint finishes, and / or simulated injection molded part color breakups all at the same time *and* from the same printer — such as the blue interior and faux carbon fiber print of this polyjet printed plastic eyewear case.

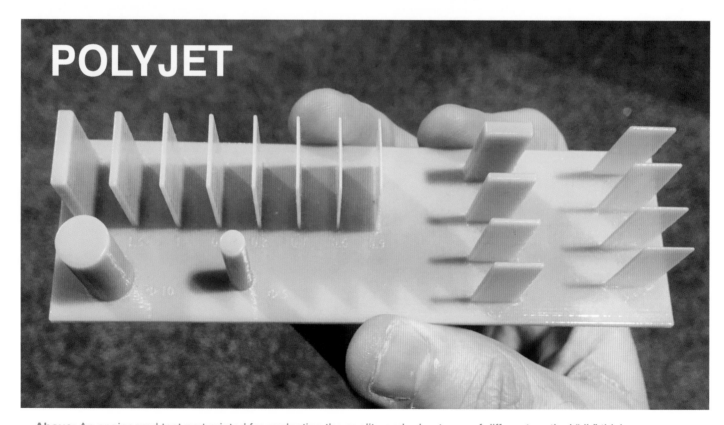

POLYJET

Above: An engineered test part printed for evaluating the quality and robustness of different vertical "rib" thicknesses.

Above: The hinge apart was 3D printed in metal (yes, metal!). The claim by 3D printer manufacturers is that these metal parts have strength and structural integrity that rivals die cast metal part. While the interior volume of this part has been spliced to save weight, material, and costs, the outer surfaces remain solid.

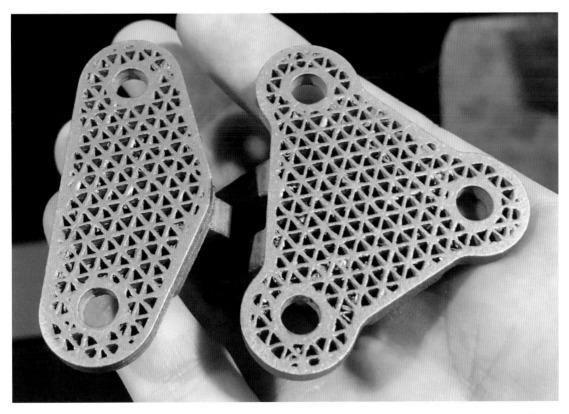

Above: This trellis formation is known as 'slicing' of a part. Slicing is an engineered way to reduce the overall internal material volume of a part, which will also reduce the material costs and printing times without sacrificing the structural integrity or external surface quality of a part.

Laser Cutting & Engraving

TIPS & TECHNIQUES

The caliber of detail which can be achieved with laser cutting can be simply INSANE. The possibilities of designs to be laser cut or engraved is endless, with makers, engineers and designers constantly pushing the envelope, with newer and more unique applications of the technology — from one-off parts sold on e-commerce shops like Etsy, to revolutions in footwear 2D pattern making design & manufacturing.

Etching / burnishing is a technique for using the laser to burn to any determined depth — creating a debossed relief effect. This is known as laser engraving, and is very powerful technique for creating custom illustrative, textural, and graphic design patterns in material surfaces.

PRO TIPS

Calibrate the laser before cutting. Also experimentation with settings and materials will need to be undertaken to get the right results for your project. Make sure to keep a log of the settings for each material type, and keep them next to your laser machine in your shop. Alternatively, Rowmark's expertly curated *Laser & Rotary Engraver Product Sample Book*, is a must for professionals, and is an excellent resource to keep on hand and refer back to regularly — including a comprehensive library of many different materials and effects in a physical swatch form.

Below & Right: Logo branding cut from two different colors of acrylic. Many businesses use this technique to give a modern look & feel to their brand.

Above: Volumetric sculpture made from stacking and gluing together independent layers of laser cut 1/8" MDF board.

Below: A '3D carved' wood relief effect can be achieved through rastering / etching wood using different laser power settings. After running a 3D CAD file through programming software, the laser cutter power / speed settings will be stored and ready to produce this type of complicated effect. As you can see, this effect can produce much more finite detail than CNC milling — without needing access to the larger, more expensive equipment and parts that come with the territory of CNC.

vided by Gantry Company

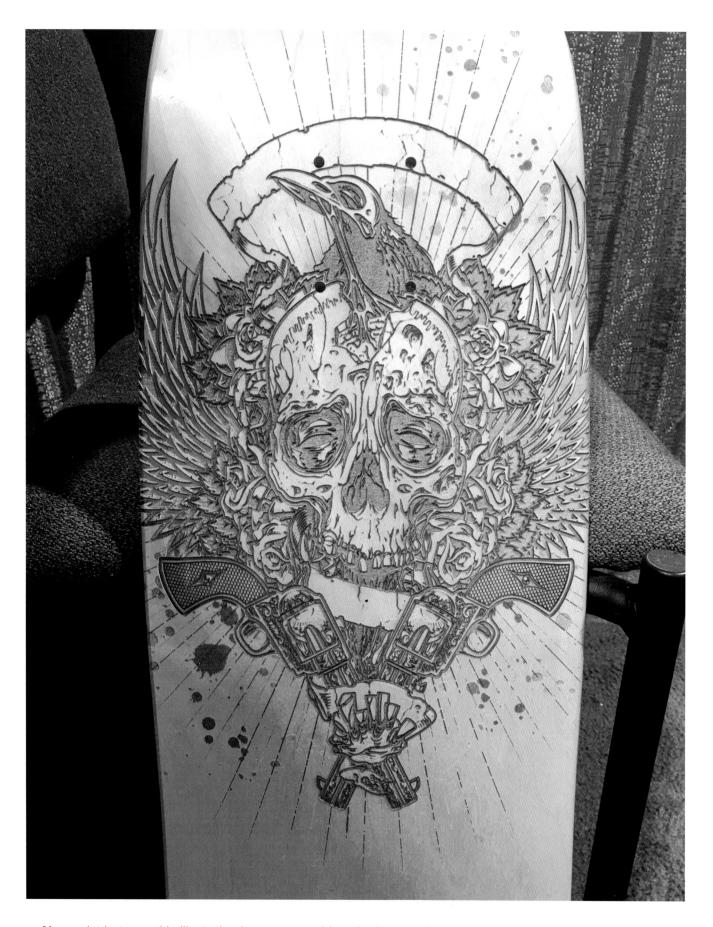

Above: Intricate graphic illustration laser engraved into the bottom of a wood skateboard deck, taken from a 2D vectorized Adobe Illustrator drawing. Because of the precise quality of laser etching, makers, designers and marketers commonly take advantage of this technology to apply custom graphic branding / logos to custom products or displays.

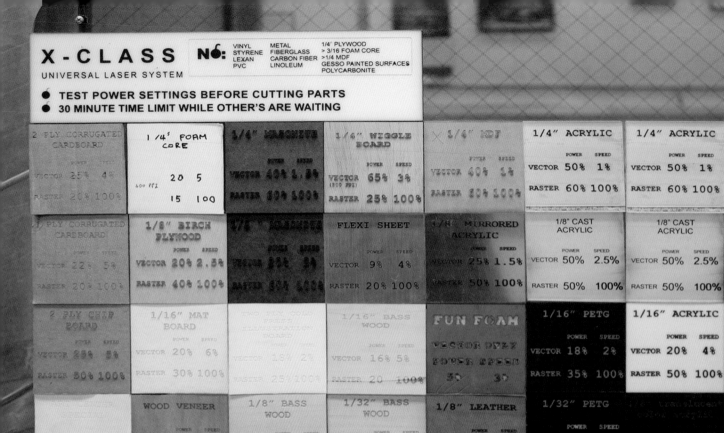

Above: The laser cutter must be properly calibrated before every cut, especially if a new type of material is used. The two major settings are speed and power. Experimentation with different settings and materials will eventually yield the right results for your project. Make sure to keep a log of the settings for each material type, and keep them close to your laser machine in your shop. For a pre-prepared book of material swatches, a supplier named Rowmark Laser offers a sample book that is considered by many in the industry to be the bible for laser cutting professionals and signmakers.

Below: Be careful about burning around edges (especially in rastered artwork, like the image shown) — which can occur if **1)** the laser power settings are too high, or if **2)** the speed settings are too low (or a combination of both). However, sometimes this can be a planned design feature rather than a bug, since this effect has a very distinct look to it.

Above: An intricate flat-pack model that is held together by mortise and tenon joint construction. Because the laser cutter is only suitable for cutting flat sheet material, small sections have been individually cut have been cut and pieced together like a puzzle. This is a very clever way of creating the curvature in this piece's vertical column sections.

Vacuum Forming

TIPS & TECHNIQUES

Vacuum forming, thermo-forming, or vacuum casting, is best used for creating thin-walled shell pieces, which would be difficult to RTV cast. This process is commonly used in the packaging industry, to create "Blister Packs" (clear bubble packages) for products such as kids' toys — it is also popular for making Cosplay costumes (i.e. Storm-Trooper armor). Vacuum forming can be used to create a positive thin shell shape, or a negative shell shape. The latter would be used as a mold. Heat and time settings should be adjusted to the material — two common materials are styrene (white), acrylic (clear) and PETG (milky white). It may take a couple of trials to dial-in the proper heat and time settings for your part. These are dependent on the type and thickness of sheet plastic material used, and also on the complexity the part. Styrene is a stiffer material and is better for taking on tight curvatures while maintaining part detail. PETG's non-stick quality makes it great for use as a mold in fiberglass layup applications. Multiple materials can be vacuum-formed over one another, as shown in the examples pictured.

PRO TIPS

Keep a log of successful temperature and time settings for the different materials you'll be forming, and keep this somewhere visible in your shop or on the machine itself — this will come in handy the next time you need to repeat the process with the same results.

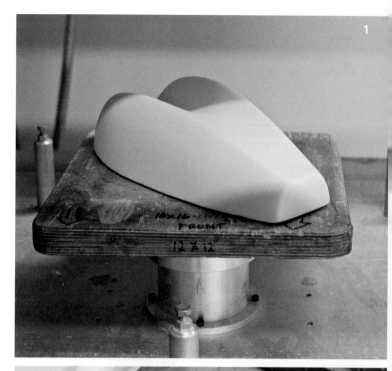

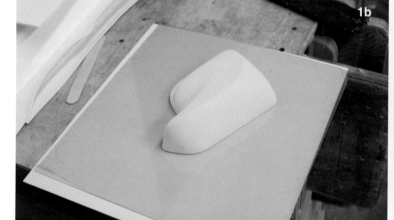

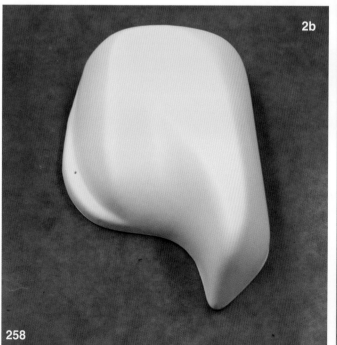

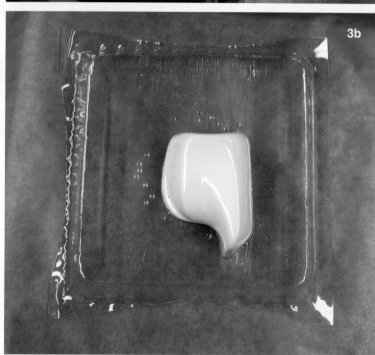

Left & Facing: 1) A 10LB foam motorcycle tank shape positioned on the platen. The 3D shape should fit within the edges of the platen for proper forming — otherwise the shape will create undercuts and not properly remove from the plastic. **2)** Styrene plastic sheet vacuum formed over the hard motorcycle tank form. Notice the extra material where the platen and former brackets were left. This excess will be trimmed off on the band saw.

Left: 3) Trimmed styrene plastic form. In this example, the styrene is used to seal the foam and create a smoother surface for the second PETG layer. This PETG layer (milky white transparent color) will be used as a mold for fiberglass composite layup. PETG is a superior mold making material due to its non-stick properties.

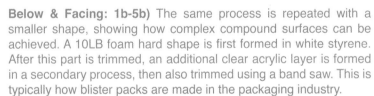

Below & Facing: 1b-5b) The same process is repeated with a smaller shape, showing how complex compound surfaces can be achieved. A 10LB foam hard shape is first formed in white styrene. After this part is trimmed, an additional clear acrylic layer is formed in a secondary process, then also trimmed using a band saw. This is typically how blister packs are made in the packaging industry.

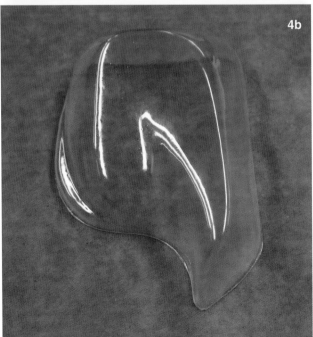

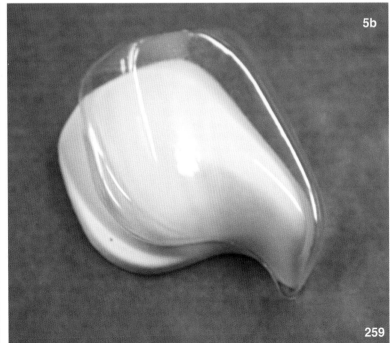

1) Overhead heaters heat the plastic material, which should start to visibly sag when softened. To test if the plastic is ready for forming, use a popsicle stick or fingernails.

2) Frame positioned over part, ready to be lowered.

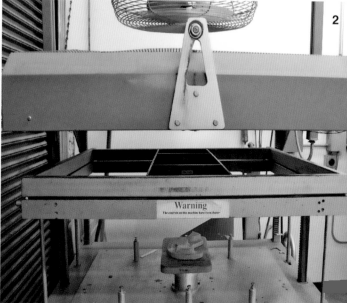

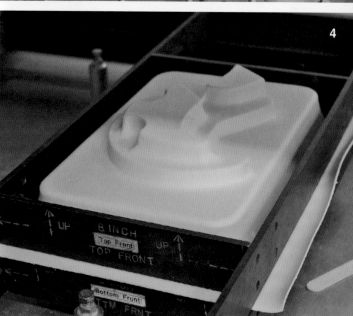

3) The frame is then lowered over the part — notice the hot plastic will start to take the shape of the form below.

4) Finally, the vacuum comes on and sucks the hot plastic down to the hard part, forcing the material to conform to the part's surface contours. Once the plastic cools, it will retain this exact shape.

Above: An example of the complex surface shapes that can be achieved by vacuum forming.

RTV Molding & Casting

TIPS & TECHNIQUES

RTV Molding - silicone cures in roughly 16 hours. A vacuum chamber sucks out any air bubbles whipped into the rubber during the mixing process. This creates a much better surface quality which will reflect in the resin castings. A one-part mold is the easiest to make, where the casted parts will have a flat back. In a 2-part mold, a pour spout will need to be designed into the mold, allowing the liquid resin casting material to be poured in through the top. Where the two mold halves come together is called the "parting line," and will show up in the final casted parts — true professionals will design the mold with this in mind, to minimize the visibility of parting lines in casted parts. Molds more than two parts are used for more complicated parts, and will need to be designed according to the part's shape. A properly designed mold will ease mold separation and eliminate any undercuts (areas which can't be separated from the mold). Mold boxes are made from non-hardening Klean Clay, with built-in "registration keys" which are used to line up the two mold halves correctly. Once the first half of the mold cures, the mold is flipped upside-down, and new silicone is poured and allowed to cure over top.

RTV Casting - urethane resin setting times will vary by the brand. This can be anywhere from five minutes, to a full hour or more. Parts can be casted as opaque, transparent, or fully clear — however, air bubbles will show if a pressure pot is not used in crystal-clear part applications. The pressure pot forces out the air bubbles which become trapped into the resin liquid during the mixing process.

Additives - metallic powders can be coated onto the inside of the mold, which fuse into the surface of the casted part. This surface can then be buffed or polished to give a realistic metal-like effect. Also, spray primer can be used in the same manner: since silicone doesn't stick to anything, the resin casts will come out with a pre-primed surface — ready for painting.

PRO TIPS

If you do not have access to a vacuum chamber, try pouring silicone from as high up above the part as possible (2-3 feet) — this will break up any larger trapped air bubbles that may effect mold reproduction quality. Use a digital kitchen scale to measure mixing portions much more accurately. The digital scale can measure in increments down to 1/10 of a gram, and are available for under $20-$30. If the molding materials are not properly mixed, the batch may take much longer to cure, or even worse — not fully cure at all. A spray release agent can prolong the life of a silicone mold.

Right: A 2-Part mold box made from Klean clay and MDF. Key holes, pour spout, and gate have been designed into the clay — pouring the first silicone mold half (below).

Above: 1-2) For best results, the liquid silicone mixture is placed into a vacuum chamber, which pulls out all of the air bubbles that were whipped into the mixture during the mixing process. This step is optional, however will produce a much better mold quality by eliminating any possible bubbles trapped into the rubber (which may explode if a pressure pot is used to cast the resin parts). **3)** If you don't have access to a vacuum chamber, the next best option is to pour the silicone from as high up as possible, which will break apart most of the larger bubbles. **4)** One half of the liquid silicone mold poured, then left to cure overnight. The mold is then flipped upside down, and the second half is poured. **5)** Since silicone is soft and flexible, structural mold supports can be made to hold the two mold halves into shape — here, scrap 1/8" masonite board is used.

Below: 1b) The 2-part liquid resin is poured separately at 1:1 ratio. **2b)** These parts are mixed together, then the mixture is poured into the pour spout at the top of the mold (the tiny hole on right side of the mold is called a "gate" which releases air pockets that can become trapped if the material fails to fully rise up into the mold cavity. **3b)** Duplicate reproduction parts are made from the same mold, with different color tints and metallic powder casting effects. Each casting pulled from the mold will slightly degrade its quality — however, one silicone mold can cast up to one hundred parts before complete failure. Using a sprayable release agent will prolong the production lifespan even longer (a common in film or special effects prop work).

Above: 1) Metallic powders, primer, and other effects can be coated onto the inside of the mold. **2)** After the urethane liquid is poured into the mold, this coating will fuse to the surface of the casted part (note the "registration" alignment posts).

Above: A professional quality 3-part mold, with an outer hinged MDF mold support box (typically referred to as a "mother mold") which holds the shape of the soft silicone rubber. This part was split into three separate because of the complexity of the cast part.

Below: The thin-walled urethane resin part below was "cold cast" using a pressure chamber or "pressure pot," which will help to force the internal 2-part liquid up the walls of the silicone mold cavity. A cold / pressure cast combination is the next closest thing to achieving similar results to injection molding, without the need for costly tooling and machinery.

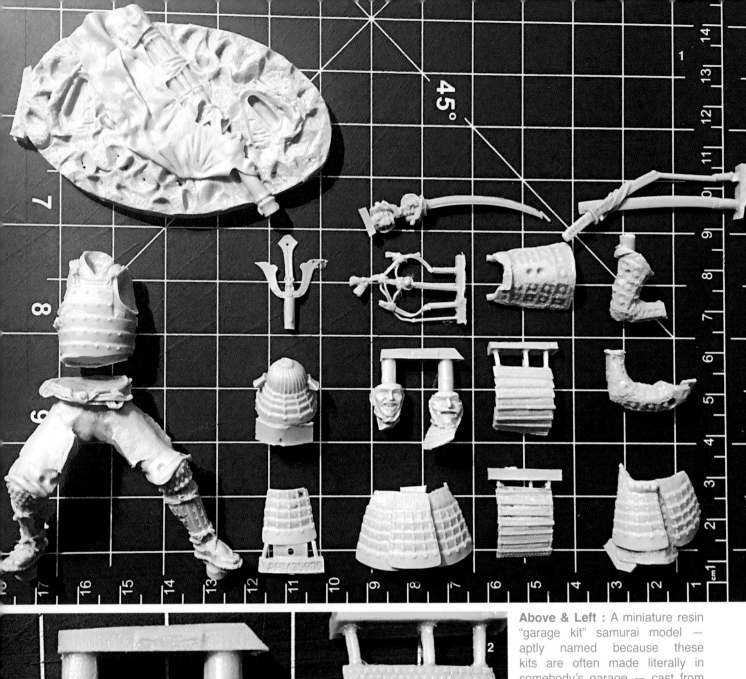

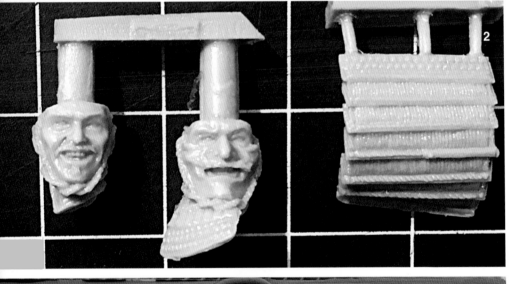

Above & Left : A miniature resin "garage kit" samurai model — aptly named because these kits are often made literally in somebody's garage — cast from a light gray urethane resin poured into an RTV silicone mold. Notice the intricate level of detail possible with resin casts shown at left. A quality silicone mold will pick up very fine textures, down to microscopic fingerprints, that will be translated to the final casted parts (each square here is about 15mm or 1/2").

REGISTRATION KEYS

SPRUE

FLASHING

CASTED PART

Left: A classic example of flashing — which occurs when excess material seeps in-between the two silicone mold halves. This can be removed with a knife (de-flashing). The leftover bowl-like shape at top is where the liquid resin material was poured into the mold gate, and is known as the sprue.

Composites Layup

TIPS & TECHNIQUES

The interior surface of the mold (here, vacuum formed PETG) is sprayed with an HVLP fiberglass-specific gel coat. This coating will produce a much nicer surface finish once the fiberglass part is pulled out of the mold. To properly create high-strength fiberglass parts, 2D flat templates must be cut from the fiber mat or cloth, eliminating any folds which can form when the cloth drapes over surface bends. The fiberglass should be cut into templates that best fit the mold contour. This method of casting fiberglass parts is called hand layup. A polyester resin mixture is brushed into the mold, along with the desired composite material — in this case, Fiberglass. Fiberglass is a nasty material to work with, so make sure to always wear gloves and a mask.

PRO TIPS

Professional shops and manufacturers of high-end carbon bike frames or race cars will precision cut patterns on a digital plotter for a near perfect, precision-fit layup.

Left: 1) 2-Part Polyester epoxy resin mixed together with MEKP hardener. The proper mixing ratio is 12 drops of hardener per ounce of epoxy resin. Working time is about 5 minutes, and the resin will fully cure in 2 hours. **2)** Fiberglass mat can be pulled apart like cotton candy. The mat is torn in half, then wetted into the mold with polyester resin. Fiberglass mat is used first, then woven cloth for strength & neatness. **3)** Polyester epoxy resin mix wetted into the mold with a brush. Notice the black gel coat on the inside of the PETG mold. This coating will be visible in the final fiberglass part after it is removed from the mold. The fiberglass part is the lightest and strongest when as little resin is used as possible — If it is too wet with resin, it is "resin rich."

Below: An MDF wood mold box supports the PETG plastic mold, for better control in the layup process.

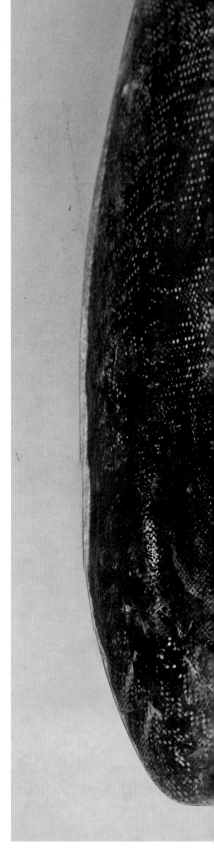

Above: Fiberglass mat is used first to fill in the surfaces of the mold, then woven fiberglass cloth for neatness. The left-over raggedy fiberglass edges are trimmed on the band saw after the part fully cures.

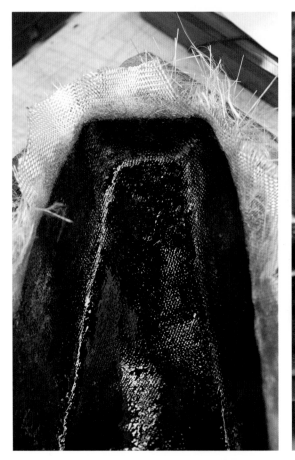

Above: Showing the final fiberglass cloth that has been wetted with resin. The layer thickness is ideally as uniform as possible, unless reinforced areas are desired. Fiberglass can be molded into complex contours — like the part pictured at right.

Above Left & Right: Final Interior and exterior surfaces of the fiberglass motorcycle tank — after the exterior has been primed, finished, and painted. Fiberglass parts are lighter and much stronger than vacuum-formed parts, making the application ideal for engineered parts. Fiberglass is also relatively inexpensive.

Spray Painting & Finishing

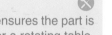

Above: dripping can result when: **1)** paint is sprayed on too heavy and / or too close to the part's surface, or **2)** the primer or paint coat underneath has not fully dried (chemical off-gassing).

TIPS & TECHNIQUES

Spray painting is both an art and a science — getting it right is no easy task. Many factors are involved, including proper surface prep to proper paint mixing ratios, dust in the room, and more. For most industrial purposes, painting follows these important steps: Surface prep —> Primer —> Wet Sanding —> Top Coat (color) —> Clear Coat. The clear coat acts as the final gloss layer that will seal and protect the painted surface underneath. Paint finishes are limited only by your imagination.

(Rattle Can) Automotive / Filler Primer - spray can version of primer. Filler primer sprays on much thicker vs. standard automobile primer, but will take longer to dry.

(Rattle Can) Spray Paint - these paints are most common at hardware stores, and are suitable for smaller models. The most common rattle spray paint types are Acrylic and Enamel — follow the application and drying time directions on the label, since each paint formula is different.

(HVLP) Catalyzed Primer - To mix, add MEKP catalyst to the primer, which causes the paint to harden and cure through a chemical reaction. Cut with Acetone first, to thin out for spraying. Less Acetone = thicker and quicker set time. More Acetone = thinner and longer set time. This 2-part primer is almost like a "Sprayable Super-Glue."

(HVLP) Spray Paint - 2-3 light coats a few minutes apart (making the last coat the heaviest) achieves far better results vs. one heavy coat. Follow application and drying time directions on the label, as each paint formula is different. Adjust spray flow, volume, pressure and spray pattern shape using the HVLP gun's adjustment dials.

PRO TIPS

PRACTICE, PRACTICE, PRACTICE. Test paint a small object first, before committing to the final part. This ensures the part is paintable. Professional quality paint results are only possible in a dust-free room. If you have a lazy susan or a rotating table, this can help to rotate an coat full 360° around a part without needing to pick it up every single time a new paint coat is applied.

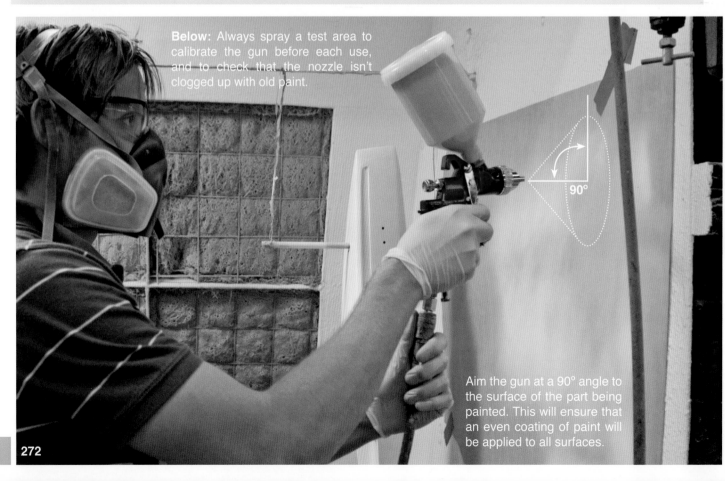

Below: Always spray a test area to calibrate the gun before each use, and to check that the nozzle isn't clogged up with old paint.

90°

Aim the gun at a 90° angle to the surface of the part being painted. This will ensure that an even coating of paint will be applied to all surfaces.

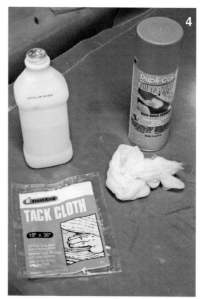

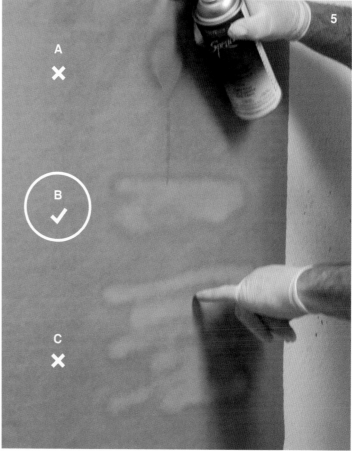

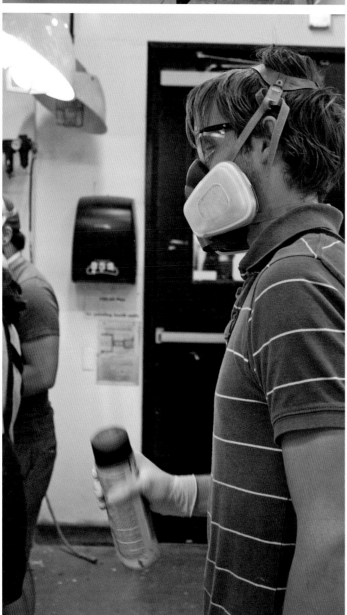

Left: 1) Catalyzed primer thinned with Acetone, then **2)** mixed with MEKP hardener. **4)** Base coat **3)** Prep the surface with auto prep or alcohol. A tack cloth is useful for removing small specs of dust. **5)** For the best results, use overlapping strokes (B) to avoid any gaps (C). Be careful not to spray paint or primer on too heavy, or it will run (A). **6)** Store the respirator mask in a ziplock bag in-between uses to extend the life of the filter cartridges.

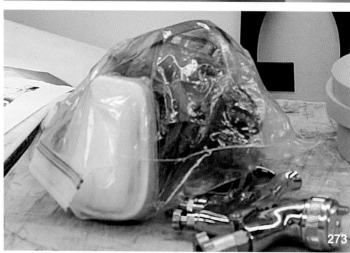

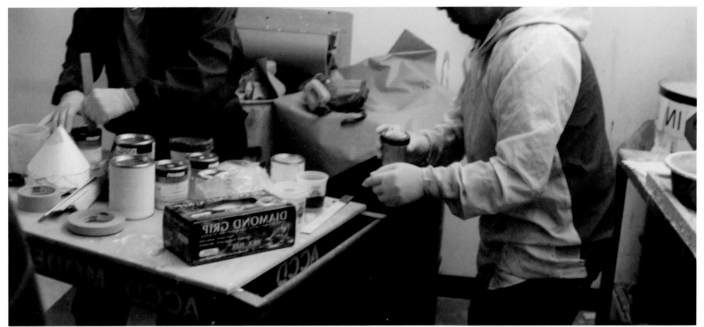

Above & Right: It's a great idea to wear coveralls to protect your clothing during the paint applications, because paint overspray and paint particulate (particle) matter in the air transferring onto clothing is inevitable.

Below: Pouring the clear coat. Clear coat must be applied in an entirely separate process on top of the base coat, top coat, and/or candy coat. Make certain your spray gun has been thoroughly cleaned beforehand! Many different automotive & specialty paint suppliers exist, this particular paint is called Dupont Nason.

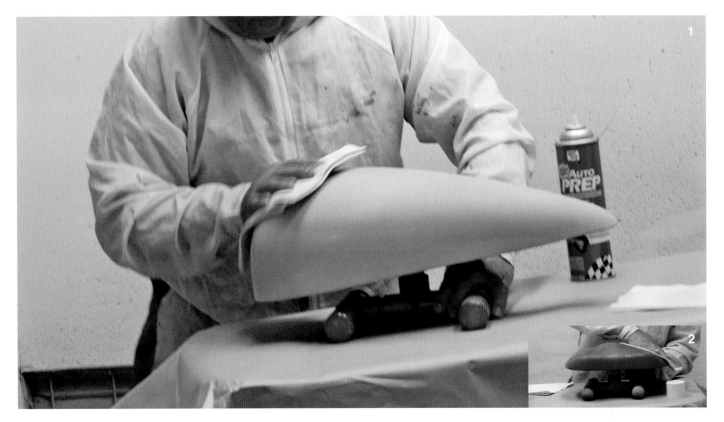

Above: 1) Surface prepping a fiberglass motorcycle tank that's been primed and wet sanded. Wiping the surface with auto prep will clean any oil, grease, or dust residue from the surface of the part — all of which could interfere with proper paint adhesion and / or show up on the final surface (including oily fingerprints)! Microfiber shop towels are used here instead of traditional paper towels, because they don't leave a trail of lint like normal paper towels do. **2)** Wiping down the surface of another part after a "color sand."

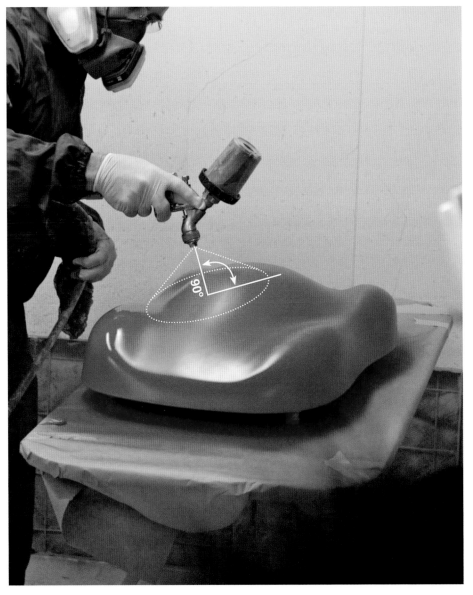

Left: The best time to apply an additional second or third paint coat (or clear coat) is when the surface begins to fog up and turn into a matte / satin sheen, which is known as an "eggshell finish." This is a clear indicator that the paint has started to cure. Applying an additional paint coat before this window occurs can lead to a nasty bubbling up of the paint coat underneath, since the solvent is still evaporating underneath, and therefore creates visible bubbles and / or cracks in the newly coated surface (such as the orange paint cracking on page 262) .

Above: Due to its oil content, clay needs to be sealed first, otherwise paint will not fully cure. Porous materials like wood or tooling foams will need to be sealed first with Shellac or several thick coats of HVLP primer / rattle can "filler primer" to make the surface smooth enough for final painting. Steps are as follows: **1)** Faber Light clay sealed with a coating of clear Shellac. **2)** This is then followed by a primer / bondo / guide coat layer to fill any valleys or pinholes. **3)** Finally, one last coat of primer is then wet sanded and ready for final paint. Almost all paint projects follow this same order.

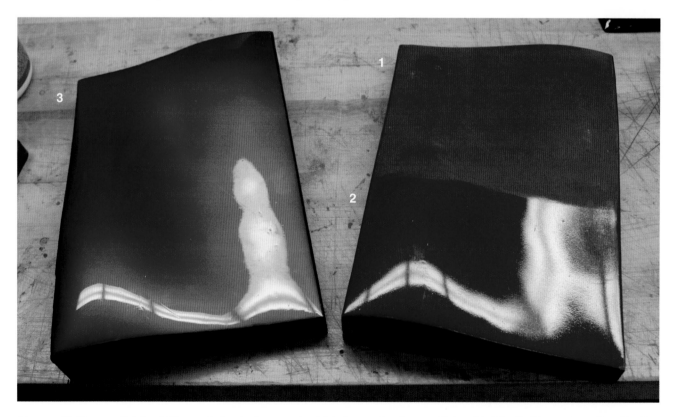

Above: 1) Bare unfinished Chavant clay before sealant (darker red color vs. Faber Light), **2)** Gloss clay after Shellac spray sealant coat, and **3)** Final automotive paint + clear coat ("candy coat") at left. Steps 1-3 are the exact same process top automakers use when creating show-ready, painted concept cars from full-scale sculpted clay car bodies.

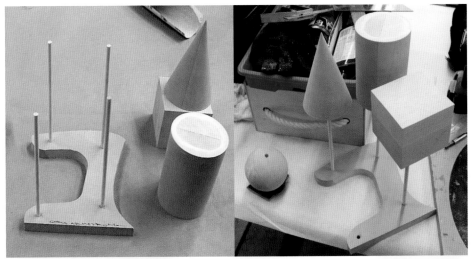

Left: Spray paint jigs are the best way to create "hand holds" and to speed up painting times. The parts can be held by a dowel stick or wooden pencil while the full 360° of the piece can be painted. This is also very useful for drying, since the pieces have no contact with a flat surface. Make this jig by drilling a small hole in the bottom of the part (choose a spot hidden from sight), and another hole in a scrap piece of wood or other material (the base). Parts that cannot easily be propped up this way can be hung with a hook or coat-hanger, and hung for drying (i.e. following spread). Again, custom jigs come in handy here.

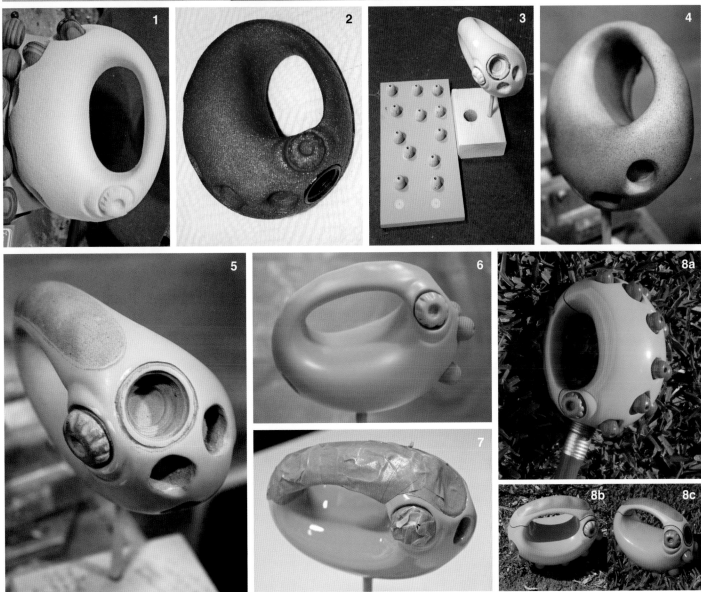

Pro-Level Spray Painting Process: 1) PU foam model with finished surface details **2)** Shellac is sprayed or brushed onto the foam to seal large surface pores (this step is needed for porous foams or woods only) **3)** First primer layer of all parts, layered on thick to create a smooth surface. **4)** Primer is sanded and Bondo'd several times, until a final guide coat is lightly dusted over the top (use a rattle-can for this). This coat is used as a guide to show which areas have been completely wet-sanded — and which have not — before final paint is applied. **5)** Guide coat has been fully wet sanded off. The primer surface is now ready for painting. **6)** Rattle-Can base color paint coat applied as evenly as possible. **7)** Once the base color dries, mask off contrast color / texture break areas with blue or green non-stick painters tape. A thick clear coat is then applied. **8)** Final painted model at right — lower red knob areas are painted separately, allowed to dry, then epoxy glued onto the model.

Spraying an Irregular Object: In the case that the object being painted cannot be easily propped up using the dowel stick method, the object must be hung via a hook instead — here, a simple hanging hook was fashioned from a metal paper clip and fishing line. A special area must be set aside to spray and paint parts like these (i.e. Urban Workshop's DIY spray booth pictured below). Keep in mind that high-quality industrial painting will need to be done in a fully enclosed, dust free indoor space with ventilation — however, spray booths don't always need to be ultra-fancy and cost tens of thousands of dollars. Most important of all, the booth must be covered, and well ventilated (preferably outdoors).

Primer: Because there is no flat spot on this pair of sunglass frames, it is hard to paint without the appearance of an unsightly dry spot. To counter this, the piece is hung with fishing line tied to a spot on the object that will be unnoticeable in the final paint finish (in this case, the inside of the ear-stem hinge). The frames are first covered with 2-3 full coats of automotive rattle can primer. They are then and left to dry for at least an hour, before being wet sanded or readied for final paint.

Paint: 1) While holding onto the object by the fishing line hook (wear gloves), the sunglasses can be spun and rotated to evenly cover surfaces all over. **2-4)** Notice a first light 'mist' coat, which is then **5)** followed by one to two medium wet coats a few minutes apart. Be careful not to apply too heavy of coats here, or the paint will run, meaning the process of primer then sanding and paint will need to be repeated all over again!

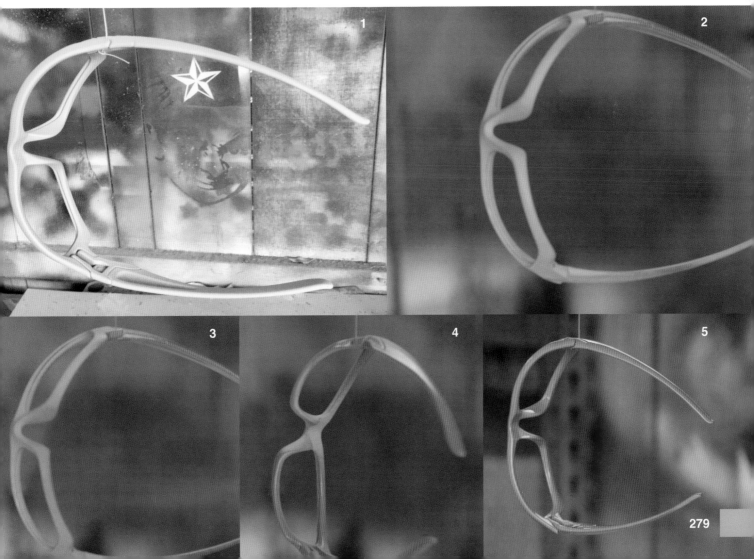

Drying: 1-2) After the final paint coat has been applied, the sunglasses are left to hang overnight. **3)** Make sure your painted piece is in a place that is both covered and undisturbed, to avoid ruining. You may also want to leave a note with your name and contact info next to the piece, if this is a shared space.

Below Spread: Final paint coat in all its glory. In my experience, a good quality rattle can paint can come very close to achieving a level of finish that is visually on par with that of a high quality HVLP spray gun. However, the key differences are the size of objects which can be painted, as well as the longevity of the finished paint surface. Objects being handled often may start to chip or rub off vs. HVLP which is more permanent. One way to counteract this is to apply a sprayable clear coat once the color coat has been allowed to fully dry.

Below: Paint effects are only limited by the imagination. The effects here can be created either by heat wrapping the surfaces with a printed vinyl, or by masking separate areas with tape, before spray painting one by one.

Left & Below: Automotive brands like Lamborghini and Ferrarri will create their own color pallettes with special (often proprietary) color formulas — each with unique names to boot. The speed forms below are used by automotive design firms and custom paint bodyshops to show how surface highlights and reflections will appear up on complex forms & curvatures.

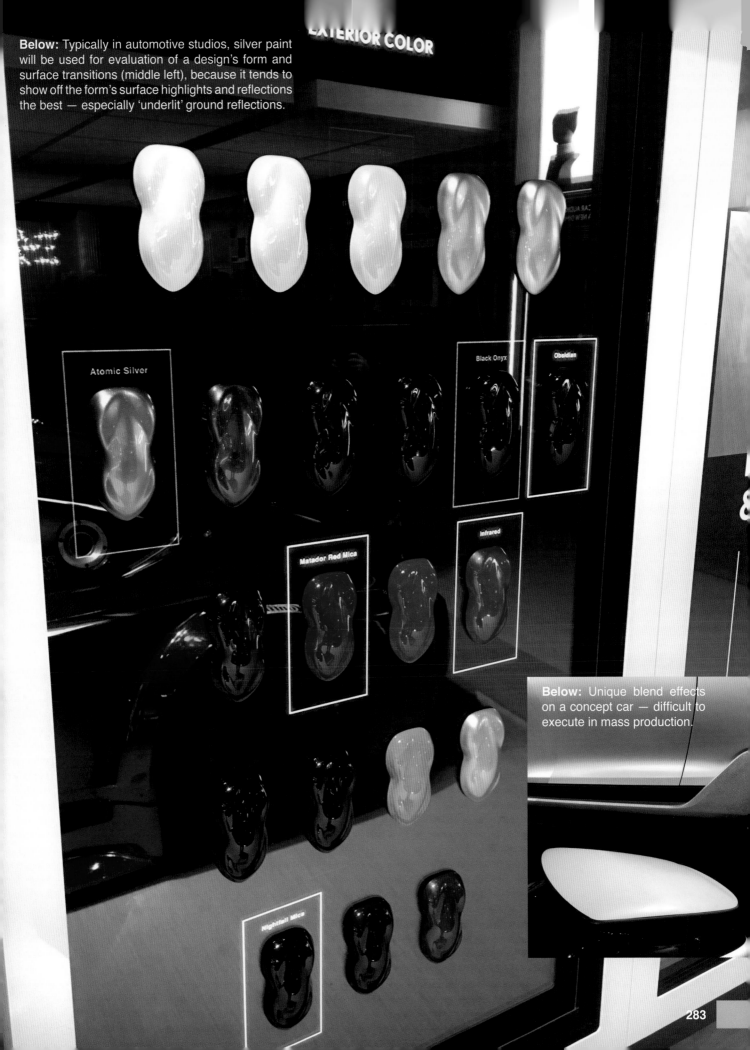

EXTERIOR COLOR

Below: Typically in automotive studios, silver paint will be used for evaluation of a design's form and surface transitions (middle left), because it tends to show off the form's surface highlights and reflections the best — especially 'underlit' ground reflections.

Atomic Silver

Black Onyx

Obsidian

Matador Red Mica

Infrared

Below: Unique blend effects on a concept car — difficult to execute in mass production.

Nightfall Mica

Above: Custom painted mountain bike frame by a pro paint shop in California. This bike frame follows the same industrial HVLP paint process covered in this book, with pin striping added by hand with a brush.

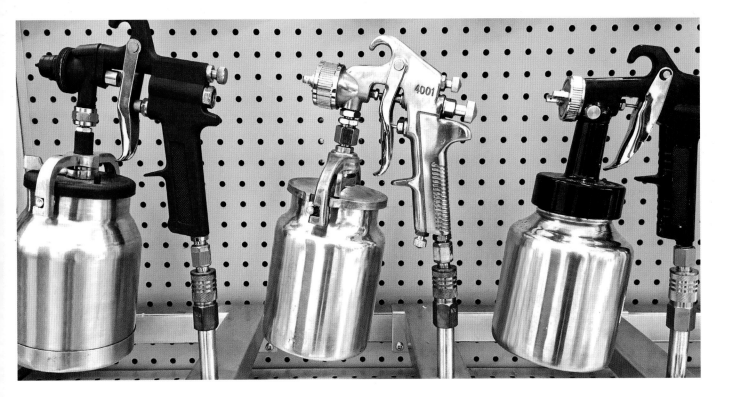

Spray Painting Cheat Sheet

For most industrial purposes, painting follows these important steps (works with both Rattle Cans and HVLP Gun):
1) Surface Prep —> 2) Primer —> 3) Dry Sanding —> 4) Wet Sanding —> 5) Painting —> 6) Drying

1) Surface Prep - sand and prep every surface before each step listed. Make sure the part being painted is dust and lint free. Clean away oil & grease with a lint-free rag or tack cloth, wetted with alcohol or auto prep degreaser spray. To protect from overspray, mask off all areas of the model which are not to be painted using blue or green painter's tape.

2) Primer - prepares the surface to be painted, essentially creating a new surface "skin" that can once again be sanded, wet sanded, or finished with body filler. Slick surfaces should be roughened with sandpaper before priming.

3) Dry Sanding - lower-grit sandpaper with heavier tooth, for removing more material. Dry sanding is used to sculpt a material, or to roughen a surface in the pre-primer stage.

4) Wet Sanding - finer-grit quality sandpaper, used for polishing in the post-primer stage. Wet sand (with a few drops of dish soap added to water mixture) up to 600-grit sandpaper to create a glass-smooth surface ready for painting. Wet sanding is used as the last and final surface prep just before the final paint coat — always make sure to keep in mind that the final paint coat will pick up the exact finish quality of the underlying surface (including oily "Cheetoh Finger" prints!)

5) Painting - once primer surface has been sanded to the desired finish (typically 600 grit wet sand for gloss finish, although a matte finish can make due with lower grit — i.e. 320) and cleaned with degreaser, it is time to paint. Always paint using riser support stands and / or hangers — this will double or triple the overall paint and dry time efficiency, and give more control to rotate parts and apply coats evenly. Work in a dust-free, well-ventilated area. Using overlapping paint strokes, spray 2-3 light coats a few minutes apart, making the last coat the heaviest. After a few minutes, the paint will begin to set and develop a satin "egg shell" appearance. An optional clear coat can now be applied during this "window". The clear coat is the final gloss layer that will seal, protect, and improve overall gloss level of the painted surface underneath.

6) Drying - primer dries much quicker than spray paint, and will typically be dry to the touch within 1 hour. Paint typically takes 24 hours to fully dry. When drying, store parts in a safe, dust-free place where they will not be disturbed — especially when using a clear coat. Clear coat will attract microscopic dust particles in the air, so it's a good idea to place a cover over the entire piece. Otherwise, all of your hard work could literally be ruined overnight!

Specialty & Exotic Finishes

1) Vinyl-wrapping **2)** Plasti-Dip® rubber grip + electrostatic spray chrome

TIPS & TECHNIQUES

Anodizing - an extremely robust, weather and scratch resistant coating applied to metals through an electrostatic process.

Bead Blasting ("Sand Blasting") - using an abrasive bead or grit that is blown at high pressure to roughen up a slick surface. Typical bead blast spec is light, medium or heavy (heavy being the roughest). When you see frosted glass (slightly opaque), this technique has been used.

Electrostatic Spray Chroming - produces a true chrome or metallic finish using a special electrically-charged paint process.

Hydro Dipping (Water Transfer Printing) - a method of applying printed graphics to 3D objects using a hydrographic film that sits on the top surface of water. When an object is submerged, the print will be transferred to the surface of the part. Can be applied to any paintable surface (substrate) such as plastic, metal, wood, and more. Also known as immersion printing.

Iridium Coating - a mirror-like colorful protective coating that originated in the aerospace industry, where fighter jet canopies were coated in gold iridium to help defend against intense heat and radiation from the sun experienced at high altitudes.

Plasti-Dip® - a dippable or sprayable vinyl rubber, used to give a rubberized coating and / or grip to parts.

Powder Coating - a durable finish applied electrostatically as a free-flowing powder, then cured under heat or UV light.

Vinyl Wrapping - 4-color process graphics are printed on a gloss or matte vinyl plastic sheet, which is then shrink-wrapped over a 3D surface using a heat gun. Since this is a non-permanent application, it tends to abrade much more quickly than paint.

PRO TIPS

With the exception of only a few, most of the finishes shown here are better left to a specialty shop, due to their complexity.

Right: Anodized precision machined hubs fabricated by a small company based out of Portland, Oregon. Anodizing not only looks cool, but it also ensures a lifetime of cleaning, by providing a strong barrier of protection against rust and harsh outdoor elements.

Below: Hydro dipping is used to apply graphics or special prints onto complex surface contours — such as video game controllers or helmets — where screen printing would fail.

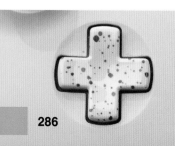

Iridium Coating: A large jig platform used for applying iridium coatings to the outer side of high-end sunglass lenses. Iridium is avaialble in a rainbow of metallic colors, and the machines used to create this finish are very expensive. Below are protective polycarbonate goggle lenses coated with iridium.

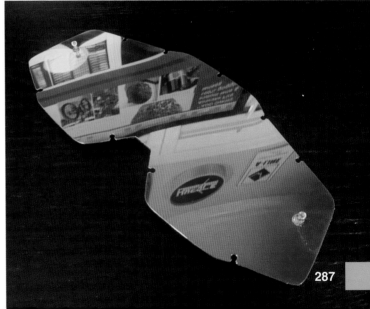

Anodizing: Anodizing is available in a wide range of different colors, and is instantly recognizable by it's distinct metallic look. The rainbow aluminum swatch sample above is from an industrial hardware supplier, and is used to select accurate colors to spec in a product design. The photos below and facing show different uses of the anodizing effect — both as a functional and aesthetic design element.

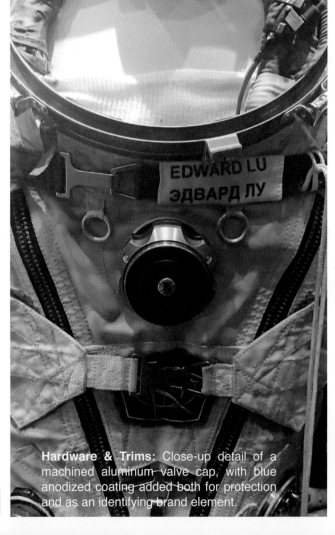

Hardware & Trims: Close-up detail of a machined aluminum valve cap, with blue anodized coating added both for protection and as an identifying brand element.

Above: Anodized machined aluminum pivot link and bolts.

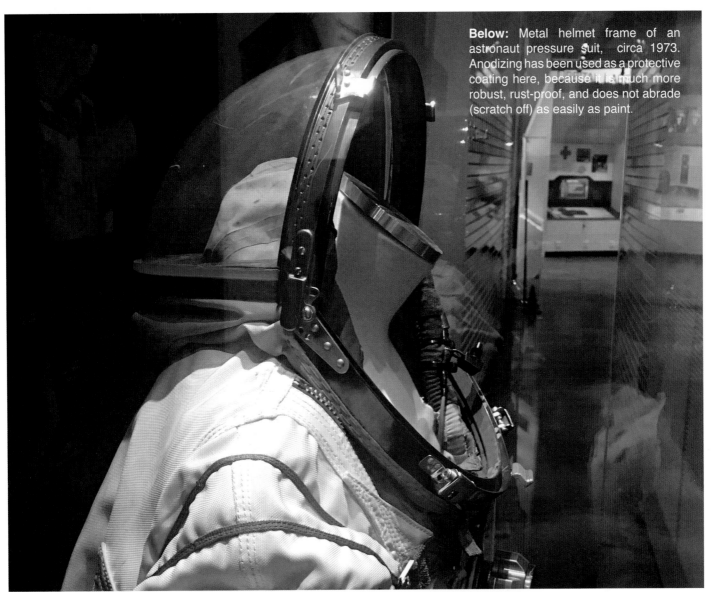

Below: Metal helmet frame of an astronaut pressure suit, circa 1973. Anodizing has been used as a protective coating here, because it is much more robust, rust-proof, and does not abrade (scratch off) as easily as paint.

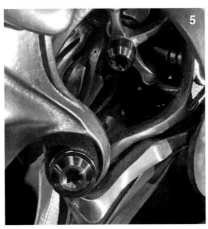

Left: 1-2) Mountain bike components with anodized finishes. Beyond looking so damn cool, the anodizing effect itself protects the metal from harsh elements and rust. **3)** The color-changing decorative finish applied to these titanium bolts is known as "oil slick" — and can sometimes be found on flashy / decorative specialty knife blades. **4)** Anodized threaded rim nut on the wheel of a performance luxury automobile **5)** A metal sculpture using anodized titanium screws, which give a nice visual design accent or "color pop."

Lifecasting

TIPS & TECHNIQUES

Molding - referred to as the "negative." When mixed at a 1:1 ratio with water, alginate will cure into a flexible mold within 15 minutes. The mold is only good for a one-time single use. Since the rubber gives off moisture from water content, only a limited number of materials can be cast — such as plaster. The mold will last for up to 24 hours, after which it will start to shrivel and crack. Make sure to hold body parts into position, with as little movement as possible for the 15 minutes the material is setting — otherwise, casted parts will come out distorted.

Casting - referred to as the "positive." The most common casting material to use in an alginate mold is either plaster of Paris or gypsum. Heating parts or storing them in a heated environment can sometimes help them to cure more quickly (problems may occur in the wintertime when temperatures drop too low).

PRO TIPS

If a full body or head cast is needed, apply a structural exoskeleton over the flexible alginate mold, using plaster or gypsum bandages. Once hardened, this "mother mold" will help to hold the shape of the mold while the plaster is being poured. This is the exact process used to create the Batman and Iron Man suits of armor in the movies — which are perfectly fitted to Christian Bale's and Robert Downey Jr.'s body shapes. This process can then be repeated, making a silicone mold of the plaster life cast — with fiberglass mother mold support.

Below: Alginate mixes 1:1 with water, and is comes in different colors depending on the brand.

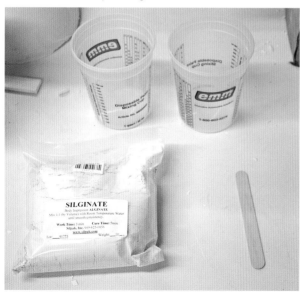

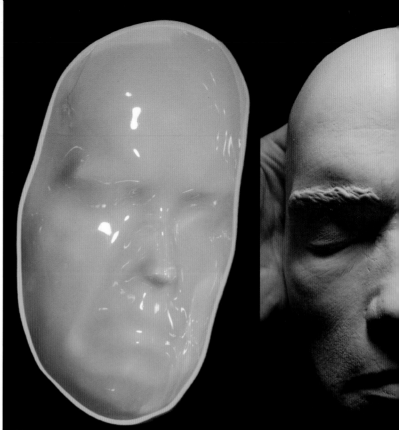

Above: Lifecasting is common in the prosthetics & special effects industries. This life mask was created from an original alginate mold and plaster cast, where a silicone mold was then created to allow for a a slip cast or rotational cast ("roto cast") of this thin resin part. A flesh-tone pigment from was added into the 2-part urethane.

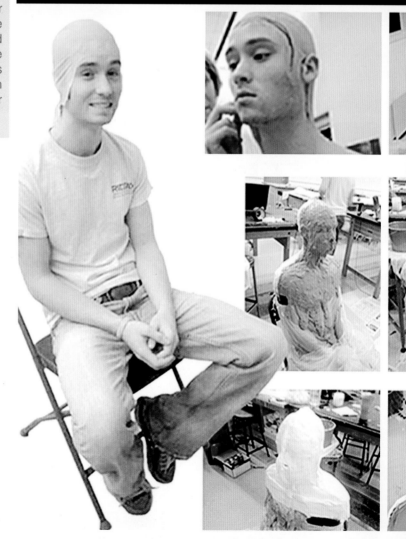

Below & Facing: A plaster head cast removed from Alginate mold, then finished with primer. A full head cast requires the model to wear a bald cap (or alginate will stick to hair) and to breath either through his nostrils, or through a mouth straw tube.

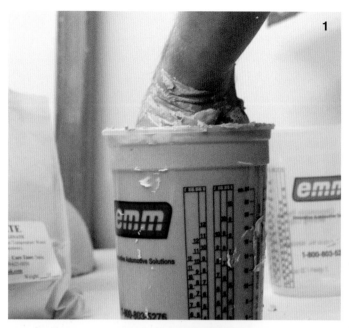

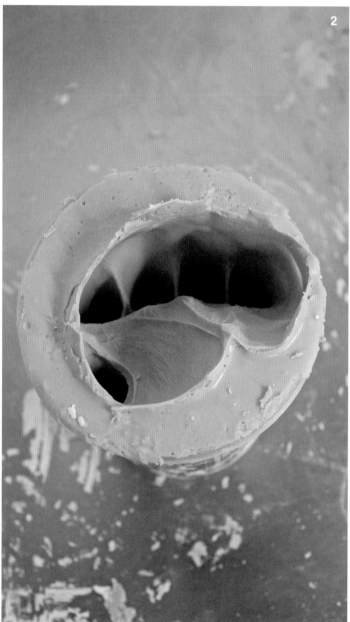

Molding & Casting: 1) Alginate powder is mixed with water at a 1:1 ratio, poured into a container, then hand is inserted. After holding a pose in place for about 15 minutes, begin to wiggle your fingers free from the mold. **2)** At right is the negative mold impression left over once the hand is removed. Now that the mold is ready for casting **3)** mix plaster to pour into the mold. The plaster will also cure with water (the plaster is exothermic, giving off heat through a chemical reaction). To properly mix plaster, sift the plaster powder into water until the water will no longer absorb any of the powder — a small mound of plaster should sit on top of the water, and the mixture should now have a pancake-batter like consistency. The plaster mixture is poured into the mold and allowed to harden overnight.

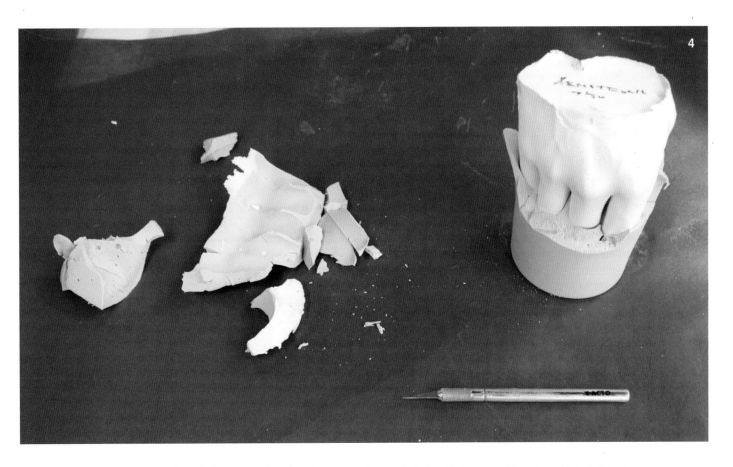

4) De-Molding: Carefully separating the plaster casting out of the Alginate mold with an X-Acto blade.

5) Final Cast: The plaster cast removed from the alginate mold will capture every last detail — down to skin pores and even fingerprints.

Kit-Bashing

TIPS & TECHNIQUES

Kit Bashing is a technique made famous in the original Star Wars film franchise, where it was first pioneered to create the intricately-detailed concept fighter jets like the X-Wing, and even the Death Star itself. This technique is blazingly quick, and still quite effective for making very convincing props for film or special effects. The process uses parts Frankensteined together from various model kits, hardware store parts, and various scraps. The final design can then be primered and painted, to give a realistic model prop effect.

The Kit Bash build process described here has been adapted from a class I formerly taught with John Park at the Red Engine School of Design, and later Concept Design Academy (CDA) called Advanced Vehicle & Mech Design.

PRO TIPS

Make sure to pick up a good variety of parts. Don't feel like you have to constrain yourself to the pre-designed kits like the military or Gundam kits. Most importantly be sure to pick up some armature wire, this will be used for the main skeleton structure for all other parts to be placed on top.

Above: Armature wire can be found at hobby or art supply stores. It's used to build support frames / skeletons for models.

Kit Party: The more kits the merrier!

Below: Random box kits from the hobby store. A good mix of military & Gundam style kits work very well.

Details: Once you've built a handful of kit-bashed models, you'll start to collect a random library of spare parts. Keep a spare box just for such parts, as this will come in VERY handy later on.

Below: John Park and I co-teaching a kit-bashing demo at Concept Design Academy (CDA) in Pasadena, California. John is an innovator and legend in kit-bashing and mech design.

PGS. 306-309

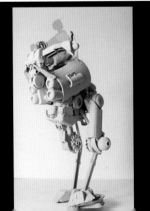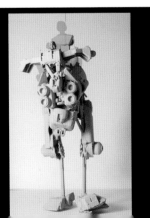

Left: An ostrich inspired bi-pedal kit-bash mech design model, with a simple coat of gray primer. A driver for scale was later added in Photoshop.

Injection Molding

TIPS & TECHNIQUES

One of the most iconic examples of injection molding is the classic LEGO™ brick. While it may look like a simple piece, there is actually a whole lot more to the engineering of these parts than meets the eye. The initial setup is much costlier than other rapid prototyping technologies, but once properly setup, injection molding benefits from massive economies of scale — with high volume, low cost parts. Injection parts can be any size, from a small LEGO™ brick to a large upright vacuum cleaner frame or outdoor plastic patio furniture. The low cost and speed (replicability) of injection is unrivaled by almost any other process, which is why its widely used in manufacturing. You'd need a 3D printing farm with many machines going at once just to come even close to the output of a decent injection molding machine. Injection parts can also have glass fibers or carbon fibers added to the plastic formula, and are available in an infinite variety of colors and finishes. Two of the most common types are thermoplastic and thermoset.

Thermoplastic Injection Molding - Injects a molten liquid plastic melted down from pellets. The most common process used.

Thermoset Injection Molding - Injects a 2-part thermosetting material. The least common of the two.

PRO TIPS

Injection molding can be used to make a small run of prototypes, but is much costlier to set up than a 3D printing machine, which doesn't require any special tooling. It is therefore most effective when used for production vs. prototyping.

Below & Right: A Pantone® color guide is an essential tool that should be in every serious designer or product developer's toolkit, and is a must for maintaining color accuracy between suppliers. Other standards exist, however Pantone® is the most trusted color standard in the world. Specific guides are available for textiles (TPX), CYMK print, and coated (glossy) or uncoated (matte) parts. Most importantly, be sure to work from the same standard as the team or factory you are working with, so that everyone is speaking the same language. If you have the budget for only one set, choose the solid coated — which works well across many different material types.

Righ: The part shown matches Patone 3005 C — which is the exact engineered spec number for this color. No "Happy Blue" or "Tickle Me Pink" here — colors are made to be strictly functional, so that there's as little room for errorneous interpretations as possible.

Above: Pantone adds new colors regularly, so it's good practice to work from a book that's no more than a few years old. That said, an old book is still better than no book.

Above: Injection molding can achieve an endless spectrum of different colors. Because the plastic material itself is already pigmented, this means it is much more robust and will not abrade (scratch off) like paint does, which is only surface-level deep.

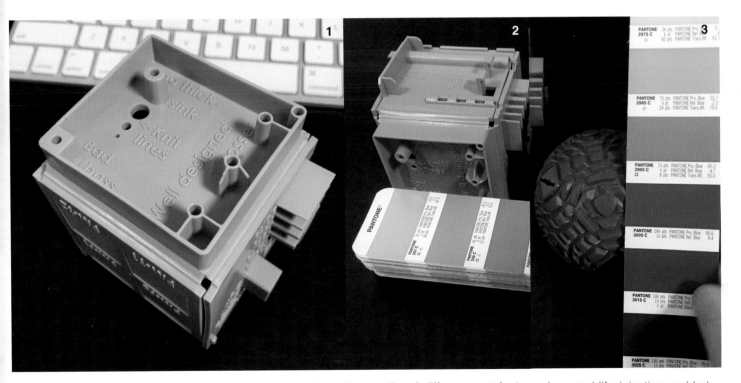

Aove: 1) The part above is a sample test part to check the quality of different part features in a real-life injection molded part application — an extremely useful tool! **2 & 3)** Checking an injection molded nylon plastic and an injection molded TPE (thermoplastic elastomer) rubber part with a Pantone® color guide. TPE is one of the most common types of injection molded rubber and can be specced in a wide range of shore durometers.

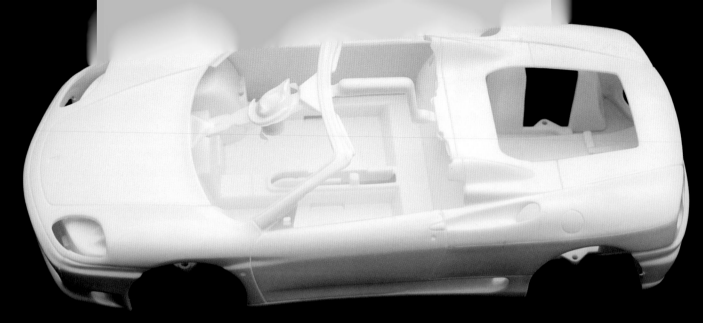

Above & Below: 1) An injection molded nylon plastic 1:24 scale model. The top, bottom, and rear bumper of the car are have been shot as two different plastic parts, then assembled together via a snap pressure fit. **2-3)** Notice the runners and sprue intersecting the windshield at the center — this shows how the molten plastic flows through the mold. These areas can be trimmed off with a sharp X-acto or Olfa knife. **4)** Injection nylon motorcycle handlebar protector. **5)** A complex snowboard binding assembly, consisting of an injection molded nylon plastic highback, base and straps. TPE or PU rubbers can also be co-molded into the plastic (mesh area).

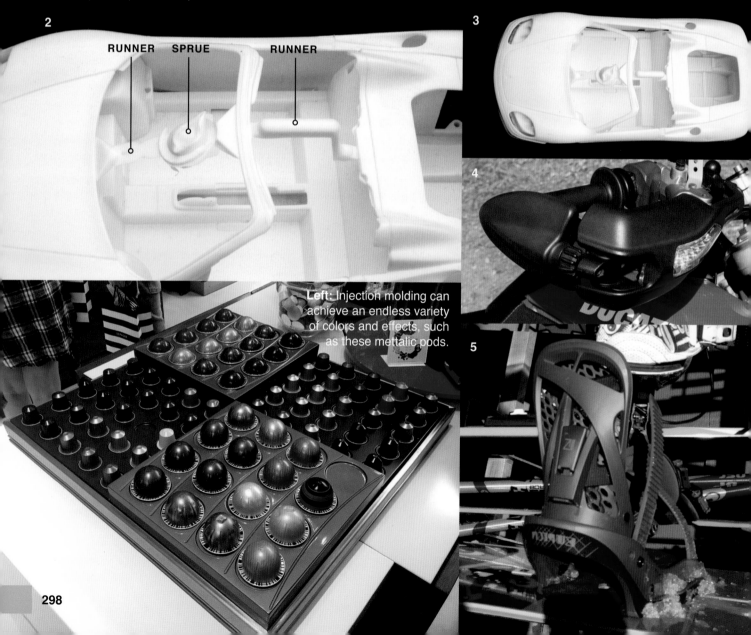

2

RUNNER   SPRUE   RUNNER

3

4

Left: Injection molding can achieve an endless variety of colors and effects, such as these mettalic pods.

5

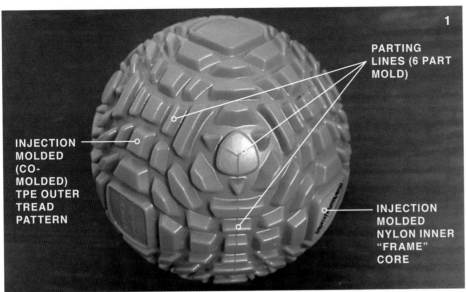

PARTING LINES (6 PART MOLD)

INJECTION MOLDED (CO-MOLDED) TPE OUTER TREAD PATTERN

INJECTION MOLDED NYLON INNER "FRAME" CORE

Left & Below: 1) Due to the complexity of this part, it is much more difficult to de-mold and requires a 6-part mold wrapping the spherical shape. TPE grip area has been co-molded to an internal nylon plastic core. Co-molding is a process whereby two materials are 'shot' together in one mold (i.e. soft toothbrush handle grips) **2)** Transparent injection nylon tail light on an Italian hypercar. Injection molding can be used for small and large scale production parts alike..

Below: 1) Mold textures can be selected, which will be applied to the inside of the mold and will show up on the injection plastic part. There are many standard textures you can select (using code numbers), or you can create your own. **2)** Ideal material sidewall thickness, cored out vs too thck (creates a depression called "sink"), ideal rib thickness — from too thick to too thin. **3)** Bosses are reinforcement ribs on the internal side of an injected part. **4)** Straight pull shows how the part will exit the mold **5)** Knit lines show up where the material "knits" together under heat and pressure, leaving lines around the edges of an opening **6)** Crystal clear nylon plastic parts can also be created. Here, a sandblast texture has been applied in-mold to certain areas. This roughenged texture helps the part bond to another assembly using glue, which wouldn't hold as well to a slick surface.

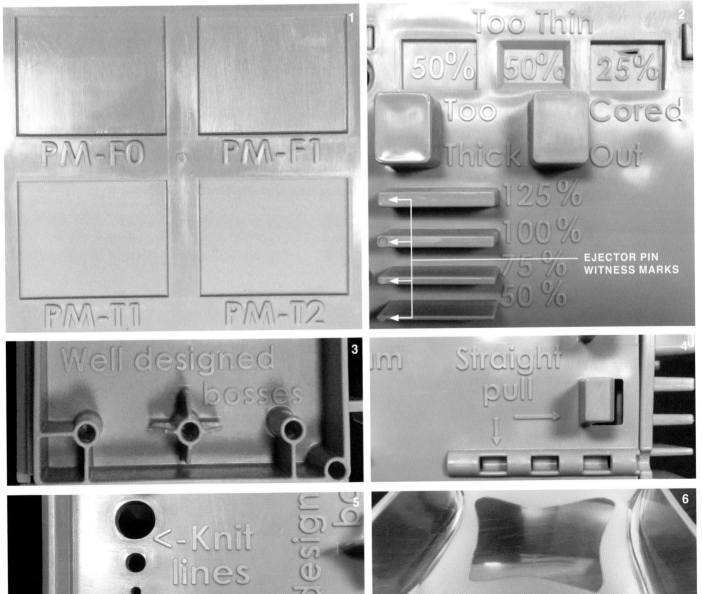

Above: A production plant stocked with an injection molding "machine farm." The entirety of the factory floor, including all robotic, automated and human labor contributes to a full assembly line. 301

Welding & Soldering

TIPS & TECHNIQUES

Welding - the quality of the welding job ultimately boils down to the quality of the weld beads — since a better, cleaner, more consistent weld bead will produce a much stronger, long lasting connection between the parts that are being welded together. This requires a steady hand. Jigs are often created for precision fitting of parts together. Welding is a true skill and is difficult to master. The difference between a pro welder and an amatuer is day and night in terms of quality. Wear proper protection, including a light-activated dimmer mask & skin coverage.

Tack Welding (Spot Weld) - welding or "tacking" separate parts together in key spots, which holds them in place in preparation for the full welding.

Soldering - operates at much lower temperatures than welding, making working with soldering much more forgiving, where it is much easier to practice without the fear of scorching yourself or damaging your eyesight with bright welding sparks. Still, make sure wear eye protection and work in a well ventilated area, since molten soldering wire can tend to smoke and produce toxic fumes. Soldering is a key process used in electronics and robotics, with many OEM kit parts such as PCB boards available.

PRO TIPS

Proper heat and power settings on the welder must be set for the specific type of metal you're welding together in order to lay down a nice bead.

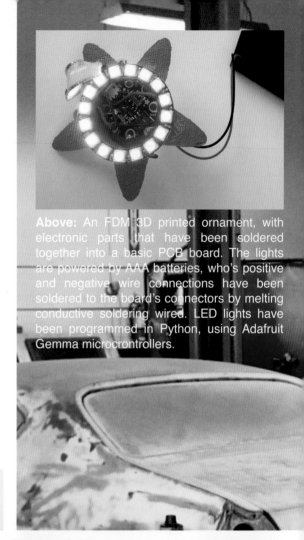

Above: An FDM 3D printed ornament, with electronic parts that have been soldered together into a basic PCB board. The lights are powered by AAA batteries, who's positive and negative wire connections have been soldered to the board's connectors by melting conductive soldering wired. LED lights have been programmed in Python, using Adafruit Gemma microcrontrollers.

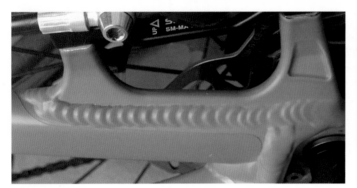

Standard Weld Bead: A typical overlapping TIG weld bead, shown here on an aluminum mountain bike frame. These welded aluminum pieces have been industrial spray painted on an assembly line afterward.

TIG Weld Bead 1: Notice how the aluminum chassis of this Japanese sport bike were first cast into part sections, and then tiled together. The weld lines here are less integrated vs. the example below, making the parting seams much more obvious.

Post-Processed Weld Bead: A TIG weld bead (shown here on titanium) that has been ground down with an angle grinder to clean it up in post.

TIG Weld Bead 2: Notice how the weld lines on this Italian motorbike swingarm have been very carefully designed to accentuate the forms, and to make the seams less noticeable.

Below: A welding setup. The red PVC screen at right — this screen in used to shield other people and machines from sparks, slags, UV light and other potential hazards. Fully hydraulic automotive lifts here are shown, which makes it much easier to get up underneath and wrench on cars.

"

My years inside the Skunk Works, for example, convinced me of the tremendous value of building prototypes. I am a true believer. The beauty of a prototype is that it can be evaluated and its uses clarified before costly investments for large numbers are made.

Ben Rich

ENGINEER / DIRECTOR,
SKUNK WORKS - *SKUNK WORKS: A PERSONAL MEMOIR OF MY YEARS AT LOCKHEED*

Chapter 6 — Advanced Projects

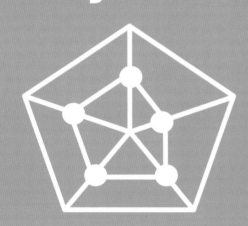

1

SHOP OVERVIEW

2

MACHINES

3

HAND TOOLS

4

MATERIALS

5

APPLICATION

6

ADV. PROJECTS

Kit-Bash Model: Mech Design

DESIGN & BUILD PROCESS

The building process for the kit-bash mech will need to start with a general idea for a mech in mind. Once a silhouette is established, start blocking out the stance with armature wire, kit parts, and hot glue.

Feel free to slice-and-dice the parts as you see fit, since what we're looking for here is an overall shape language. The parts will look Frankensteined in the beginning, but it's important to always keep in mind the silhouette. A general breakdown of kit parts and where they can be used is shown in the diagrams below.

Right: Starting the design process with a quick silhouette sketch done with a brush pen. The design will change quite a bit differently from this original intent, however the blocking of the overall volumetric masses will help guide the design throughout the kit-bash process.

1 Building blocks and styrene build up the inner mass "guts" of the mech.

2 Large surface parts make up the bulk of the outer "skin"

3 Mechanical bits and pieces for functional parts. Kit posts make perfect hydraulics

4 High fidelity/texture information bits. Save these for the end

Parts Breakdown

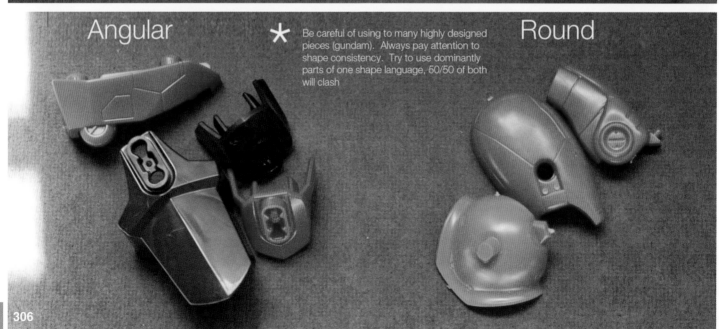

Angular

* Be careful of using to many highly designed pieces (gundam). Always pay attention to shape consistency. Try to use dominantly parts of one shape language, 50/50 of both will clash

Round

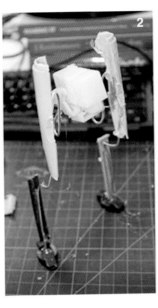

1) Initial armature wire bending and hot gluing of the feet, so the piece can stand on its own.

2) Block-out general mass areas with "filler" parts. Keep in mind these areas will be covered later.

3) Add joints and adjust the stance. Airplane kit fuselages work well for the upper leg portions, having a convex cone shape to cover the armature wire.

4) More details are added at this stage from the model kits. Also, a cut up credit card has been use to as a knee protection plate (styrene can also be used).

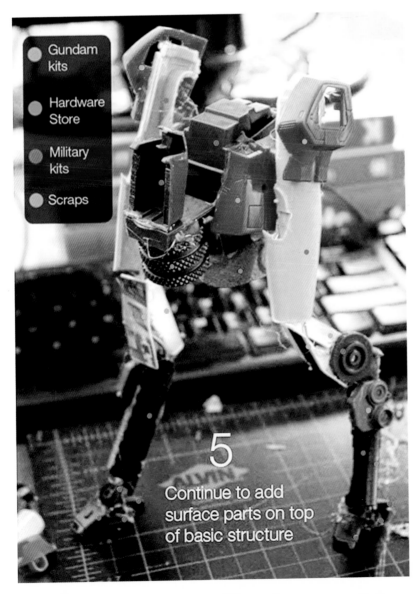

Gundam kits
Hardware Store
Military kits
Scraps

5
Continue to add surface parts on top of basic structure

5) Diagram showing how parts can be found from anywhere. It may look like you've ransacked the spare parts department at your local Fry's Electronics or ACE Hardware in these initial stages. Once a design silhouette is established with bulk parts, glue and an armature skeleton, the model kit parts are then added to give another layer of textural design interest.

Below: Top view of the finished model after a couple of coats of primer. Notice the areas of high detail and areas of simple shapes — or "areas of interest and rest." This is a core principle of a good design. Too much detail everywhere and the design will be too busy, too simple and the design will be dull and boring.

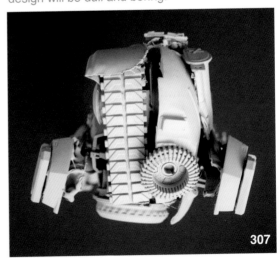

FRONT

Above & Below: Once all of the parts have been glued in place, it will look like a kaleidoscope of different mismatched colors botched together. Don't worry, these parts will all be unified nicely after a coat of primer.

BACK

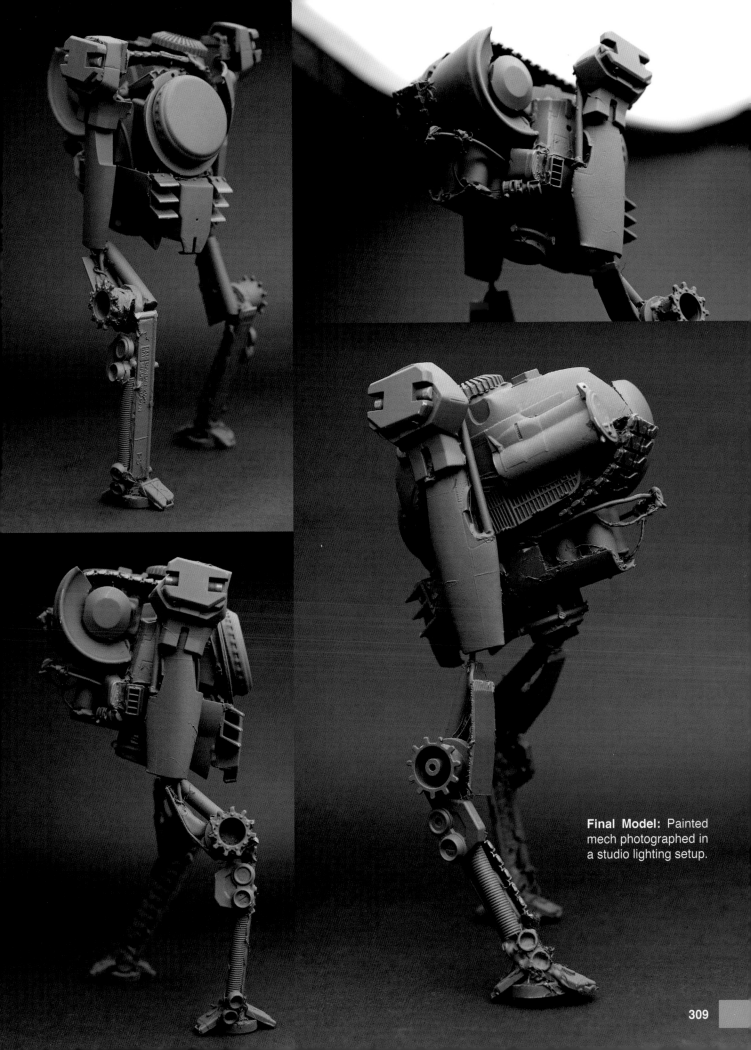

Final Model: Painted mech photographed in a studio lighting setup.

Paint Process: 1) Kit-bashed parts shown ready for primer. For basic cylinder shapes, cut up glue sticks can be used. **2)** Two heavy coats of automotive rattle can primer are applied and allowed to dry for an hour. **3)** A matte O.D. (olive drab) acrylic enamel is applied by rattle can. This coat is allowed to dry overnight. **4)** Final orange color accents are applied with a small paintbrush and acrylic enamel.

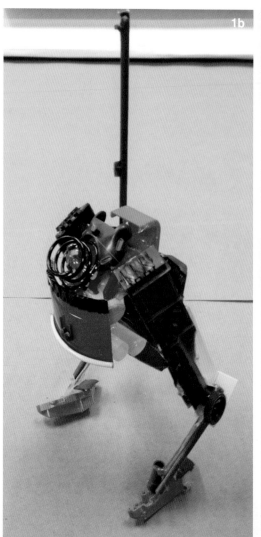

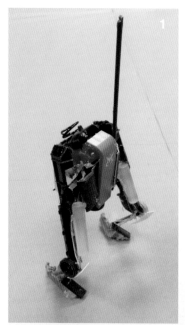

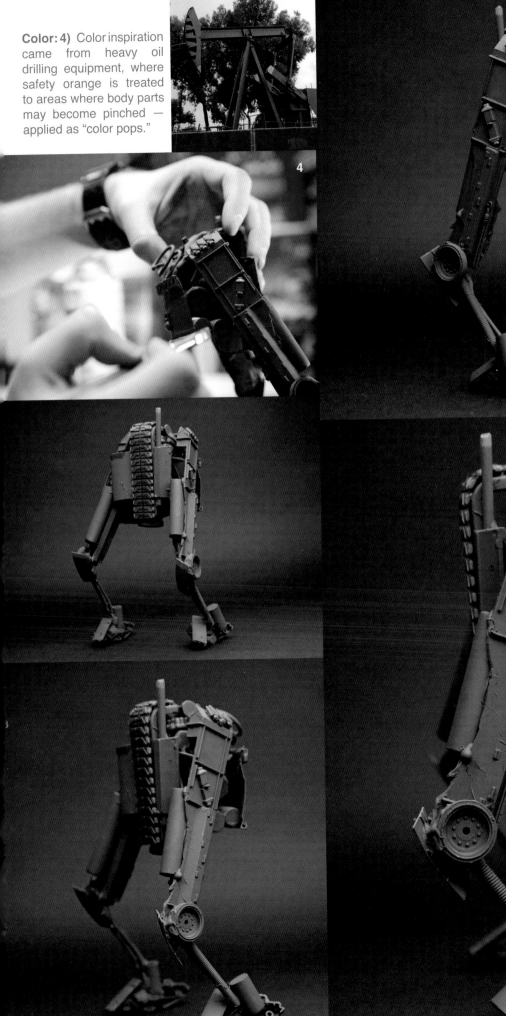

4

Final Model: Painted mech photographed in a studio lighting setup.

Product Design Prototype: Shovel

DESIGN & BUILD PROCESS

Here we will use a children's gardening shovel concept as an example. The building process for this prototype tool begins after the Industrial Design portion has been completed. The design process includes sketching, research, and competitive market analysis. In an R&D office, the prototype model will either be built by the Industrial Designer himself, or will be made by a professional model maker. Both scenarios will follow the same process regardless.

Once the final design sketch is signed off on and is ready for 2D CAD blueprint. This blueprint is a 1:1 orthographic line drawing, showing the key design elements of the shovel — silhouette, proportion, and styling design lines. The goal of model making is to accomplish as closely as possible this original design intent into a 3D volumetric form — which is more difficult than it sounds, since a 2D drawing can be open to many interpretations. Having a tighter design sketch up front can alleviate this problem.

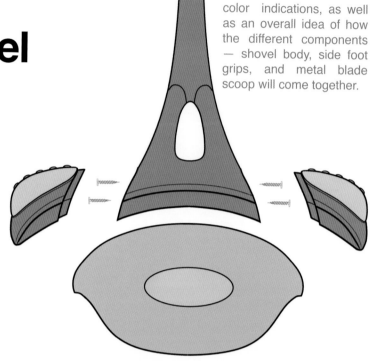

2) Original shovel design sketch with initial material/color indications, as well as an overall idea of how the different components — shovel body, side foot grips, and metal blade scoop will come together.

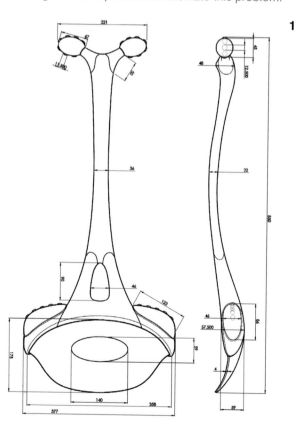

1) Orthographic 1:1 scale line drawing is created in Adobe Illustrator. This draft view drawing will be used as a guide to cut the initial silhouette out of a 10LB foam block.

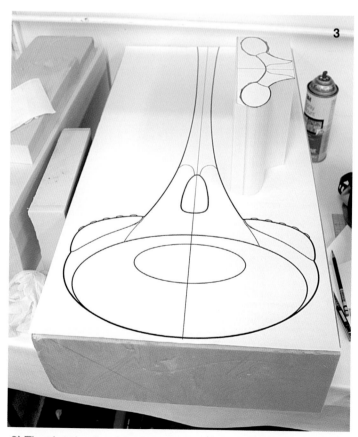

3) The drawing is printed at 100% full size, then adhered to the face of the foam block with spray adhesive. A side draft view is also attached to the side of the block. Notice this block was not large enough, so another smaller piece needed to be epoxied over top, which then is the handle.

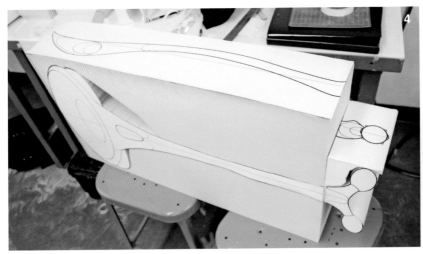

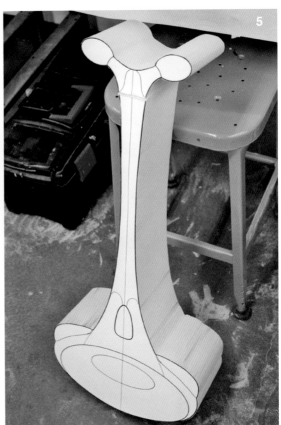

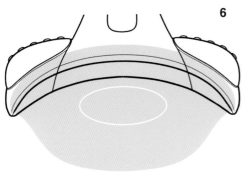

4) Top and side "orthographic" shovel design views are printed on paper at 100% scale and adhered to a large foam block with spray adhesive. **5)** This large block of 10LB tooling foam is then cut on the band saw, to give overall volume, shape, and profile. **6)** Diagram sketch of how the shovel scoop will fit into the main shovel body.

7-8) The pre-cut foam buck is shaved down with a Surform rasp, before finer details are added with files, sanding sticks, sponges, and dental tools. **9)** Grip details are made using a silicone mold, then making urethane resin casted duplicates. **10-11)** Clear plastic bubble scoop shape is made from acrylic on the vacuum former.

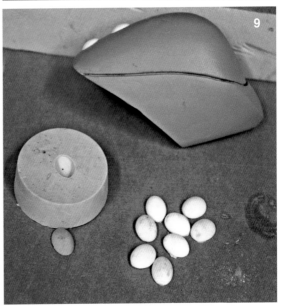

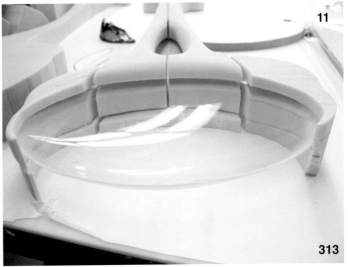

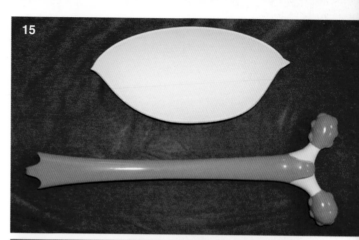

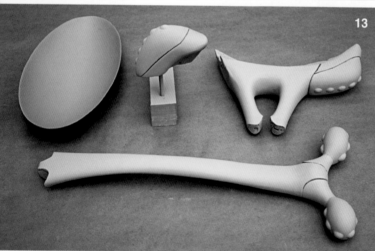

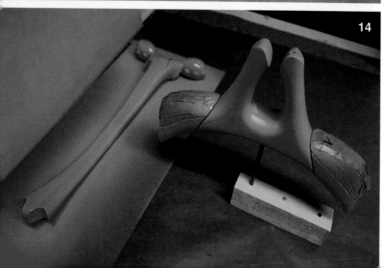

12) Model edges are rounded out using a Surform rasp, then finished with sanding sponges for fine surface control. **13)** Once the design details are locked in, HVLP spray primer is used to seal the pores of the foam before spray paint is added. **14)** Color areas are spray painted with rattle-can paint. Different color areas are masked-off separately with blue painter's tape. **15)** Electro - metalized spray chromed parts added through a separate process. The areas to be chromed were wet sanded and sent to a shop that specializes in spray chroming. **16)** This process is superb to any off the shelf chrome rattle can paint, which creates a dull silver effect. **17)** Clear Plasti-Dip® was applied to shaft portion and handles for grip. The yellow dot is a vinyl decal.

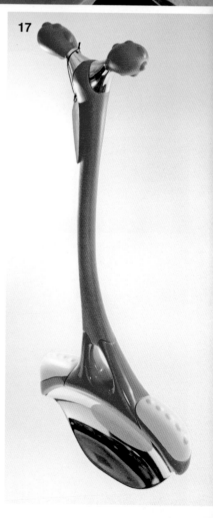

Final Model: While the prototype is not functional, it is a very convincing 'appearance model' of what a real mass produced product would look like — and is used for various photo shoots, etc.

PG. 277

PG. 237

Racing Helmet: Custom Paint & Vinyl Graphics

DESIGN & BUILD PROCESS

Below is the process used to create world champion BMX racer's custom helmet, which was commissioned by his largest sponsor — DEVO Training Academy. The goal of this project was to create a custom piece that would make Jason stand out on the race track. Starting with graphic color and orientation explorations, or 'comps', one final design is selected to take into production. This includes building the design into a scale spec showing all views and how the graphics will wrap around the complex 3D curvature of the helmet. The better and more accurate information you can give to the fabricator behind such a project, the greater likelihood the final results will be more of a success with little being lost in translation.

Several processes were tried, before settling on paint for the final paint work. I've included this to show that sometimes a design or build project doesn't always go completely as planned — which is a fact of life and comes with the territory — so this is where you'll need to learn to roll with the punches and have the grit and determination to see a project through to its full completion.

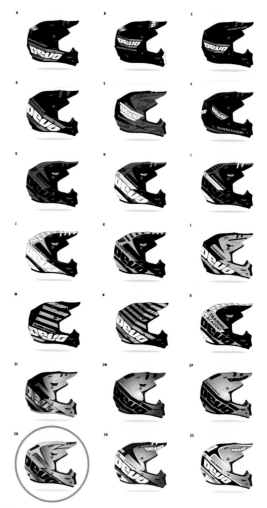

Above: A few rounds of graphic explorations or "comps," ranging from mild-to-wild. The more ideas explored = the more creative and unique the end results. Alphabetical labels were used to easily distinguish the designs, where "2" indicates second round. 2H was selected by the client to move forward into final production.

Above: Building the 2D line drawing (aka '2D CAD') to full scale in Adobe Illustrator, based on the helmet's dimensions.

PRINTED HELMET GRAPHICS : 2H-A

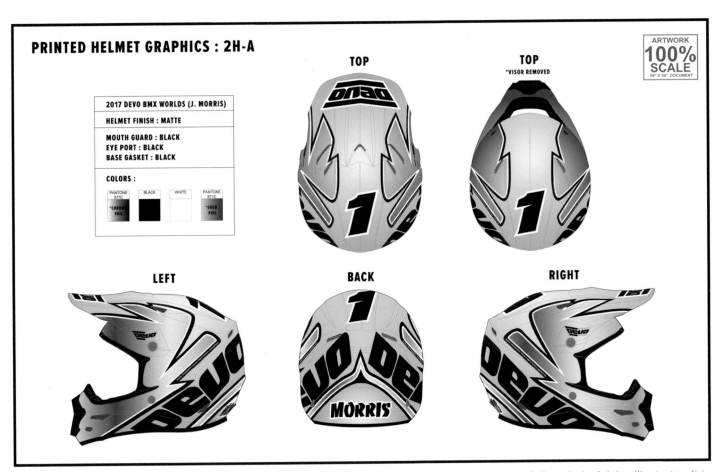

| 2017 DEVO BMX WORLDS (J. MORRIS) |
| HELMET FINISH : MATTE |
| MOUTH GUARD : BLACK
EYE PORT : BLACK
BASE GASKET : BLACK |
| COLORS : |

PANTONE 877C *CHROME FOIL | BLACK | WHITE | PANTONE 871C *GOLD FOIL

TOP

TOP *VISOR REMOVED

LEFT

BACK

RIGHT

Above: An example design spec, where the different helmet views were built at 100%, or 1:1 full scale in Adobe Illustrator. It is important to treat the design spec (or 'tech pack') as a precision-engineered document — working to include as much detail as possible to whoever will actually be building out your design. Critical elements here are a title bar and accurate color descriptions.

JASON MORRIS 2018 SIGNATURE BMX HELMET

Above: The line drawings from the scale spec were then taken into Photoshop, where a medium-fidelity rendering style was applied for presentation to the client. The addition of indicational light, shadow, and metallic effects show much better how the graphics will actually wrap across the 3D surface contours of the helmet, and can save an arm and a leg, as well as valuable time and effort trying to figure that out in real life — by building sample upon sample, and having to learn from mistakes!

Above: The flat 2D pattern coming straight out of a large format vinyl printer / plotter. The pattern has been formatted to fit the 2D dieline for this specific surface geometry of this helmet model, which ensures that it will wrap properly over the surface curvatures. Different helmet models will have different dielines, and dielines will scale up or down depending on the size of the helmet (this is true for any product using a pattern dieline). One-off custom team branding for sports like LaCrosse are made this way.

Above: Vinyl decals applied with a heat gun over a bare white helmet base. Due to the limitations of the vinyl template process, it is difficult to achieve the same level of quality as spray paint. Because of this, production was switched to a custom racing helmet paint shop known for doing professional NASCAR, motocross and funny car racer helmets based out of Southern California. High end mountain bike frame decals are applied using a process known as ink transfer, using an ink transfer tape.

Final custom painted helmet for world-champion Pro BMX racing athlete, Jason Morris. Painting is usually reserved for one-off helmets only, as the process is very labor intensive and costly. Mass produced graphics will usually be made through a process known as hydro-dipping (this is also the same process used to create graphics on video game controllers). Color and graphics designed by Christopher Armstrong, final paint by Beam Designs. Client: DEVO Training Academy.

"

If the Maker Movement causes more parents and grandparents to recognize the pattern of a maker in their children, we will give those children a boost for the future. I also wonder, will the world of work be different for these children? Will they be able to take advantage of their talents and continue developing them over the course of their lives? Will they feel that they are in control of their lives? Will they understand that the world can be hacked, tinkered with, taken apart, and put back together? That is what is means to get hands-on in making the world better.

Dale Dougherty

FOUNDER & CEO,
MAKER MEDIA - *FREE TO MAKE: HOW THE MAKER MOVEMENT IS CHANGING OUR SCHOOLS, OUR JOBS, AND OUR MINDS*

Appendix

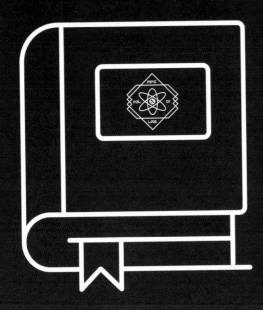

Jobs in the Trade

INDUSTRIAL / PRODUCT DESIGNER (I.D.)

These are the folks who give life to products, and handle innovative new ideas, functionality, ergonomics, and aesthetic appeal of products. The design process includes sketching, research, and competitive market analysis. Responsible for Color, materials and finishes (CMF). While not engineers, industrial designers will oftentimes have an eye for functionality and be mechanically inclined. Heavy involvement in / experience with building proof-of-concept prototypes or appearance models is a must in this profession. Depending on the size of the R&D office, the prototype models will either be built by the industrial designer directly, or will be made by a professional model maker. Both scenarios will follow the same process regardless.

ENTERTAINMENT DESIGNER

These are the visionaries who give life to vehicles, props, characters / creatures, and environments in the world of film, TV, animation, and video games. Entertainment designers will often use sketching and visual communication tools like Photoshop to communicate ideas, which will then be translated into physical props or vehicles by model makers. Many entertainment designers who work on vehicles or spaceships for film will be hired with a background in the transportation design industry.

CONCEPT DESIGNER

A concept designer is an umbrella term for any designer who works with "blue-sky", or ideas in the limitless concept phase. This term used to refer to entertainment designers, before the term came into the fold. Concept design is still a term used to identify designs which have little to no consideration for cost, manufacturability, safety, or engineering — although, sometimes elements will be pulled from these type of concepts and turned into real mass-produced products. Some larger product-based companies will invite their best designers to be a part of their "special projects" or "think tank" innovation teams — which will be tasked specifically for research and development of advanced new materials and technologies to be used 10-15 years in the future.

MODEL MAKER / PROP BUILDER or MASTER

The hidden craftsman and tinkerers of the film & TV industry. Think of professional model makers as similar to "Q" in the James Bond films — they can rig up anything on the fly, and use a slew of hat tricks to cobble together something on-set that might seem like magic to others. Model makers will work hand in hand with entertainment designers, concept designers, and film directors to build the right props to fit the story. The goal of model making is to transform original design intent in 2D form into a 3D volumetric form — which is more difficult than it sounds, since a 2D drawing can be open to many interpretations. Having a tighter design sketch up front can alleviate this problem. This is a high-pressure job where

handling accidents or emergencies such as broken props are a part of everyday life, and come with the territory.

MECHANICAL / HARDWARE DESIGN ENGINEER

Are the brains behind all things mechanical in a product. Functionally driven to the core, will oftentimes have backgrounds as tinkerers in early childhood. Mechanical engineers will often work hand in hand with Industrial / Product designers and electrical engineers to bring new products to life. ME's will handle functional concerns like strength & stress testing /analysis, manufacturability, cost considerations. Much of the staff at a company like Dyson are mechanical design or "hardware" engineers. Creation of functional prototypes and/or proof-of-concepts is common.

TOY DESIGNER / SCULPTOR

One of the oldest maker professions. Toy design still uses classic production methods like clay sculpting (by hand) and RTV silicone mold making. Toy designers themselves may also come from a background in entertainment or concept design — where sketching and visualization of concepts are a must.

TRANSPORTATION / AUTOMOTIVE DESIGNER

Planes, trains, and automobiles! These designers fall within the umbrella of industrial design, although under a special category which deals with objects that move vs. ones that are static — i.e. boats, bicycles, motorcycles, roller coasters, scooters, monorails, various watercraft, aerial drones, etc. Oftentimes transportation designers will be tasked with designing the outside exterior of a car or airplane — while it's up to mechanical engineers and electrical engineers to focus on the structural chassis, internal guts, engine, that will ultimately propel it forward. It's common for transportation designers to work side-by-side with automotive clay sculptors, who will bring their designs to life at full 1:1 scale for internal corporate review. Automotive interior designer is another specialized trade all in itself, which is responsible for hand-selecting the interior fabric, trims, and color details that can really heighten a driver's experience within the car. Typically these professionals will have a background in product design or interior design.

AUTOMOTIVE CLAY SCULPTOR

These professionals are true elite craftsmen. They are tasked with taking a sketch in raw idea form, and translating it into the surface body design of the car. Much of the car design process is being done in 3D CAD software nowadays, although highly skilled clay sculptors are still a heavily entrenched part of the automotive design world — and are likely here to stay.

3D CAD MODELER or TECHNICIAN

The computer wizards that turn a designer's vision into reality. Many industrial designers will have experience with 3d modeling software packages as well, however specialists in the field have their place in many applications — freeing up designers to do more of the creative work involved in coming up with new ideas. These specialists will also have a wide variety of experience using different CAD packages, including best practices for preparing part files for rapid prototyping and/or manufacturing.

COSTUME DESIGNER / FASHION DESIGNER

Typically these professionals will have a background in fashion design with thorough knowledge of the cut & sew production process, but not always. More and more, entertainment designers are fulfilling the role of costume design within film, TV & video games — which is closely tied to character design.

INTERIOR DESIGNER / RETAIL DESIGNER & MERCHANDIZER

Designs the interior look & feel, and functional layout of a building, home or office space — sometimes referred to as the "ambience" or "Feng-Shui." Interior designers can also be skilled in retail store fixture design, and highly creative merchandizing displays (often known as Point of Purchase) that drive interest, interaction, and heighten the overall in-store buying experience. Sometimes these professionals may have an educational background in fashion merchandising.

EXHIBITION or ENVIRONMENTAL DESIGNER

These professionals will design environments for trade shows, outdoor festivals, large display exhibits for conventions, etc. Similar to interior design, with the difference being that exhibit designers focus more on interactive environmental experiences — which are often times temporary installations (i.e. Museum, trade show display booths, event exhibits).

PRODUCT DEVELOPER (AKA. DEVELOPMENT ENGINEER)

Product developers will work side-by-side with designers to turn their ideas in raw sketch form or renderings into real products. Will have vast experience in manufacturing, and will travel overseas often to communicate with production partners. Will also handle scheduling and product management concerns, as well as cost considerations.

MATERIALS SCIENTIST or RESEARCHER

These research scientists will be primarily tasked to develop advanced materials for big chemical suppliers such as 3M, Corning or Dupont, which can then be licensed for applications in aerospace, architectural construction, transportation, or consumer goods manufacturing. Will often have a background education in chemical engineering or physics. Large firms like Nike or Apple may have a dedicated R&D team specifically tailored to allow the company to create new and unique materials and / or processes, which can then be protected by trademark or patents and used in new & upcoming products.

INDUSTRIAL or MANUFACTURING ENGINEER

A trade focused primarily on the development of sohisticated mass production machinery, and its use in assembly line optimization. Often includes factory automation and robotics.

THEME PARK DESIGNER / IMAGINEER / BUILDER

A dream job for many! Coming up with the fun, themed rides we all know and love. Often with a wide variety of the experience combining mechanical engineering, architecture, illustration or entertainment design. Will work side by side with model shop production crews or prop departments. Disneyland has hundreds of such designers and builders on staff, at each one of their popular park locations.

SET DESIGNER or BUILDER

Build sets for plays, opera, theater, indie performances, indie films, etc. A great way to get started in a field that involves building things, many of people from this profession may move into interior design, architecture or environmental design.

INDUSTRIAL SPRAY PAINTER

Yes, there are jobs just for professionals who spray paint for a living! Large custom-paint shops like Trek Bikes' 'Project One' and Troy Lee Designs (TLD) have many full-time pro spray painters on staff — to paint everything from custom bicycle frames to helmets for sponsored athletes. While robotic arms are common for mass assembly-line paint applications for automotive manufacturing, pro painters still have a place for small batch production or one-off custom paint work.

MACHINIST or METALWORKER

This title refers to the folks who use lathes, mills, and CNC mills to fabricate high-precision parts primarily out of metal. Machining, when done well, is an art form — just look at the machined titanium / carbon fiber jewelry from the company Rogue DZN (founded by a former Oakley watch designer), or the futuristic machined art sculptures by Chris Bathgate!

SHOP TECHNICIAN or MANAGER

Shop techs are tasked to maintain the machines in the shop. They will handle all service, maintenance & repair work as needed, and will make sure all machines are up and running — from CNC mills to 3d printers, to table saws and everything in between. They will also help to ensure safety best practices of shop members / staff. Shop techs will typically have a wide range of knowledge and be versed on the many different machine types — mostly what NOT to do, or how NOT to break them!

PROP DEPARTMENT ASSISTANT

This assistant will handle the logistics of all incoming and outgoing props for a film production set. A good place to get your foot in the door in the model making industry.

ROBOTICS DESIGNER or ENGINEER

Professionals who primarily focus on automation and robotics in any capacity. Often designs and maintain robotic machines on a assembly line (ie.Kuka or Fanuc industrial arms on an assembly line, or experiemental bots used by DARPA or other R&D firms.

ARCHITECT

Architects often work with sketching, drafting, AutoCAD, Revitt, or Google Sketchup for quick design mock-ups. When working with tall buildings or those with unique constructions, an architect will work with a structural or civil / construction engineer, who often runs an anaylsis on the viability of the structure before it can be built. Architects work with floorplans and plan drawings, and make sure that buildings are built to code and follow all local, state, and national regulations.

PROJECT / PRODUCT MANAGER (PM)

Handles all organizing, scheduling and execution of a project, typically using spreadsheets and other PM tools. This is an important role, since creative endeavors can be quite chaotic.

DESIGN MANAGER

Like a project manager, but will manage an entire design team. Works side-by-side with design director or VP of design.

CIVIL or CONSTRUCTION ENGINEER

Overlaps with a structural engineer, often focusing on large construction and building projects, such as tunnels, airports, bridges, and skyscrapers; making sure they meet cerfification.

PACKAGING DESIGNER

Yes, there is such a thing as a packaging designer. Often stems from a background in industrial design, it is a packaging designer's job to dress up the first consumer touchpoint of a product, which is its protective box. Since the packaging can heighten the "reveal" and the experience of owning a product (see: YouTube unboxing videos), much attention is often paid to unique or creative packaging, beyond just protecting the contents inside (the primary job of packaging) . Can be constructed from cardboard, acrylic, vacuum cast plastic, or any number of materials. Packaging design is to what a book cover is to a book — and say what you will, people do judge these details and the level of care taken to making them sing! Also inlcudes add-on features such as product hang tags, manuals, etc. Structural designer often has an engineering backgroung, aesthetics will come from an I.D. background.

CMF DESIGNER

Colors, materials, and finishes. Often comes from a fashion or an I.D. background. These touches can make a big difference in the overall tactile and visual experience of a product, so this has become a highly specialized profession in it's own right. At larger firms, CMF designers will work side-by-side with product designers or interior designers (such as in a luxury jet-liner or yacht design application).

URBAN PLANNING DESIGNER

A trade responsible for designing large scale infrastructural projects for cities and towns to develop, preserve, and enhance the built environmnent — including subway stations, outdoor shopping malls and civic arenas, etc. Interacts with architects, landscape architects and civil engineers.

ELECTRICAL or ELECTRONICS ENGINEER

An engineer that designs novel electronic systems or components. Often works with the internal wiring of a product or device not seen by the naked eye — such as computer motherboards, PCB boards, CPU's and computer chips, electrical wiring, and batteries or reusable energy that power many of the devices that we take for granted every single day (i.e. smart phones, electric bikes, electric or e-scooters).

PROSTHETICS DESIGNER / ARTIST

Responsible for creating functional, surgical, and reconstructive prosthetics, as well as disguishes for some spy bureaus (á la real life *Mission Impossible*), and finally for SFX in film and TV. Often has a background and / or training mechanical engineering, I.D., or makeup art. Artists will work with lifecasting techniques, using alginate molds to create life-like foam latex or silicone castings with realistic painted skin effects. Artificial aging is often done this way, including Marlon Brando's famous jaw prosthesis in The Godfather.

SEAMSTRESS / SEWING MACHINE OPERATOR / PATTERN MAKER

Sewing of everyday garments and products is still done largely by hand and by humans — believe it or not. Seamstresses are highly skilled technical craftspeople, especially where designs can be quite complex such as technical cut & sew design. A pattern maker is a highly skilled trade in itself, requiring a specialty craftsperson who will work closely with designers and developers to create accurate 2D patterns to which will then translate into 3D volumes — where fit, form and function fit are very important. A few milimeter-adjustments here and there to the patterns can make a huge difference.

FREELANCER / CONTRACT CONSULTANT

Depending on the project scope, some designers will often be hired on a project by project, or contract basis (freelance).

UI & UX / INTERACTION DESIGNER

User interface and user experience designer. Demand for this profession is raidly becoming more sought after, as the switch to digital and online shopping becomes more and more popular. Designs the visual flow, sequence, and interactive animations behind a digital interface. Often has a background in graphic design, industrial design, or software development.

ART DIRECTOR or DESIGN DIRECTOR

Directs a design team, usually staffed with designers, engineers, and product managers. Larger companies will have separate design / art directors per each division.

CREATIVE DIRECTOR

Responsible for managing the visual and stylistic brand messaging direction, or simply "creative." Works with a team of web, graphic, print, film and photography designers. The creative department typically handles all advertising and marketing consumer touchpoints, including everything from ad photography, to catalog layout, to packaging, film, social media, film and promotional video content, etc.

JUNIOR or MID-LEVEL DESIGNER / ENGINEER
Someone just entering the workforce with little or no experience in an industry is known as a junior. Mid-level refers to someone above a junior but below senior level.

SENIOR DESIGNER / ENGINEER
The title of senior is reserved for a professional who has a few years of experience under his or her belt, with a proven track record and ability to get results. A senior person will often serve as a mentor for junior and mid-level staff in an office.

STAGE DESIGNER or SET BUILDER
Responsible for building the stages and / or sets for theater, plays, stage shows, broadway musicals, film, and music videos. Will work closely with environmental designers, interior designers, or concept / entertainment designers. Often will have a background in model making, carpentry or architectural design / build projects.

SPECIAL EFFECTS / PRODUCTION SUPERVISOR
Oversees a cross-collaborative team of practical effects artists, model makers, and craftspeople. Often promoted from a track record of working on successful film projects.

TECHNICAL / SPORTSWEAR DESIGNER
A designer who specializes in cut & sew and soft goods, which is a combination of fit, function, fashion and style. Often has a background in industrial design, fashion, apparel development & manufacturing, or all of the above.

FOOTWEAR DESIGNER
Like a soft goods designer, except specializes specifically in footwear. Footwear design and development itself can be quite sophisticated within it's own vertical product category — requiring a finely tuned eye for certain features, details or nuances that will make the product successful in the marketplace. Involves trend research, sketching & mock-ups.

ARCHITECTURAL VISUALIZATION (ARCH VIZ)
This field is becoming more and more important as high-end build & development projects are becoming more in-demand. Creates convincing, often photo-real renderings or 3D visualizations of what the space will look like when completed — often in 3D CAD software and Adobe Photoshop.

EXECUTIVE PRODUCER
Producers are to film what investors are to businesses. These are the folks who front the production capital (at their own risk) to finance a project and see it to life — in hopes of reaping the rewards of a successful film at the box office.

CHIEF DESIGNER or VP / HEAD OF DESIGN
Just like in a tribe, the chief is the head honcho on the team and has the final word in all decision-making. Typically promoted to such position from a proven track record of producing results for the organization and the ability to lead & manage a team. Involved in all high-level decisions, working closely with all senior, mid-level, and junior designers / engineers on staff.

DESIGN ENGINEER or PROJECT ENGINEER
A title used at some companies such as Dyson, to describe a holistic integration of both design and engineering disciplines — as opposed to being independent from one another. Keep in mind that terminology will change from firm to firm.

CARPENTER or WOODWORKER
A specialized trade revolving around working with wood as a building material. Involves a high degree of craftsmanship.

INDUSTRIAL WELDER or FABRICATOR
A great welder is worth his or her weight in gold. Applications range from aerospace, automotive, commercial, defense, etc.

FURNITURE DESIGNER
A designer specializing in the design of furniture. The power couple / design duo, Charles and Ray Eames, are perhaps two of the most famous furniture designers in history — although their broad title would be industrial designer.

SUPPLY CHAIN MANAGER
Will manage all of the incoming and outgoing logistics behind all of the independent links in a supply chain. At larger companies, which produce many different types and variations of product styles (SKU's), the task of managing these logistics can become quite combersome.

LEAD DESIGNER / ENGINEER
A leader on a specific project, usually promoted from within a company because of a track record of proven results.

DESIGN or ENGINEERING INTERN
Similar to junior-level in terms of experience, but often a temp.

FUTURIST or VISUAL FUTURIST
Buckminster Fuller, Syd Mead, and other visionaries who don't fit into a traditional category are referred to by this label.

SOURCING SPECIALIST / MANAGER
This professional will have a wide range of experience working with different suppliers and supply chain networks.

QC SPECIALIST or MANAGER
Quality control specialist, responsible for ensuring that the products are free of defects or quality issues.

PRODUCTION DESIGNER
An open-ended title used in the film and SFX industry to describe a designer who works on a film set or production.

SPECIAL EFFECTS TECHNICIAN
Works closely with production designers and production managers on a film project. Similar to a model maker combined with a mechanic. More of a support staff role.

PATTERN MAKER
Creates 2D flat patterns for cut & sew applications, such as apparel, bags and backpacks, footwear, etc. Accurate patterns are very important for establishing the proper fit & function of a design.

R&D Terminology

ABRADE or ABRASION RESISTANCE
The scratching off of a material's surface coating. Material scientists often assign a resistance rating to some coatings.

ABS
Acrylonitrile butadiene styrene. A plastic that's stronger PVC.

ACCELERATOR (CHEMICAL)
An accelerator is a compound or substance that is added into a chemical mixture to speed up the catalyzation process. For example, baking soda is an accelerator for CA superglue.

A-CLASS SURFACE
An A-Class surface is a term used primarily in automotive design, to describe the highest caliber surface qualiy of a 3D design surface, without any lumps, depressions, or waves that could impede de-molding or cause mold breakdown in production. A-Class surfaces will result in much longer lifespan of mold tooling, dies, or sheet metal bending / forming jigs.

ACTUATOR
In robotics, a device that creates a mechanical action.

ADDITIVE
Dyes, fillers, pigments, accelerators or other compounds that are added to enhance certain chemical or physical properties.

ADDITIVE MANUFACTURING
Made by "growing" a part from a base, powder, or liquid vat of material, such as in 3D Printing, where a layers are 'added' on top of each another layer by layer to create a final part.

ADVANCED R&D or SPECIAL PROJECTS
A special division within a company, tasked with developing new or experimental designs (often with its own budget).

AESTHETIC or NON-FUNCTIONAL PROTOTYPE ("LOOK & FEEL")
A prototype that doesn't perform its intended function, but is built rather to assess the visual styling or tactile qualities of a design — including its size, weight, and shape — and may often be made from the same, or similar color and materials as the final design intent. Built alongside or in parallel with a functional prototype, as both will serve two different purposes.

ALLOY
A lower-quality metal mixed with a more valuable one. Coins are often alloys.

ALONG THE BIAS
Orienting woven fiber strands along the "bias" or surface slope of a feature or part, mostly in carbon fiber layup.

A PILLAR / B PILLAR / C PILLAR / GREENHOUSE
Names used to describe the upper architecture of a car, where the greenhouse or "glass dome" is held together by pillars.

APPLIQUÉ
Ornamental needlework in which pieces of a patch of fabric are sewn or attached to a larger piece or garment. This technique can be achieved either by hand or machine stitching.

ARCHITECTURAL HANDWRITING
All caps handwriting is typically referred to architectural handwriting. Pay attention to the quality of your handwriting — as it will pay dividends in your design sketching ability!

ARDUINO / RASBERRY PI
A electronics kit that's become popular in device and robotics programming. Created by an Italian industrial designer rather than by an engineer, with an emphasis on ease of use.

ASSEMBLY or ASSEMBLIES
When two or more separate components are joined together. 3D CAD files are often built as assemblies.

ASSEMBLY LINE
The division of labor into specialized tasks, which are arranged on an efficient line. First pioneered by Henry Ford in 1913.

AUTOMATION
Automating a machine process in order to maximize its production efficiency, often requiring little human involvement.

BAR TACK
A high density zig-zag stitch, used as a strong reinforcement or where heavy loads will be applied (i.e. backpack straps).

BASE COAT
Also known as the color coat, followed by the top (clear) coat.

BESPOKE
Exclusive, ultra limited, tailor-made, or made to order.

BLOW MOLDING
The process used to make plastic soda bottles. A machine extrudes a hollow tube of molten plastic between two mold halves, then after the mold closes, a needle pumps air into the tube and forces the plastic to follow the shape of the mold. Parts can either be made from ridged plastic or elastic TPU.

BOM
Build of materials. Outlines the exact material composition of

a product, similar to the ingredients list of a recipe. A BOM will itemize every single material and component used to construct a product, right down to where it is sourced from and the exact quantity or volume used (essential for costing).

BONE LINE
A surace line that sticks prominently above a surface.

BORING
Cutting out a hole in a part.

BOSS or BOSSES
In injection molded part housing construction, bosses create contact points where an assembled product can be fastened together, and also give structural strengh to hollow parts. Oten threaded to allow for screws to join two part halves together.

BOTTLENECK
An engineering, development or production choke point that will suffocate the forward progress of a system or procedure.

BILLET or BLANK
A solid block or cylinder of material (i.e. aluminum, clay, steel, plastic) — usually how it arrives in raw / bulk form, before being processed by machining, stamping, sculpting, welding, forging, cutting, etc. A billet is similar to a blank or an ingot.

BLIND SEAM
A seam that is folded into itself, hiding the stitching from sight.

BLUE FOAM or STYROFOAM
Polyester styrene "insulation foam," which is commonly used in design to create the internal bulk volume for a buck.

BLUE SKY
Meaning "the sky's the limit," where budget and/or manufacturing constraints, limitations or restrictions are non-existant. Constraints are a practical reality of bringing a product to market profitably, but can tend to stifle radical design thinking. Entertainment and concept design are perfect examples of blue sky thinking — where gadgets, vehicles or architectural designs seen on film give more focus on cool factor and less on to how they actually be made or how they will function (structurally or mechanically) in the real world. These are the types of projects every designer dreams of!

BUCK
A buck is the majority or underlying bulk volume of a design.

BRAINSTORMING
A creative problem solving process that involves tossing out every idea or sketch that comes to mind, starting as free and wide range as possible, in an effort to arrive at novel solutions.

BREADBOARD
A type of prototype used in electronics / electrical engineering.

BUILT TO SCALE (1:1, 1:4, 1:10, ETC.)
Building to a precise smaller or larger scale, usually in early concept stage. Small items can typically be built at 1:1, or 100% scale, whereas larger items will need to be scaled down while still retaining relational proportions. (1:1 = 100%, 1:2 = 50%, 1:4 = 25%, 1:10 = 10%, 1:100 = 1% and so on).

CAD
Computer aided design. Typically refers to 3D design models, however in apparel and footwear, 2D vectorized designs created in Illustrator are also often referred to as "CAD's."

CAM
Computer aided manufacturing. Rather than how a part is shaped or how its assemblies fit together (CAD), CAM is useful for evaluating a manufacturing process such as machining, before a physical part is ever committed to. CNC toolpaths and CFD flow simulations are common uses of CAM.

CANDY COAT or PEARL COAT
A pearelescent paint coat applied over a base color coat, which derives its name because the visual effect of a candy coat is similar to a wet or carmelized "candy apple" look. Commonly seen on hot rods to make the car body surfaces shimmer under sunlight, giving that little bit "extra." "Hot Rod Red" is a popular automotive candy coat. Some Rolls Royce cars have up to 23 layers of paint, totalling 100lbs just in coat!

CASE STUDY
A study tracking the beginning to end project or "case" — from inception to final outcome, as well as any processes, procedures and lessons observed or learned along the way. Case studies are commonly used in the business world, however design case studies make for strong portfolio pieces.

CATALYST or ACTIVATOR
A catalyst is a liquid or chemical compound that causes a liquid or paste-like material to catalyze or "cure" into solid form after it is added or mixed in proper ratio. MEKP is a common catalyst for epoxy resin, as used in fiberglass composites.

CATEGORY KILLER or CATEGORY KING
A leader in a category or specific market / industry vertical. This phrase is similar to "killer app."

CFD ("FLOW SIMULATION") / FEA
Computational fluid dynamics (CFD), also known as "flow simulation" is software used to test aerodynamic airflow, liquid flow for injection molding, or air flow for air conditioning & heating, etc. in the computer. Finite Element Analysis (FEA) simulation software is used to "stress test" or analyze the structural and / or thermal properties of a part or component.

CHARACTER LINE or DESIGN LINE
In styling or "surfacing" — a line that defines the shape, flow, and direction of a product / vehicle design and gives a strong "character." Typically, character lines are designed in a way that accentuates certain elements and to keep the eye moving or flowing around a design. The most important line is known in the automotive industry as the "principal line," and can create the attitude or the emotion of car (what the Italians are well known for).

CLEAR COAT or LACQUER COAT
Final protective coating that is applied over a paint coat, which adds an extra layer of protection from scratches, handling, and wear from outdoor elements and to prolong paint life. Rolls Royce applies two clear coats on every one of their cars.

CLOSED CELL FOAM
Foam with pores that are closed and encapsulated. EVA shoe midsoles and foam gym / yoga mats are closed cell foam.

CMF (COLOR MATERIALS & FINISHES)
The full range of color, materials and finishes of a product, specified in minute detail. CMF has the ability to make or break a product, and has turned into a specialized discipline.

COGS
Cost of goods sold, which includes all of the necessary expenses to produce, ship, advertise and sell a product.

COLD CASTING
Casting a liquid 2-part thermosetting resin with ground metal powders or lead shot, in order to give cast parts the additional feel and weight of their molten or "hot" cast metal counterpart.

COLOR BLOCK or BLOCKING / COLOR POP
In color design, solid graphic areas are known as color blocks. Co-ordinating these blocks is known as "color blocking."

COLOR DAM
A raised ridge and / or groove in a mold to stop the flow of rubber. Color dams will cleanly divide all the colors on a part.

COLOR MIGRATION
When a color unintentionally migrates or seeps into other areas of a part or garment, sometimes due to a defective or improper process / application. Also known as "color bleed."

COLOR-WAY (COLORWAY)
Refers to the unique color combination of a product or design. One product may have multiple different color-ways, each requiring it's own SKU or part number for inventory purposes.

CO-MOLD or OVERMOLD
The process of shooting to separate molten materials into the same mold is known as a co-mold (i.e. tootbrush handle grip).

COMPOUND or COMPOUNDING
Mixture or recipe of chemical ingredients in a rubber formula.

COMPOSITE
A hybrid material composed of two or more different materials (i.e. epoxy resin + fiberglass). Aka composite plastics.

COMPUTER STITCH
Stitched by precision CNC, rather than by a human operator.

CONCEPT CAR
A design concept put together by an automotive studio's in-house design & engineering team, which serves several purposes: 1) pushing the envelope of current trends and technologies, 2) inspiring futuristic visions into possible directions the brand could head towards, and 3) to keep things fresh and engaging for the company as a whole — which could get very stale if the business is only focused on profit and loss each quarter. Concept cars are often built as one-off prototypes out of clay, that are painted to look like real production cars. Concept cars which have no engine and must to be towed to a location are known as "runners." Prototypes that have an engine and can drive are known as "drivers." If a concept is extremely well received by the public, sometimes an automotive manufacturer will turn the concept into a production car (i.e. the BMW i8 and i3 are two examples, designed by former chief exterior designer Richard Kim).

CONTRACT MANUFACTURER
Many, if not most manufacturers today are contractual based — meaning that they are not owned by any one brand or parent organization, but are contracted out to fulfill a specific order. One factory often works with multiple brands at a time.

CONTROL DRAWING or ENGINEERING DRAWING
Similar to a blueprint, a control or engineering drawing is a technical document consisting of precise line drawings. Primarily used in electrical or mechanical engineering to communicate the inner workings of a prototype part.

COO / COUNTRY OF ORIGIN
Refers to the origin in which the product or goods originate. This is often required by law as part of the product care label.

COOLING FLUID
Machining or millng metal produces a tremendous amount of frictional heat, which puts undue stress on the tool or cutting bit and can cause expensive breakage to the tool and / or mold. To reduce this amount of heat, a special lubricating fluid is sprayed onto the parts during the cutting procedure.

COPYRIGHT
Protects any work in "copy" or in print, wherein the rights holder is granted ownership or "rights" to the work for a certain number of years, which will vary by country or region.

COSTING / COST ENGINEERING
The process of engineering parts in the most efficient and cost effective way possible. Costing can also refer to the process of negotiating individual material / part costs with suppliers (per the BOM's), which can be an extremely tedious process if many separate factory & supplier components are involved.

CRADLE TO GRAVE or PRODUCT LIFE CYCLE
A sustainabiliy practice of tracking the resources used in the production of a product, and the decision whether to re-use or repair, or to disposal of (i.e. the landfill would be the "grave").

CROSS-COLLABORATION
Multi-disciplinary teams working together across departments.

CROSS SECTION
Shows the internal volume, material composition, and / or 3D

surface contours sliced through a given object. Cross sections are often included in design specs and / or blueprints, to show additional pieces of supportive information that can be used to clarify the design intent. Cross sections are also often used in sketches to communicate three-dimensionality of an object.

CURING TIME
The time it takes for a 2-part material to "set up" or cure — typically refers to RTV silicone, urethane resin, or epoxy glue.

CUTTING LOSS
Amount of waste material that is lost due to cutting procedure.

CUTTING STEEL or "TOOLING UP"
Slang terms used for the machining of steel mold tooling.

CUTTING YIELD or MATERIAL CONSUMPTION
Refers to the amount of waste material yielded by a particular pattern design, where the parts are arranged like Tetris pieces on a sheet of fabric or leather hide, in order to minimize cutting loss in an effort to reduce costs and waste. Smaller / simple patterns = high yield. Larger / complex patterns = low yield.

DART
In cut and sew, a triangular-shaped cutout in a piece of fabric, allowing it to bend into a 3D curvature when stitched together.

DE-BOSSED
Sunken or lowered surface element or detail (valley).

DEBURRING or DEFLASHING
Removing of excess flashing material from a casted, injection molded or layup part — commonly at parting line or where the two (or more) mold halves come together.

DECO STITCH
Decorative stitch — a non-functional, aesthetic finish detail.

DEFECT / DEFECTIVE
The part was produced with an unintended error. Having a strong QC system in place is important to minimizing errors.

DE-LAM or DE-LAMINATION
A weak or improper bond between two material surfaces causes them to de-laminate.

DELIVERABLES
A full set of items clearly outlining exactly what will be delivered as part of a project. Typically prepared in the project brief.

DELRIN®
The trade name for Polyoxymethylene (POM), a type of engineering thermoplastic developed by DuPont, and similar to PP. Commonly used in injection molding applications, where small plastic pellets are melted down and then "shot" into a steel mold cavity at high pressure. Widely used in the consumer electronics and automotive industry. Also known as acetal or polyacetal. Can be re-melted and re-used.

DENIER / THREAD COUNT
Measurement of linear mass density, or the weight of a given length of fiber. Essentially this translates into the density of a fabric weave material.

DESIGN AESTHETICS (AKA STYLING)
The emotional look & feel appeal of a given design.

DESIGN BRIEF / PROJECT BRIEF
An onboarding document prepared at the beginning of a new project, to give a brief synopsis of the project's goals and expected outcomes — including deliverables and timeline.

DESIGN DNA
The DNA of a design is just like the genome of an organic species, effectively encapsulating the entire philosophy and personality of a design. One of the rarely known secrets of design is that a brand's logo is a distillation of its DNA — which ultimately translates itself into the product or automobile design. As a result, brands will often change or modernize their logo after the old one gets stale, or becomes synonymous with a tarnished reputation. Alternatively, a company might create an independent or offshoot logo to represent a new sub-category within the parent brand, instead of engaging in a entire brand re-design and / or costly overhaul. A design's form langauge, branding, and aesthetic / functional elements all combine together to form what's known as the DNA.

DESIGN FOR MANUFACTURING (DFM) or PRODUCTION-READY
When a product is designed in a way so that it can actually be made in a mass production setting. This is something many first time inventors don't think about until it's too late.

DESIGN ITERATION
A unit of variation, sometimes major, sometimes minor, used to explore either the look & feel, or the function of a design (or both). The typical design process is one of refinement, or a process of elimination — whereby many iterations are explored upon in order to arrive at one or two final design outcomes. The best approach is to start out wide, tossing out many ideas, then to narrow down the selections over time.

DESIGN PATENT or ORNAMENTAL PATENT
Unlike a functional patent (harder to obtain) a design patent protects an aesthetic or ornamental styling element only.

DESIGN REFINEMENT
Refers to the process of elimination, using design iterations to arrive at a final refined, polished, and massaged outcome.

DESIGN RENDERING or VISUALIZATION
A more polished version of a sketch, including more realistic highlights, shading, and reflections for presentation purposes.

DESIGN SKETCH
A quick and dirty drawing for the purpose of visually communicating a design's intent (both form and function).

DESIGN "SPRINT" / PROJECT "SPRINT"
The typical Hollywood blockbuster film model of assembling a team (usually contractors) to come together for a short burst of concerted effort; similar to running a sprint vs. a marathon.

DEVELOPMENT TIMELINE
A schedule which tracks the development of a project from beginning to end, sometimes to meet a seasonal release.

DIE CAST / PRESSURE DIE CAST
Hot or molten material (usually metal) cast into a "die" mold.

DIE CUTTING / DIE STAMPING
Using a sharp steel cutting die, which looks just like a cookie cutter, to cut out a pre-defined pattern from a flat sheet of metal or fabric. A production run of soft goods products will require dozens, if not hundreds of different cutting dies — scaled up or down per product size. Every part of the product needs its own die. Sheet metal car body panels are die stamped.

DIE-LINE / TEMPLATE
Most commonly used in packaging and folded cardboard or paperboard boxes, as well as in cut and sew design and development. Anything where a printed pattern must be properly aligned, including sublimation printed graphic kits for the sport of motocross and mountain bike racing. A template is any pre-defined shape or individual 2D pattern, where the die-line serves as the outline around where it will be cut.

DIGI-KEY
A well known USA electronic components catalog / supplier.

DUAL SOURCING
Sourcing the different parts or material from two or more separate suppliers, in order to "fill in the gaps" based on each supplier's core competencies. If you live in California and have ever had to make a grocery stop at both Ralph's and Trader Joe's in one trip — you know exactly what dual sourcing is all about! Dual sourcing is also used for insurance, or to ensure redundancies against material shortages, quality issues, or that all of your eggs aren't placed in one basket — which can expose a project to vulnerabilities if complications arise.

DUROMETER or SHORE HARDNESS
A unit of measurement used to determine the density of a solid plastic or rubber material. Density is measured in pounds per square foot. The two primary measures of durometer are Shore A and Shore D. Shore A is for softer rubbers, and Shore D for harder plastics. Lower durometer rating = softer material. Higher durometer rating = harder material.

DRAFT ANGLE
When the walls of a part are greater or less than 90°, this is known as a "draft angle" The reason a draft is designed into parts is facilitate their removal from a mold (de-molding), typically RTV silicone or machined steel tooling. For instance, injection parts will expand after cooling, locking them onto the tooling and making them difficult, if not impossible, to remove without destroying the part and / or mold in the process.

DRAFTING or TECHNICAL DRAWING
In the traditional trade of architecture, the process of creating 2D technical drawings ("design drafts") is known as drafting.

DYE SUBLIMATION
A process that uses a computer to print a full color design onto transfer paper. When applied to the material surface and heated, the ink vaporizes and transfers onto the material. Great for 4-color process photographic graphics and artwork. Swim trunks and athletic racing "kits" are made with dye sub.

ECONOMY OF SCALE
The price per single unit or item is vastly reduced, and total overall cost savings achieved, through a process of purchasing or producing large quanities of items at scale.

EDGE BINDING or PIPING
An edge that is folded and stitched, added to a fabric material to prevent it from fraying (i.e. elastic nylon stretch binding).

EDGE TREATMENT
A subtle yet powerful design element that's often exploited in the realm of industrial design to heighten aesthetic appeal. Common edge treatments are bevel, radius, and chamfer.

EDM
Electrical discharge machining (metals).

EGGSHELL FINISH
A state where a paint starts to fog into a satin matte appearance, usually after a few minutes of being coated.

ELASTOMER
An "elastic polymer," or a polymer with viscoelasticity (both viscosity and elasticity). Used interchangeably with rubber, as almost all rubbers fall within this category.

EMBOSSED
A raised surface element or detail (peak). Used quite often as a decorative pattern or as a stand-alone design element.

EMBROIDERY
A decorative fabric element applied by needle and thread, that can be either hand sewn or computer stitched to give an ultra precise, highly detailed effect.

EMPIRICAL METHOD or EMPIRICISM
The process of solving problems through a process of trial and error, which can lead to breakthroughs. James Dyson built 5,127 prototypes for his original bagless vacuum cleaner, and he swears that the 5,126 failures were learning experiences — whereby he slightly improved upon each iteration to finally arrive at the 5,127th. This method of tinkering is opposite to the academic approach, which uses mental models instead.

END MILL
The machining bit used in manual and CNC milling applications, used in conjunction with a tootpath (or cutting

route). A ball end mill is typically used on surfaces that are 3D shaped, so that it doesn't leave any hard edges anywhere.

ERGONOMICS
A human-centered approach to design that focuses an object's shape to fit with natural human anatomy & biomechanics.

EXPLODED VIEW (DRAWING)
A drawing where the separate parts of an assembled product or design are "exploded" out into a 3D space, in order to show how the individual components fit together.

EXTRUSION
Forcing a material through a pre-shaped die. If you've ever made Play-Doh spaghetti as a kid, you're familar with the extrusion process. Material is extruded through a die which gives the part its final shape. Metal iPod housings are made from extruded aluminum that is then anodized and cut to size.

EVA
Ethyl-vinyl acetate, most commonly used in products like blown or expanded EVA foam (i.e. car seats, shoe midsoles).

FABRICATION or "FAB"
The process of building out or fabricating a design or a part, usually following a blueprint or similar set of specifications that dictate how the part should be made.

FASTENER
A permanent or removeable mechanical attachment point which joins together two or more objects, such as a linchpin, rivet, cotter pin, screw, bolt, zipper, velcro, clip, stitches, and laces. A threaded screw hole is known as a tap.

FEATHER EDGE
Refers to the a surface edge that gradually fades or "feathers" into another, usually having no defined or specific radius.

FEMALE PART or MOLD (NEGATIVE)
Typically the concave or emtpy side of a mold, which interfaces and / or joins with the male side in order to form a whole.

FOB
Free on board, or the price of a product without calculating S/H, import / export tariffs. Commonly known as "cost."

FIDELITY
Refers to the level of finish resolution or quality of a sketch, rendering, or build — ranging from low, to medium or high.

FILLET or SCALLOP
A fillet is an inner or inside (concave) radius.

FIRST ARTICLE BUILD
The first initial parts or "articles" to come out of a mold — often in injection molding — for the purpose of evaluating the quality of the mold itself. The remaining mass produced parts will be benchmarked and derived from these early parts.

FIRST ORDER RETRIEVABILITY
A shop term used by model makers to describe tools that are within arms reach and easily retreivable.

FIRST PRINCIPLES
Referred to as "reasoning from first principles," which is a foundational scientific and philosophical practice of pruning understanding down to the bare essentials.

FLAME SURFACING
This design style was pioneered and popularized by the former chief of BMW design, Chris Bangle. A sharp "knife edge" pinched surface that creates a unique, bold aesthetic.

FLASHING or MOLD FLASH
Where excess plastic material oozes out or is squeezed from the side of a mold. This happens where the halves come together, and will leave behind a parting line when this excess material is trimmed. Be mindful of your parting lines design!

FLAT PACK DESIGN
Design that works specifically with 2D flat panels, which are then joined together to create 3D volumetric pieces. Often used in furniture and / or architectural design applications.

FLOOR PLAN
A top view scale drawing used specifically in architecture or interior design, to illustrate the design layout of a space.

FLOW STATE
Entire books have been written on this deep psychological state. Flow state is characterized by a complete absorption in one's activity, and the resulting loss in one's sense of space and time. Also known as being "in the zone," where one is operating at the edge of peak performance & productivity!

FORGING
In blacksmithing — the process of folding and repeatedly hammering red hot metal over on itself, in order to make it stronger. A large oven or kiln is referred to as a forge.

FORM or PRE-FORM
A hard shape in which a softer material is conformed to.

FORM DEVELOPMENT
The process of developing a design's form language / design DNA, usually through an iterative process of sketches and sketch models, followed by 2D renderings and / or 3D CAD.

FORM FACTOR
Refers to "footprint" or internal real estate of a product. For example, electronic components that are housed within an iPhone have a much smaller form factor than an iPad or iMac.

FORM LANGUAGE
Similar to design DNA, form language is the consistent, subjective theme or design styling that's embedded within the DNA of a design's forms. Examples of different form languag-

es are fluid, organic, minimal, sleek, industrial, or angular.

FORSTNER BIT
A specialty drill bit with a unique cutting shape, which is used in countersinking to create recessed impressions in a surface.

FOUNDRY
A production plant dealing primarily with metal fabrication.

FUNCTIONAL PATENT or UTILITY PATENT
Protects a functional design feature or new invention, as long as it doesn't infringe upon one that has come before (known as "prior art"). Typically comes with a 14 to 20 year lifespan (USA & UK). Patents must be filed in every country where the invention is intended to be sold or distributed.

FUNCTIONAL PROTOTYPE
A working prototype that exibits an intended (often mechanical) function. The prototype may not be built from the desired materials, may be larger than intended, and may appear to be crude and unfinished with exposed wires and hinges; but still performs its intended function.

GANTT CHART / FLOW CHART
A graphical project management tool. Initially implemented during war time, to chart out large-scale battlefield operations.

GARAGE KIT
A small model kit, typically made from cast resin in a garage.

GEL COAT
A protective outer coating used in composites layup, which also fills in surface air bubbles. The gel coat is first diluted with acetone to allow it to be sprayable, then is applied directly onto the surface of a mold. When the composite resin cures, it fuses with the gel coat in the catalyzation process.

GENERATIVE DESIGN
One of the newer and most powerful technological developments in CAD / CAM software, generative design uses A.I. and machine learning to generate structurally-efficient engineering solutions that outperform similar human-derived structures. Many of these structural designs offer vastly reduced weight, while dramatically reducing material usage — resulting in significant cost savings as well. Car manufacturers have experimented with this technology for race vehicle chassis, and NASA in Mars rover undercarriages.

GIGO
"Garbage In, Garbage Out," a software development phrase meaning outputs are only as good as inputs (i.e. code data).

GIRTH
The measurement around the circumference of an object.

GOLDEN RATIO / GOLDEN MEAN
Fibbonacci sequence, also known as the golden spiral. A key element of proportion and aesthetic beauty / appeal.

GRAIN
Can refer to wood or leather grain, where wood grain is a unique pattern that varies by species, leather grain is the top or outermost layer of the cowhide or animal hide.

GROMMET
A grommet is essentially a rivet with a hole in the midldle.

GAUGE
Refers to the thickness and strength of a sheet metal material.

GUIDE COAT
An underlying paint coat used for even surface sanding.

"HALO" PRODUCT
Refers to a premium or top-tier aspirational product in a line.

"HAND FEEL" / "HAND"
A term used to describe the tactile touch and feel of a piece of a soft 2D fabric material, such as a leather or suede.

HAPPY ACCIDENT / SERENDIPITY
A happy accident is an unpredicted occurance which leads to an unplanned but pleasant outcome. Don't try to fight happy accidents — learn use them to your advantage instead!

HARD GOODS / HARD LINES
Solid 3D products that are either cast or injection molded.

HARDWARE & TRIMS
Pieces that are arranged around a garment, such as metal or plastic zippers and zipper pullers, die-cast metal snap buttons or rivets, plastic injection hardware, molded TPR parts, etc.

HEAT CUT
Using high heat to create a cut, such as with a hot knife, laser, or ultrasonic radiation welding.

HEAT SHRINK
PVC plastic tubing that "shrinks" over a part with heat.

HEAT TRANSFER
Using transfer ink to apply a decal with heat and pressure.

HEAT TREATING
The process of heating steel or metals in order to strenghten their molecular qualities. Similar to sintering, but is done in post rather than in the metallurgical bonding phase.

HELD IN ORIENTATION
To hold a part at a specific working angle, as in welding etc.

HERO SHOT or MONEY SHOT
A big, bold product photo is often known as a "hero shot."

"HIDE THE CRIMES"
Hiding poor craftsmanship with paint or another treatment.

HOLISTIC DESIGN (HOLISM) or "FULL STACK"
Where design and engineering are integrated as one complete, end-to-end whole — including how a product is designed, developed, made, packaged, to how it looks (both inside and outside) and how it functions. James Dyson and Buckminster Fuller are huge advocates of this type of thinking.

HOOK & LOOP
Refers to velcro construction, where the loop side is the female side, and the hook side is the male side.

HOT KNIFE
A metal knife or similar sharpened blade that is heated and used to trim the flashing off of molded rubber parts.

HOT MELT or FUSIBLE LAMINATION
Melting one material to bond and laminate to another.

HYDRO DIPPING or WATER TRANSFER PRINTING
A method of applying printed graphics to 3D objects. Can be applied to many different material substrates such as plastic, metal, wood, and more. Also known as immersion printing. The artist Hydro74 is famous for his hydro-dipped creations.

HYDRO FORMING
Similar to injection molding, but instead uses pressurized water to force a hollow metal billet to conform to the outer walls of a mold. Some high-end specialty aluminum bike frames and water flasks are made this way.

IDEATION
This is a common term within industrial design, used to describe the process of "ideating," which is essentially translates to "idea creation". A visual form of brainstorming.

IMPERIAL SYSTEM
Inches, feet, yards, miles. An older English system of measurement that's still the standard in England and America.

INFILTRATE or INFILTRATION
The process wherein a hardener or binder material is infused with a fragile material, such as SLS 3D powder printed parts.

IN-HOUSE or INTERNAL
Completing a job internally, rather than using a third party vendor. Usually refers to a firm's home office / headquarters.

INJECTION MOLDING
The process by which a molten fluid material is injected into a mold using pnuematic force and pressure. Injection molding is used to produce parts or products very inexpensively and at very high quantities. Most of modern society is fueled by products that are injection molded. Plastic injection is most common, however rubber and metal can also be injected, with different materials used to create the molds accordingly.

INK TRANSFER
A process using an ink transfer tape that peels off like a sticker, leaving behind a permanent mark. How mountain-bike frame decals are applied in production.

IN-MOLD
Means that a design element or feature (i.e. a logo) is machined into the mold, rather than attached or applied later on — i.e. screen printing, pad printing, sewn, bonded, etc.

INNOVATION LAB or INNOVATION KITCHEN
A slang term used for an R&D lab, derived from the similarities between the empirical innovation process and cooking — expermiment, bake concepts, test what works or what doesn't.

INTELLECTUAL PROPERTY (I.P.)
Unique property developed by a firm or by an individual, which is protected under law — including copyrights, patents, trade secrets, licensing / distribution and ownership rights.

ISOMETRIC DRAWING / ISO VIEW
A three-quarter object view that has been drawn without perspective. Orthographics are isometric drawings projected from the top, bottom, front, back, or sides of an object.

JIG
A structural apparatus that holds separate parts into orientation, or at a specified angle. Jigs are useful for cutting, welding, spray painting, coating, and multiple other processes.

JOINERY / JOINING / JOINT
The connection point made between two or more objects, usually at the corner. There are many design opportunities for unique joints, such as tongue & groove or mortise & tenon.

KERF or KERFING
When a piece of plywood is run through a table saw many times, to make shallow or deep cuts that are close together. Shallow cuts help with glue setup and ahesion, giving the glue valleys to grab onto. Deep cuts allow plywood to be bent on a radius, similar to an accordion or siping. The spacing between the kerfs will determine the size & bend of the radius.

KEY SKETCH
A sketch selected from a round of concept explorations, usually to move forward into a prototype or final design stage.

KNIT LINES
In injection molded parts, the lines in a part's surface where the material "knits" together under high pressure & heat.

KUKA ARM or INDUSTRIAL ROBOT ARM
Robotic arms are a cornerstone of factory assembly & automation. Kuka is the most well known name of industrial robotic arm manufacturers (German). Fanuc and Yaskawa (Japanese) are also some of the most popular manufacturers.

LAYER THICKNESS or PART RESOLUTION
Refers to the thickness of a 3d printed / additive manufactured part. Measured in microns. Thinner layers = higher resolution.

LEAD TIME / TURNAROUND TIME

Once a project or an assignment is initiated, lead time is the time it takes to receive the requested deliverables.

LEAN or "AGILE" MANUFACTURING

Made famous by the Japanese, refers to manufacturing managed by small batches and just-in-time production.

LIFE / HEAD / BODY CAST

A cast taken of the human body, often for SFX hair & makeup.

LIGHT CATCHER

This is a surface that is intentionally turned upward to catch a highlight from an overhead light source, helping to give a point of visual interest to a design. Used commonly in transportation design, often being located on lower car body panels and fenders to make the vehicle *appear* lighter.

LIGHTFAST / LIGHTFASTNESS

Refers to the ability of a material to withstand exposure to direct sunlight, or UV light. UV damage can result from a material having weak lightfastness, which causes the material to yellow or discolor quickly.

LIVERY DESIGN

Graphic design and / or branding, usually paint or vinyl wrap.

"LOOK & FEEL"

Used to describe the visual and tactile aspects of a design or a product. Commonly used in non-functional or aesthetic prototypes as a "look & feel" presentation model.

LOOM

A device used to weave fabric cloth and tapestry.

LOST-WAX CASTING or INVESTMENT CASTING

A process by which a duplicate metal sculpture is cast from an original sculpture. Commonly used in jewelry making.

MACHINE FARM

This is a collection of duplicate machines in a facility (i.e. CNC, 3D printers, injection molders), which "farm" a large number of parts. Some service firms have farms of 3D printing machines that can produce up to one million parts per year.

MAKER FAIRE

The "world's largest show & tell" expo for design & egineering.

MAKER

Due to new and pioneering technologies, the maker is in effect his or her own independent manufacturer. This term does not represent one singular discipline or practice, but instead spreads across the full range of design, engineering, architecture, model making, fabrication and construction.

THE MAKER MOVEMENT

This is the term given to the rise of the maker, made possible by advanced technologies such as desktop 3D printers, CNC machines, and laser cutters — which were once only available to large R&D institutions like NASA or DARPA. The maker movement represents a paradigm shift unlike anything other in history, empowering the individual (decentralized) versus larger, more complex traditional manufacturers (centralized) and the gatekeepers that come along with them. Sometimes referred to as *The Fourth Industrial Revolution.*

MALE PART or MOLD (POSITIVE)

Typically the convex side of a mold, which interfaces and / or joins with the female side in order to form a whole.

MANDREL

A large steel industrial roller, typically used in the carbon fiber weaving process — which is known as 'radial braiding.'

MAP

Minimum advertised price, or the lowest price a product can be sold for either in store or online (set by the manufacturer).

MAQUETTE or MINIATURE

A scale model "sketch" or rough draft of an unfinished scuplture, used to visualize forms before producing at full-scale. Clay maquettes are common in the SFX industry.

MASTER CAST or MASTER COPY

The first initial cast from a mold, used as a benchmark from which the quality of all following reproductions are to follow.

MASTER MOLD

The mold from which all other duplicates are benchmarked.

MATERIALS SCIENCE

The R&D behind the exploration and invention of advanced new materials to be used in industry. Large chemical suppliers such as Corning, Dow Chemical, Dupont, and 3M are dedicated almost solely to materials science R&D. Space exploration is another important facet here, where scientific discoveries found in outer space can be used back on Earth.

MOCKUP or STUDY MODEL

A mockup is essentially a "rough draft prototype" or 3D sketch model, which is used primarily to quickly test out an idea.

MODERN DESIGN

A design style that is characterized by clean, geometric lines and slick surfaces. Popular in furniture and architecture.

MOLD GATE

The gate is the entry hole or opening in the steel tool or rubber mold, through which hot molten plastic is "shot" into the mold (injection), or where the part is poured in from (resin cast).

MOLD REGISTRATION KEYS or PINS

Male and female indentations in the surface of a mold, to help line up precisely during resin casting or injection molding.

MASS FINISHING

Uses an abrasive media similar to small gravel particles, which will vibrate with parts pieces and can deburr, descale, brighten, polish or surface finish work pieces.

MATERIAL HONESTY

Used to describe an honest use of materials, meaning they have not been adultered or coated to look like something they are not. Using real carbon fiber versus a less costly hydro-dipped "carbon fiber print" is an example of material honesty.

MASS PRODUCTION or MASS MANUFACTURING

The process of producing goods in large quantities. The Industrial Revolution was the harbinger of mass production.

MCMASTER-CARR®

One of the top suppliers of mechanical hardware and parts in the USA, with an extensive catalog including drill taps, endmills, screws, bits, etc.

METALLIC FLAKE or PEARLESCENT

Paint with metallic powder flakes added gives it a special color-changing sheen when viewed from under different angles of light. Pearlescent paints shine even more brightly and deeply than metallics, containing tiny bits of ceramic "mica" material instead of metal, which both reflect and refract light.

METRIC SYSTEM

Millimeters, centimeters, and yards. The metric system is much more precise than the Western imperial system of units (inches, feet), and standard for working with technical drawings and factory spec requirements. Millimeters, centimeters, meters, kilometers. The metric system is far superior because of it's precision and ease of fractional incrementation, making it ideal for scale design or engineering work. Professional engineers & designers across the world will almost always work in metric (millimeters and centimeters), when needing to built parts or products to stringent requirements.

MICRON or MICROMETER

One millionth of a meter, or one thousandth of a millimeter. 3D printed layer thickness, as well as spray or powder coated layer thickness is commonly measured in microns.

MILD STEEL or LOW-CARBON STEEL

The least expensive and most commonly used of all steel.

"MILD TO WILD"

Used to explain the design practice of exploring the most conservative to the most extreme range of ideas. When running design or scientific experiments, if you don't explore the wild or radical concepts, you'll be much more likely to be pigeonholded and to default to what's safe or has already been done before — resulting in "me-too" ideas that simply follow the prevailing status quo. Don't be afraid to be BOLD!

MINIMALISM

The Zen "less is more" philosophy which originated out of Japan's restoration period after World War II, where simplicity came to epitomize sophistication in architecture and design.

MINIMUM VIABLE PRODUCT (MVP)

An MVP is an early-stage product released with bare minimum functionality only, used to test its viability or "product market fit." Popularized by Eric Ries in his book *The Lean Startup*.

MIRROR MODEL

Sometimes called a half model, a mirror model is a sculptural model (usually clay or foam) which is attached to a mirror. This gives the illusion of a complete design with both halves, and saves enormous amounts of time — since perfectly balancing and reflecting a design surfaces in clay is very difficult.

MITER CUT or MITER JOINT

An angle cut typically used for creating a joint, where a jig is used to hold the cutting blade into place.

MIXING RATIO

In a 2-part thermosetting applications, such as RTV molding and casting, or in epoxy glue, the mixing ratio is the proportion in which two material formulas are mixed together to activate the proper catalyzation — measured by weight, or by volume.

MOLD SUPPORTS

Crafted into a mold to prop up or to hold an oblong shaped part into place during 3D printing, injection molding, or molding and casting, and are removed after the part is finished.

MOLD TEXTURE

A specially-selected texture applied to the interior surface of a mold, which will then show up on the final pressed, cast, or injected part. Applied to the steel tooling mold surface by an acid etching process. Hundreds of patterns are available for selection, or custom patterns can also be created.

MOQ

Minimum order quantity, or the minimum quantity a factory or supplier requires to produce a certain part or or material. Commonly referred to as "factory minimums" or "minimums."

MORTISE AND TENON

Similar to tongue and groove construction, except pieces are held together by notches instead of slotted grooves.

MOTHER MOLD or MOLD SUPPORT BOX

An outer mold box or skeleton, which holds the shape of a soft mold such as silicone. Typically, fiberglass will be used as a mother mold in body cast applications to hold the shape of thinly brushed-on silicone after the impression is taken — since the thin mold by itself would be too soft and shapeless.

MSDS

Material safety data sheet. These will come standard with chemical-based materials such as RTV silicones and urethane resin materials, and will have useful info that runs the full gamut of material safety and handling, to working times, curing times, mixing ratios, proper storage and disposal, active ingredients, side effects, and more.

MSRP
Manufacturer's suggested retail price or "retail price" for short.

NIOSH
National Institute for Occupational Safety and Health.

NON-DISCLOSURE AGREEMENT (NDA)
A standard document protecting the confidential information of a disclosing party. Also known as a confidentiality agreement.

NON-SUPERFLUOUS DESIGN
An unnessecary element that adds no utility to a design. The practice of minimalism is to remove all superflous elements.

NON-WOVEN or SPUN-BONDED
A fabric made of polyester fibers, commonly used as a backer / substrate for synthetic materials. Also known as spun-bond.

NYLON
A type of thermoplastic. This term is also an umbrella term used to describe most injection molded plastic parts.

OEM or "WHITE LABEL" / PRIVATE LABEL
Original equipment manufacturer. Also known as a "stock mold", "open mold" or "private label."

OFF-GASSING
The chemical reaction process used in creating a material (commonly expanded foams like EVA or PU) can sometimes produce a strong odor referred to as off-gassing. That famous 'new car smell' is actually toxic for your health — and is given off by the EVA foam factory car seats and other upholstery.

OFF-SHORE / OUTSOURCING
Manufacturing or assembly is done on foreign soil, usually because of labor cost saving benefits and/or access to the specialized labor required to perform a difficult task.

OFFSITE / REMOTE or EXTERNAL WORK
Some businesses have remote satellite office locations or divisions that are completely separate from HQ. Also includes long-distance work that is done remotely by a contractor or freelancer, often over email and conference calls.

ONE-PART MOLD / "OPEN MOLD"
A mold with an open face on one side, where the material is poured. The simplest type of mold arrangement and is usually only suitable for low quantity part volume & production.

"ONE-OFF" (AKA BESPOKE)
Refers to a design or part that is made in extremely limited quanties, often as a single or just a few iterations. For example, the Batmobile is perhaps one of the most famous one-off designs — since only a few stunt vehicles are made per each film, as opposed to a mass production vehicle where tens of thousands, or even millions are made of a single model.

ON-SHORE
Manufacturing or assembly that is done on home soil.

ON-SITE / IN-HOUSE or INTERNAL WORK
Work performed at headquarters, as opposed to remote work.

OPEN CELL FOAM
Foam with pores that are open or aerated. Foam mattresses, green pottery foam, and kitchen sponges are all open cell.

ORANGE PEEL
A hammered texture surface resulting from when a spray painted color coat / clear coat is either sprayed unevenly, or is applied too thickly, causing a wavy surface resemblance to the outer skin or peel of an orange.

ORTHOGRAPHIC DRAWING / ORTHO
A planar view drawn without perspective, or facing straight-on to the top, sides, or bottom of an object. Known as an "ortho" for short. Most technical specs include some form of orthos.

OVERLAY
A part or panel which sits over another part and / or panel.

OVERLOCK STITCH or FLATLOCK STITCH
A type of stich that is usually used to join two elastic stretch fabrics together, as in underwear or compression garments.

OVERSPRAY
When excess paint or sprayable adhesive "sprays over" the intended part area. This is why masking tape is so important!

OXIDATION
A chemical reaction that occurs when a certain type of material is exposed to oxygen in the air, which will cause it to rust or to develop a patina.

PANTONE® COLOR SYSTEM
Hardcore R&D firms like Apple will often create their own unique colors not found in the Pantone® spectrum, and are often supported by a proprietary & internal color system.

PAPER PATTERN or FLAT PATTERN
A flat 2D paper pattern (often cut from a sheet of paper) is what soft goods products are constructed from. A complicated object such as an outdoor backpack or wetsuit may have many different patterns for each individual panel of the item. Each revision to the shape or size of a panel on a product will require a revision to its unique paper pattern.

PARTING LINE or PARTING PLANE
Where two or more mold halves come together creates a visible line in the part (commonly in RTV molding and casting or injection molding). Also known as a "witness line." A narrow, tight parting line is a sign of quality tooling construction.

PATENT
Legally protects a unique invention, technology, or feature —

as provisional, functional, or a design (ornamental) patent. A patent must follow a stringent approval process which references "prior art" before it can be officially registered and legally enforceable. A USA patent typically lasts for 14 years, and will need to be renewed in order to remain enforceable.

PATINA
After metal is exposed to oxygen and oxodizes, it produces a green-ish grungy surface finish known as a patina.

PC
Polycarbonate, which is perhaps the strongest of all the thermoplastic polymers, and is commonly used in thermoformed NFL helmets and bulletproof "glass."

PCB BOARD
Printed circuit board. The backbone of electrical engineering, PCB boards support and connect electronic components by conductive tracks, pads and other features etched into sheets of copper and laminated between sheets of a non-conductive substrate (i.e. computer motherboards and RAM sticks).

PE
Polyethylene, a thermoplastic polymer that is the most commonly used plastic today. Kitchen cutting boards are PE.

PERF or PERFORATION
Perfing is an abbreviation for perforating a material, which means cutting holes into its surface. Beyond pure function, there's room for many unique decorative / textural elements.

PERSPECTIVE DRAWING or VIEW
Drawn in one-point, two-point, or three-point perspective (vanishing points) — which is how our eyes naturally percieve objects in physical space. Used in sketches or renderings.

PINHOLE
Small holes in a surface, which can be filled with body filler.

PITCH DECK
A sales document used to raise a round of investor funding.

PLAN VIEW DRAWING or ELEVATION DRAWING
Architectural landscape views (exterior or interior) are known as plan view drawings. Often used in early design blueprints.

PLASTI-DIP®
A brand of dippable or sprayable rubberized vinyl coating.

PLASTISOL
One of most common "inks" used in screen printing (i.e. graphic t-shirts), which consists of a dyed liquid plasticizer with polymer particles. When heated, the plastic particles dissolve and turn to a solid gel (how fishing lures are made).

POLYMER
A chemical compound or mixture of compounds formed by polymerization. Often used as a synonym for plastic or resin.

POST-PROCESSING
Processing done after original or primary part processing. Most parts require additional processing such as assembly, powder coating, or screen printing for completion. Many post processes are performed for aesthetic purposes, including degating, deflashing, cleaning, painting, coating, polishing, silk screening, pad printing, laser engraving, deburring, bead blasting, anodizing, powder coating, and decorating.

P.O. or PURCHASE ORDER
Purchase order. Used when placing orders from a factory and / or supplier, often accompanying a purchase agreement.

POCKET
In machining, sunken areas of a tooling is known as a pocket.

P.O.P. or POINT OF PURCHASE DISPLAY
A consumer-facing display meant to draw attention to a product. With thousands of products lining the shelves of a retail store, the goal of a P.O.P. is to make a product stand out against the sea of competition by offering with a unique experience. Often made from die cut corrugated cardboard and printed with photographic artwork, branding and graphics.

PP
Polypropylene, a thermoplastic polymer that is similar to polyethylene, but is slightly harder and more heat resistant. Hard case travel luggage is commonly thermoformed PP.

PPS SAMPLES or SALESMAN SAMPLES
Pre-production samples, or final product samples that are prepared just before mass manufacturing, typically in a limited quantity. Commonly known as salesman samples.

PRACTICAL EFFECTS
Means physical form (models, props) rather than CG (computer generated). Stan Winston FX and Weta Workshop are two of the most famous practical effects studios for film. The film Iron Man used a seamless combination of both practical effects and CG for Tony Stark's armored suit, which gives more realism than effects that are purely digital alone.

PRECEDENT or BENCHMARK
Nelson Mandela famously remarked "It always seems impossible until it's done." A process that sets the example for what is possible is a precedent. The first runner to break the four-minute mile is a great example of a new precedent.

PRE-FAB / PRE-FABRICATION
Pre-fabrication. Often refers to architecture and / or homes built from pre-existing structures, such as shipping containers.

PRE-PREG / PRE-IMPREGNATION
Reinforced carbon composites that are pre-soaked with a thermosetting laminate such as epoxy, to save on time and labor costs in the layup process. Also known as "wet fabrics," are typically stored in refrigerators to prevent early curing of the resin. The alternative, or standard type of carbon fiber cloth is known as dry fabrics.

PRESSURE CAST

When a 2-part liquid resin is mixed together (i.e. urethane casting), air bubbles are whipped into the mixture and will embed themselves into the final part. A pressure pot is used to force these air bubbles out of the mixture before it has a chance to fully catalyze or cure into a solid part — which improves the final part quality, especially in clear or transparent parts where air bubbles will be visible. The casted part that results from this process is known as a pressure cast.

PRESSURE FIT / PRESS FIT

When two pieces interlock with one another at such high tolerances that the frictional pressure itself creates a strong mechanical bond between them.

PAIN POINT

A problem or certain point of pain or frustration for the consumer while using a product.

PRICE POINT

The price range or scale that a product is set at. For instance, a range of products within a vertical category may have different price points depending on quality and / or complexity.

PRODUCT CATEGORY

Describes what specific market vertical a product falls into.

PRODUCT LIFE CYCLE / "CRADLE TO GRAVE"

A product's full service life, from manufacturing to disposal — often in a landfill. Commonly referred to as "cradle to grave."

PRODUCT MARKET FIT

A term popularized by tech investor Marc Andreeson. A product or market may be good in its own right, but there must be a market fit for the product for it to be successful.

PRODUCTION SHARING

A modern manufacturing practice where raw materials come from one region of the world, are processed in another part of the world, and are assembled in another part of the world.

PROFIT MARGINS / "MARGINS"

The percentage or "points" of profit made per item.

PROJECT BRIEF

A project brief will usually include a list of line items or deliverables, and explain the background as well as the desired outcomes for a project.

PROVISIONAL PATENT

Essentially a "patent hold," meaning the patent is reserved but not completed. Much less expensive and time consuming of a process vs. filing for a full patent, and is thereby interimly used often while a full patent application is being registered.

PROOF-OF-CONCEPT

A prototype, model or mock-up built to prove out a particular functionality, useability, or validity of a new design idea. This term is also used widely in the field of business & investments.

PROP / MOVIE PROP / PROP REPLICAS

Items or "props" that are used on a film set, which are still commonly in concept form, and do not have any real function beyond looking cool and fitting within a story. Because they are specifically designed and produced for one film, RTV molding and casting has been typically used to make small batches of extras — although 3D printing is increasingly becoming more common.

PROPRIETARY

A process, system, design or technology that's often unique to and exclusively owned by a particular individual or firm, and is often a trade secret as well.

PUCKERING

Bunching / wrinkling in a 2D fabric material, usually occurring at a seam. Commonly due to the fabric being sewn too tightly.

PVC

Polyvinychloride. A common rubber or plastic used in TPR's.

QC / QA

Quality control or quality assurance. Maintaining individual part quality becomes increasingly difficult at larger scale.

RADIUS / EDGE RADIUS

The roundness of an inner or outer edge of a part and/or mold.

RAPID PROTOTYPE or PROTOTYPING

Using rapid technologies such as CNC, additive manufacturing, or 3D printing, as opposed to mass production techniques which require costly tooling and long lead times to setup.

RASTER / RASTERING

Similar to etching, but is produced by the heat from a laser.

RAW EDGE

An unfinished edge with no backer or support material, such as an edge binding or a hem. Some materials, such as leathers, work well while others like textiles will tend to fray.

RAW MATERIAL

A material in it's natural state, or how it is mined directly from the Earth. Must be processed into a consumable product.

REDLINE or REDLINES

Drawing revision lines, comments, or notations over the top of a design, spec, or blueprint document (usually red in color).

RE-CYCLING

Re-using an old product or device, or melting down the raw materials to make a new copy of the same product or device.

REGISTRATION KEYS or BUSHINGS

In RTV mold making, registration keys help to properly line up or "register" the two or more mold halves together.

RELEASE AGENT
A specially formulated non-stick coating that's either sprayed or brushed onto the inner surfaces of a mold to facilitate the release of casted parts, or to prolong the life of a mold. Sprayable release agents are typically derived from silicone, but will vary depending both on the material of the mold and of the casting material used.

RENDERING
A rendering is a polished form of a sketch, typically used to refine both the form and the function of a design for presentation purposes. Can either be 2D or 3D, and range in fidelity from a stylized to a photo-realistic work with accurate light, shadow, reflection and / or convincing material indication.

REPLICA PROP or REPLICA
A copy of an original. Often known as a copycat or a fake

RESEARCH AND DEVELOPMENT / R&D
The process for discovering & impementing new technologies. Investment into R&D is essential for breakthrough innovation.

RESIN
A liquid or semi-solid chemical substance that converts into a solid polymer through a chemical reaction known as thermosetting, or through UV light reaction (SLA 3D printing).

RETOOL / REJIGGER
Revising, re-working or creating new and improved tooling.

REVERSE ENGINEERING or BACK ENGINEERING
Dissecting a product or material specimen to learn about its mechanical, chemical, or electronic makeup or construction.

RFP / RFQ
Request for proposal or request for qoutation, sent at the onset of a new project.

RIVET
A permanent mechanical fastener consisting of a metal bolt with a round head, hammered into a punched or drilled hole.

ROBUST / ROBUSTNESS
Refers to the durability of a material, finish or coating.

ROI
Return on investment; how outputs ultimately match to inputs.

ROLLED GOODS
Refers to rolled sheets of material (i.e. fabrics, foams, rubber).

ROTATIONAL "ROTO" MOLD or SLIP CAST
A rotational mold, also known as a slip cast, is the process of spinning a mold in 360° direction, causing the liquid resin to evenly coat to the sidewalls by gravitational pull (similar to those old carnival rides that suck you against the walls). An effective way of creating large part casts with thin side walls.

RTV (ROOM TEMPERATURE VULCANIZATION)
A term used to describe a chemical vulcanization process of a rubber material that sets at room temperature.

RUNNERS
In injection molding, the channels by which the material flows or 'runs' through a mold and into the separate part cavities.

SACRIFICIAL BOARD or PART
A scrap piece of material placed under another when cutting.

SAMPLE
An early trial build of a design, material, or finish process for evaluation. Often synonymous with prototype.

SAMPLE ROOM
A room — either internally or externally — within a firm or factory, where samples are made. Typically staffed with sample developers and pattern makers, rolls of various different fabrics, a material library, and other basic hand tools and machinery for making samples quickly and on the fly.

SAND MOLD / SAND CASTING
Sand can withstand extremely high heat, and is used as a mold to pour-cast molten steel or aluminum. This process is commonly how engine blocks are made.

SAND BLAST / BEAD BLAST
Using an abrasive bead or grit which is blown at high pressure to roughen or apply texture to a slick surface. Bead blast can be specced as light, medium or heavy (heavy being the roughest). Frosted glass is an example of bead blasting.

SCOPE OF WORK (SOW)
A document provided at the onset of a project, that gives a rundown of a project's agreed upon deliverables, timeline, and the billable costs for each. Often is included in a contract.

SCOPE CREEP
Anything falling outside of a project's SOW is known as "scope creep" and usually entails extra costs and delayed delivery.

SCORE CUT / SCORING
Cutting halfway through a flexible material to allow it to have a live hinge, which can then be snapped off for a clean break.

SEALANT
A coating that seals and protects the surface underneath. Varnish, shellac, and laquer are all examples of sealants.

SELF FABRIC
In cut & sew, refers to the main fabric being sewn to "itself."

SERVOMOTOR / "SERVO"
A small but powerful rotary or linear actuator, which is one of the backbones of robotics engineering and industrial systems design. Found in remote controlled cars, drones, and in-line manufacturing to control precise linear position, angle, veloc-

ity and acceleration. Two major types are brushed or brushless (costlier & longer lasting), available in AC or DC.

SFX / VFX

Special effects or visual effects used in film or TV. Two major types of SFX are practical effects (physical props) and digital effects (CGI or computer generated imagery). The first Iron Man and Terminator films used a combination of the two for best results (Stan Winston Studios worked on both films).

SHELLAC

A protective wood finish derived from tree bark resin, which is diluted with alcohol and acts as a sealant, primer, and varnish.

SIDEWALL THICKNESS or SHELL THICKNESS

A thin wall of a part, typically in injection molding design. Shelling out a design keeps it lightweight, and gives room to place internal components such as electronics.

SILK SCREENING or SCREEN PRINTING

A very old technology and still the most common way to apply graphics or designs to a material's surface, using traditional screens and ink. A new screen must be set up for each color.

SINGLE / DOUBLE / TRIPLE NEEDLE STITCH

Refers to the number of rows of stitching, where the number of rows is determined by the number of needles loaded into the sewing machine. A single needle stitch is most common for most applications. Double needle or triple needle stitching is used where high strength and reinforcement are needed.

SINK

In injection molding, where thick bosses, ribs, or features can cause surface warping (sinking) on the other side of the part.

SINTERING

During sintering, parts are heated at a temperature below the melting point range of the base metal, but high enough to metallurgically bond the individual particles together. Sintering further densifies the parts, increasing strength. Metal parts are heated in a sintering furnace, which metallurgically bonds the individual particles.

SIPES / SIPING

Die or laser cutting slits — known as sipes — into a material, allowing it to flex (similar to kerfing but not cut on table saw).

SIZE GRADING / SIZE GRADE

Refers to the process of grading — or scaling up or down proportionally — the 2D patterns or 3D geometry of an object or design. A correct size grade is essential for maintaining both the correct form and correct function of a product, across a range of different product sizes (i.e. S, M, L, XL).

SKETCH / SKETCH MODEL

A sketch can be either 2D or 3D, made by hand or in the computer. Essentially translates to thinking out loud to communicate an abstract design idea visually and concretely.

SKIVE / SKIVING

Thinning of the edge of a piece of leather using a sharp tool. Also known as a split cut.

SKU

Stock keeping unit, pronounced "skew." Each unique size and color of a product will have its own SKU, or part number.

SKUNK WORKS

A fully autonomous division within a larger parent organization, often operating under high secrecy and with the goal of developing radical R&D innovation. The sole purpose of such unit is for exploring technological / material / product breakthroughs not restricted by a set budget. The term also is used for highly confidential "stealth" or "black projects". The origin of the name comes from the aerial defense contractor Lockheed's World War II Skunk Works division, which was tasked for developing some of the most advanced aircraft ever produced, such as the F-117 stealth fighter jet, SR-71 Blackbird, and U2 spy plane.

SLAG

Steel waste material which is often thrown off by the machining process; resembles sharp curlicues.

SMALL BATCH PRODUCTION

Making only a few units of an item at a time, in small or as-needed quantities. Small batch size allows for less waste and for rapid pivots to be made during the middle of production. Derives its name from small-barrel craft bourbon production.

SMU (SPECIAL MAKE UP)

Usually a limited edition and / or limited quanity of a product featuring a custom graphic, branding or corporate identity treatment is known as a special make up. A custom racing kit, embroidered apparel, or custom gear set specially made for a sponsored athlete would be considered an SMU.

SNAP or LINE TENSION

Also known as accelerating and decelerating curvature. This is a detail exploited by transportation designers, to create a sense of taughtness or "tension" between two points on the surface of a speed form or directional shape. A slack or drooping line is the antithesis of a taught line, which will result in an uncontrolled and therefore undesireable visual aesthetic — drawing similar parallels to a powerful, athletic physique vs. one which is weak and out of shape.

SOFT GOODS / SOFT LINES (CUT & SEW)

Soft products made from 2D patterns that are sewn together.

SOFT LAUNCH or HARD LAUNCH

In product launch lingo, a soft launch is a gradual product rollout, whereas a hard launch is a full and complete rollout.

SOURCING

Where will your raw materials come from? Where will all the component parts be assembled? This is very important aspect of product development, and is known as sourcing.

SPEED FORM
An abstract, directional sculpture created in the early stages of a new car design, usually for the purpose of establishing a fresh new form language or design DNA — which will set the precedent for the actual car design going forward. Typically appears in advanced concept cars that are still decades out.

SPEC PROJECT
A non-comissionsed "what if?" thought experiment project, often created to highlight a designer's core competencies.

SPI / STITCHES PER INCH
A unit of measurement that refers to stitching concentration, where the number of stitches per inch determines the strength of a seam. Too few stitches will create a weak seam, too many can lead to a perforation effect that can weaken the materials being sewn together. 9 to 11 SPI is common, with 5 SPI used for softer rubber channels.

SPLINE
A tool used to check the taughtness of a material's surface, which is known as "snap." Think of a clothesline that is strung tightly between two posts — this is snap. Automotive and transportation design is often referred to as the "battle for line tension." Tight lines = strong. Droopy lines = weak.

SPRUE
Excess molten or cast material left over inside of a mold gate.

SQUARE / SQUARED EDGES
Being square means having right angles with 90° corners, which is essential for creating furniture, boxes, etc.

STAGE GATE
A key or major milestone in a project's development timeline.

STARTUP ACCELERATOR / INCUBATOR
Where a startup business goes to "accelerate" it's launch, usually consisting of a vast investor / mentor support network that is meant to serve as launching-off point for startups.

STEEL TOOLING / MOLD TOOLING
A mass production mold set up for injection molding or rubber pressing, which is precision machined or "tooled" from chromium steel — a high durability metal that can withstand repeated high pressure of injection plastic. Molds for injected rubber or metal are built from different types of metal, but using the same techniques. The machining of the mold tooling is referred to as "cutting steel." The terms mold and tool are used interchangeably with one another.

STEM / STEAM
Science, Technology, Engineering and Math, which are essentially the builder-in-training fields. STEAM is an alternative acronym with an additonal "Art" discipline added.

STEPPER MOTOR (CNC)
Stepper motors are the motors that drive CNC machines, and why visible layers in a machined part are known as "steps."

STITCHING CHANNEL
A channel groove built "in-mold" into a plastic or rubber part, to allow it to be stitched on top of a soft fabric material.

STITCHING GAUGE / THREAD SIZE
The thickness of a stitch, usually selected or specced by a designer for aesthetic reasons. It's all in the details!

STYLE GUIDE / BRAND STANDARDS GUIDE
An internal branding document on par with holy scripture; dictating every visual logo, font type, and color usage detail for maintaining proper consistency (aka brand identity system).

SUBTRACTIVE MANUFACTURING
Material is taken away, but cannot added. Think of the marble sculptures made by the ancient Greeks or Romans. By comparison, clay is both an additive and subtractive medium.

SUBSTRATE
An underlying "backer" material, often used to give structural support to an otherwise brittle or flimsy material.

SUPPLIER / VENDOR
The "source" of the supply, or where certain raw material goods are purchased or supplied from. These can be highly specialized factories or firms who do one thing only (and well).

SUPPLY CHAIN / SUPPLY CHAIN NETWORK
The chain of all suppliers, vendors, and production partners within a given manufacturing and distribution network.

SURFACE BLOOMING
A bad chemical reaction arising to the surface in a material, typically in rubbers. This can also happen when a paint coating hasn't properly cured and is bubbling up underneath.

SURFACE CROWN
A crown is typically the highest point in a curved surface.

SWATCH
A reference sample taken from a larger piece of material, sheet or fabric, often cut into small squares.

SWATCH BOOKS or SWATCH CARD
Swatches assembled into a book or one-page card for comparison and evaluation, before making a final selection (i.e. dyed colors of material, different grades of leather).

SWATCH LIBRARY or MATERIAL LIBRARY
A collection of swatch books and material samples from different suppliers that are assembled into a reference library.

TAP SCREW
A self-tapping (or self-threading) screw that can tap its own hole as it is driven into the material.

TAPE DRAWING
A legacy tactile method that is still widely used in automotive and transportation design, involving the use of black vinyl

tape of different widths to establish a design's character lines, often done on a large sheet of thick vellum. Tape drawing uses the natural tactile tension of the tape to give the lines a tight tension or "snap." Tape drawings are commonly drawn at 1:4 scale, but sometimes at 1:1 at some car design studios.

TARIFF or DUTY

Materials that must be imported may be subject to fees, taxes or import duties, which will vary depending on the material composition or by the product type.

TASTEMAKER or TASTEMAKING

The early adopters driving the latest trends in fashion, design, and culture. Also known as purveyors of "good taste."

TECHNICAL DESIGN

Widely used in cut & sew. Technical essentially means "high tech" or made with engineered materials such as waterproof Gore-Tex® fabrics, rip-stop nylons, taped seams, etc.

TECH PACK / SPEC PACK or DESIGN SPECS

A tech pack, short for "technical package" (also referred to as a design spec) is your primary mode of communicating all design requirements to a factory — including every color, material, and detail of a design — down to the last millimeter. Each separate page is built to scale, and formatted to a size that can be easily printed out on paper (i.e. 8.5"x11" or 11"x17") and assembled into a "pack." Tech packs are industry standard in soft goods development, but also used in hard goods development. Each page will have the name of the individual designers or developers involved, and are sent electronically through email (although once upon a time they were actually scanned in one by one, and then faxed !).

THERMOFORMING or VACUUM CASTING

The process of taking a sheet of plastic material, heating until malleable, then forming it with the aid of a vacuum into a 3D shape. Thermoforming, vacuum forming, and vacuum casting are all terms used to describe the same process.

THERMOPLASTIC

A plastic that sets through a combination of thermal heat and pressure — creating a physical, non-molecular change. Thermoplastics are most commonly used as injection molded plastics and rubbers. Once melted down, they can be remelted and remolded again, making them recyclable. Physical change (no molecular change) = non-permanent.

THERMOSET or THERMOSETTING PLASTIC

A plastic that sets through a chemical reaction, usually when combined together as a 2-part mixture — where one part is the base material, and the other is the catalyst. Once the change takes place, the material can't be melted down again without destroying the part, and is therefore non-recyclable. Chemical change (molecular change) = permanent.

THINK TANK

Used to describe an group or committee of independent scientists, researchers and bright minds from all different fields, backgrounds, and geographical locations who are brought together to solve a specific problem — including research into advanced tehnologies. The Manhattan Project is a famous example of a government sponsored think tank.

THREE-PART MOLD

Some more complex shaped parts will be difficult to remove from a standard one or two-part mold, and will therefore require a three or more separate mold parts.

TILE or TILING

A common practice in 3D printing, where the machine's print bed will limit the part size that can be printed. Tiling allows for very large parts to be printed in sections and then assembled together, either with epoxy glue or by mechanical joinery.

TONAL or "TONE ON TONE"

Matching the same color, or +/- a few shades lighter or darker. A dark gray logo on a black t-shirt would be considered tonal.

TACTILE "TOUCH & FEEL"

Used to desribe the tactile nature of a material, product or process, as opposed to purely digital processes such as CAD.

TOLERANCE or TOLERANCES

Tolerance refers to the amount of "play" or wiggle room built into the assembly or construction of two or more parts. Low tolerance = slack / more play. High tolerance = tight / less play (i.e. machined to +/- 0.05mm tolerance or less).

TONGUE AND GROOVE

A construction technique using a slotted groove system instead of glue, nails or screws to hold pieces together. Common in traditional Japanese architecture and woodworking.

TOOLPATH

In CNC machining, the path along which the cutting endmill part or 'tool' follows in order to complete an operation.

TOP COAT

Follows the color base coat, also known as the clear coat.

TPR or MICRO INJECTION

Short for Thermoplastic rubber, which is injected into a tiny mold with a syringe (typically PVC or PU rubber is used). Small TPR's are commonly known as "jewel pieces." Infinite styles, colors, and super-fine details are possible.

TRADE SECRET

Proprietary knowledge, processes, technologies or information that is hidden to the outside world and confidential in nature, often considered to be "top secret." Trade secrets are not patentable, but are still often jealously guarded and protected, such as secret recipes or formulas. The secret formula for "Coke" is one of the most famous examples.

TRADE SHOW or TRADE EXPO

An industry expo where new brands debut new products and

product line announcements. Some trade shows are closed to the general public or are invite only, where access is granted to destributors or retailers looking to carry the new products.

TRADEMARK
A name or logo "mark" (wordmark) used in a commercial ("trade") setting that is legally protected by law. Trademarks are considered as a form of intellectual property or IP.

TRANSITION
A transitional area connecting two or more separeate surfaces together. Automotive design is all about creating flowy, sexy transitions between a car's exterior surface volumes. Well designed transitions can heighten the appeal of an otherwise bland or static design. Also known as a surface blend.

TWO-PART MOLD
A mold consisting of male and female mold halves, which come together to complete a whole mold cavity or enclosure.

TWO-WAY STRETCH / FOUR-WAY STRETCH
Stretch fabric that stretches in only two directions (planes), or in four directions (planes). Also known as lycra spandex.

UNDERCUT
You want to avoid these at all costs in moldmaking! An undercut is where a part volume creates an "overhang" that makes it difficult to remove from a mold (de-mold) without destroying either the part or the mold (or both).

UNDERLAY
A part or panel which sits under another part and / or panel.

UNOBTANIUM
An unknown 'mystery material' that either doesn't exist, or is obscenely expensive if not physically impossible to produce.

UP-CYCLING
Re-purposing a used / old product or device as a new product use (i.e. neoprene coozies cut from old wetsuit sleeves).

USE CASE
Describes the unique setting or scenario where a product may be used. One product may have several various use cases.

VACUUM BAGGING
The process of using a vacuum and large bags (similar to freeze drying) to suck out any excess epoxy laminate material impregnated into a cloth or mat, in composites layup manufacturing. This produces a stronger bond, and results in a much lighter part with an increased strength-to-weight ratio.

VENEER
A thin facing layer glued onto core panels, such as wood or MDF. Often veneers can be decorative in nature, using higher quality material as a outside aesthetic covering. Plywood plys are thin sheets of veneer that are glued and stacked on top of one another, forming a sandwhich construction.

VINYL WRAP
A stretchable vinyl wrapped over a part in a non-permanent graphic application. Not as robust as paint and tears easily.

VISCOSITY
How well a liquid flows, also know as its fluidity. Alchohol = high viscosity. Maple syrup = low viscosity.

VISUALLY ACCURATE or "EYEBALLING"
Eyeballing or building to "visual accuracy" is one of the core differientiating modalities between the model maker and that of the engineer, where the former only needs to make a model or prop look good on film or in photos, but lacks precision.

VOCATION / VOCATIONAL
A hands-on, practical job trade and / or skillset.

VOLUMETRIC
A 3D volume derived from independent 2D sections.

WET SANDING
Adding water to sandpaper to improve the sanding quality by helping to remove any excess sanding dust. Usually follows dry sanding, and is primarily used to polish rather than to roughen a surface — as in the pre-paint preparation stage.

WEATHERING / "BATTLE DAMAGE"
A technique model makers to do make their props look grungy, used, and interesting (i.e. District 9, Iron Man, Blade Runner).

WATERTIGHT
Watertight CAD models are needed for 3D printing or proper machining and / or manufacturablilty — meaning that there are no holes in the part surface, and that all structures and assemblies are properly joined / knitted together or "closed."

WAX
Wax has multiple uses, but one of the most popular is as a protective / gloss finish used to seal the pores of wood.

WITNESS MARKS
In injection molding, areas left over by the ejector pins or parting line of the two or more separate mold halves. Typically these are hidden on the undersid of a part and out of view.

WONKY
An industry term used to describe a funky or distorted detail.

WRENCHING
Working on mechanical parts or machinery (i.e. cars or bikes)

X-FACTORY
"Exit factory date," or when a shipment leaves a factory.

ZIG-ZAG STITCH
A stitch that's literally in the shape of a zig-zag, commonly used in overlock or flatlock stitch construction, or for decoration.

Suppliers Reference

SANDING
3M Wetordry	www.3m.com
Motor Guard	www.motorguard.com
Dura-Block	www.dura-block.com

SPRAY PAINTING
Rattle Can:
Rust-Oleum	www.rustoleum.com
Tamiya	www.tamiyausa.com
Dupli-Color	www.duplicolor.com
Montana Can	www.montana-cans.com
Klean Strip	www.kleanstrip.com
Seymour	www.seymourpaint.com
SEM (filler primer)	www.semproducts.com

HVLP Spray Gun:
Evercoat	www.evercoat.com
House of Kolor	www.houseofkolor.com
PCL Poly Primer	www.pclautomotive.com
Iwata	www.anestiwata.com
DevilBliss	www.devilbliss.com
Sata	www.sata.com
Dupont Nason	www.dupont.com
Annex	www.annex.com

3D PRINTING
Form Labs	www.formlabs.com
Stratasys	www.stratasys.com
Maker Bot	www.makerbot.com
Ultimaker	www.ultimaker.com
Shapeways	www.shapeways.com
3D Platform	www.3dplatform.com
Carbon 3D	www.carbon3d.com
Markforged (metal)	www.markforged.com
Prusa Research	www.prusa3D.com

RTV MOLDING & CASTING
Alumilite	www.alumilite.com
Smooth On	www.smoothon.com
Silpak	www.silpak.com
BJB enterprises	www.bjbenterprises.com

LIFE CASTING
Monster Makers	www.monstermakers.com
Silpak	www.silpak.com

GLUES & ADHESIVES
ZAP	www.zapglue.com
Super 77 (3M)	www.3m.com
Tacky Glue	www.aleenes.com
System Three Epoxy	www.systemthree.com
Loctite	www.loctite.com

AUTO BODY FILLER
Bondo (3M)	www.3m.com
Evercoat (glazing putty)	www.evercoat.com

HAND TOOLS & HARDWARE
Harbor Freight	www.harborfreight.com
Home Depot	www.homedepot.com
Lowes	www.lowes.com
Orchard Supply Hardware	www.osh.com
Ace Hardware	www.acehardware.com
X-Acto	www.xacto.com
Olfa Knife	www.olfaproducts.com
McMaster-Carr	www.mcmastercarr.com

LASER CUTTING
Trotec Laser Cutter	www.trotec.com
Epilog Laser Cutter	www.epiloglaser.com
Universal Laser Systems	www.ulsinc.com
Rowmark (swatch books)	www.rowmark.com

INDUSTRIAL MODELING CLAYS
Chavant	www.chavant.com
Eberhard Faber (Staedler)	www.garieinternational.com
Kochi Clay	www.kochico.com

HEAVY MACHINERY
Delta	www.deltamachinery.com
LeBlond	www.leblondusa.com
Laguna	www.lagunatools.com
Powermatic	www.powermatic.com
Allen Bradley	ab.rockwellautomation.com
Kent-USA (lathes)	www.kentusa.com
Tennsmith (foot shear)	www.tennsmith.com
Roper Whitney (foot shear)	www.roperwhitney.com
Bolton Tools	www.boltontool.com
Miller	www.millerwelds.com
Craigslist (used machines)	www.craigslist.org

CNC ROUTERS
HAAS	www.haascnc.com
Laguna	www.lagunatools.com
Fadal	www.fadal.com
Cincinatti Machine	www.cinmac.com

VACUUM FORMERS
Sibe	www.sibeautomation.com
Atlas	www.atlasvac.com

SAFETY
3M AO Safety Respirator	www.3m.com